THE DEADLY FEAST OF LIFE

The Deadly Feast of Life

DONALD E. CARR

DOUBLEDAY & COMPANY, INC., *Garden City, New York*

1971

LIBRARY OF CONGRESS CATALOG CARD NUMBER 75-135712
COPYRIGHT © 1971 BY DONALD E. CARR
PRINTED IN THE UNITED STATES OF AMERICA
FIRST EDITION

To Sigrid and Sven Lassen

CONTENTS

INTRODUCTION

The plan built into this book follows a literary architecture which I have adopted in other books (*The Sexes, The Known and the Forgotten Senses*, and *An Ark of Wiser Animals*, the last two of which are not yet published); namely, to see if by a watchful cruise of the whole animal kingdom, an insight into the games evolution has played and the aspects in which man resembles and in which he differs from other animals we can obtain a clearer picture of man as a creature with a future. In each book we proceed by walking up the evolutionary steps, pausing now and then to turn over a worm or to confront a tiger.

In *The Sexes* the reproductive habits as well as the family and social techniques of the animal classes were analyzed. We concluded among other things that man was not only absurdly oversexed but that he had lost the instinct, possessed by nearly all other animals, for population control.

In this book we first examine food and eating; we proceed to find how species become extinct and finally we inspect the way animals use poisons. When we apply these categories of examination to man we review the old and newer ways of avoiding hunger and malnutrition, man's continuing erasure of his planetary companions and the poisons that man scatters or hoards in such enormous amounts that they threaten his own extinction as well as that of all animal life.

Throughout all four books runs the idea of transcendental memory—the non-physical inheritance of complex behavior patterns, not only with regard to whole animals but to the incomprehensively intricate and delicately timed chemical functioning of single cells which are viewed as small, social, precise universes of their own.

It is biochemistry and zoology rather than sociology and political science that seem to me the important ways by which to clarify and inspire the soul of the human community.

THE DEADLY FEAST OF LIFE

PART I

Life Consumes Life

THE GREAT CHAIN OF FOOD

The single greatest branching in the tree of life was, of course, between organisms that could chemically make their own food (plants) and those that had to scrounge for it (animals). An argument persists among those theorists who believe a plantlike single-celled creature preceded an animal-like protozoan. If their opponents (the animal-firsters) are right, what did the animal-protozoans eat before the generous kingdom of plants was evolved to provide forage? The theorists are waiting for you on this one; even Darwin had the answer a century ago. They ate the same kind of proteinaceous soup that gave birth to them in the first place. The soup was there since there were, of course, no bacteria or yeasts to ferment it or compost it. If the archaic life-producing process started all over again on a newly drowned planet, the soup as served up would hardly last a few minutes. But the earth at the time of the birth of life was as sterile as the sun and perhaps nacreous, much more sterile than the moon, whose virginity is beginning to come under suspicion.

From the start of life the process of finding food and eating it has become the primary preoccupation of every animal from the single-celled to the trillion-celled. The animal must reproduce, of course, but to reproduce he first has to live. Philosophically one can regard all the somatic embellishments and logistics of the animal as stratagems to preserve the germ cell (It was the egg, not the chicken that came first), but this does not detract from the naked primacy of the search and handling of food. Even the simplest bacterial virus, a travesty of life, has to have its single germ molecule (DNA or RNA) clothed in a tight coat of protein. It is also philosophically valid to remind oneself that all the evolutionary traits that man accumulated—those which we now consider peculiarly human—came from the fight for food. Whether the hunter's hand tool enlarged the brain or a swelling brain made inevitable the hunting tool is irrelevant. Both appeared simultaneously and in irreducible concatenation.

Single-celled organisms, plant or animal, provide the first link of a stupendous food chain that winds up directly or indirectly in the stomachs of philosophers. (I say indirectly, because if the philosopher is eating a steak, he has relied on the cellulose-digesting bacteria present in the steer's stomach, and essentially the same thing is true if he prefers chicken soup.) The tiniest flagellate animals eat bacteria. The more aggressive and complicated ciliate protozoans eat flagellates or microscopic algae. The ciliates are in turn eaten by bigger ciliates and by lowly solitary worms and small crustaceans. The worms and crustaceans are eaten by larger or more aggressive creatures. And so onward and upward it goes until we find *Homo sapiens* eating almost anything that was once alive, including members of his own species. (Unluckily he cannot digest cellulose, but that may be rectified.) In the midst of such chains we find some cheaters—the parasites. Their food habits are necessarily so complicated that it has infected their reproductive habits. Life cycles of barely traceable intricacy make them seem not to be single creatures but multiple split personalities, all villainous.

Consider two typical food chains, the arrows marking an eating event: In the sea, *microscopic green algae→surface protozoa→small crustaceans* (e.g. copepods and water fleas)→*small fishes→larger fishes→sharks*. On the land, *plant juices→aphis or plant lice→ larvae of ladybird beetle→birds* (*or spiders*)→*owls and hawks*.

There is an inherent lack of efficiency in such a natural chain, since Nature is not a very good economist. Although modern fowl factories are able nearly to attain the maximum of one pound of live chicken from one pound of selected feed, the predatory and digestive efficiencies ordinarily depend on many factors, some of them still unknown. If, for example, one substitutes man for the shark in the typical ocean-food chain given above, it takes about 10,000 pounds of green algae or plankton to make one pound of man. It is lucky for the multicelled animals that the tiny basic biscuits of the chains are produced in numbers so huge that the mind boggles. For example, the Baltic sea normally provides a billion copepods (small crustaceans) per cubic yard. This is what keeps the herring going. When, as in the fifteenth century, the copepod crops fail in the Baltic, whole financial and political dynasties crumble. The Hanseatic League loses its power to the fishing potentates of Holland.

Yet we give a false impression of ferocious omnivorousness if we assume that even among the carnivores everything bigger will eat anything smaller. Among fierce mammals, such as members of the wolf genus and men, and even among invertebrates, there are often curious restrictions, indicating an almost psychotic influence of behavior patterns or of ritualistic taboos—to the extent that the animal may die amidst abundant calories but not the calories he will accept. The arctic fox will starve if the lemmings are scarce. He will not accept a substitute. The robber crab will eat only coconuts. He will also starve if the coconuts fail. Chinese and Japanese peasants for centuries were stunted from calcium and vitamin deficiencies because they would not or could not drink cow's milk.* (It is a reasonable hypothesis that the relatively small size of the Far Eastern Mongoloids is due not to lack of food but to unreasonable eating taboos and finickiness. This seems to be demonstrated by the fast-increasing stature of modern Japanese children, reared with more cosmopolitan food habits, and also by the fact that the native Mongoloids of North and South America were often fairly tall people.)

In the interest of understanding animals and their relationships to each other, let us go to the bottom of the phyla and return upward to man, noting typical menus *en route*.

* As we shall discuss later, there may be a reason why such peasants *cannot digest* milk.

THE SMALL EAT THE SMALLEST

It must be admitted immediately that even the humblest and simplest animals have diet problems. The non-photosynthetic flagellates feed on bacteria or microscopic algae which they swallow whole. They also absorb directly the dissolved remains of tiny dead plants or animals. Through the microscope they can be observed grazing on the bottom, pushing particles into their mouths, using their little whiplike flags as chopsticks or simply waiting for the nutrient molecules to drift through their cell membranes. When the raw food is inside the cell, the digestive processes are chemically almost indistinguishable from ours. Some of the flagellates, the more primitive, cannot synthesize thiamine (vitamin B_1) and must obtain it in their diet. This nutrient supplement is as necessary in these one-celled creatures as it is in man and for the same purpose—for carbohydrate metabolism. Without it the intermediate pyruvic acid accumulates in the system and poisons the organism. Other flagellate species can make the thiamine molecule if they are provided with the two molecular halves of it—pyrimidine and thiazole. The majority of these protozoans are able to put vitamin B_1 together from simpler raw materials. Yet this chemical art has, for the most part, been lost during the evolution of the higher animals. It is a fantastic oversight on the part of evolution and has undoubtedly been responsible for the initial failure or the ultimate decline of otherwise promising evolutionary models.

With the amoeba, a big aggressive protozoan, we see the beginnings of the hunter complex. *Amoeba proteus*, to cite a well-studied species, moves about by streaming some of its liquid cell contents into temporary fingers called pseudopods. The pseudopod moves forward to touch a surface and the rest of the amoeba, so to speak, catches up with it. As a beast of prey, the amoeba, in making contact with a flagellate or ciliate, suddenly hugs it by extending several pseudopods. The captive is ingested into the amoeba and can for a while be seen struggling unhappily within the cage of protoplasm. Then a food vacuole is formed and a powerful enzyme is introduced into this bundle of ingested animal plus water. This is a surprisingly selective operation. When digesting a green alga, the vacuole-enzyme system acts differently than when breaking down a ciliate. As the vacuole moves around in patterned cell currents in a process called cyclosis, the digestion products are transferred into the surrounding endoplasm. The amoeba has dined and is ready for a brandy and a cigar. But the vacuole proceeds around, now accumulating wastes, and heads for the so-called "anus spot." Thus the vacuole system has in succession functioned as a digestive "organelle" and as an excretory agent. It has played the role of stomach, blood, intestines and kidney. There is also in such protozoans as *Amoeba* a permanent contractile vacuole whose function is to maintain the water balance. Since an amoeba is much more concentrated in water-soluble molecules than the aqueous surroundings, water tends to diffuse into it by a process known as osmosis. The contractile vacuole can thus be looked upon as a sort of bilge pump which eliminates excess water. This matter of water balance is extremely crucial, especially in aquatic organisms, and it will be seen that many organs first regarded as mysterious have eventually been identified as water-balance stabilizers. In marine animals, where the concentration of sea salt reduces the osmotic process, such stabilizer pumps are not so common.

The idea of using vacuoles equipped with enzymes (or enzymes equipped with vacuoles) for internal digestion is a bright one and foreshadows the use in multicellular animals of specialized wandering phagocytes for the same purpose. The sponges perform their digestive processes in the single cells, but the *ingestion* mechanism often relies on the co-operation of two kinds of specialized migratory cells. The choanocytes seize the food particles and pass them on to the amoebocytes. The amoebocytes are peculiar in that they are not only migratory but are capable of changing into other cell types. This is as if you sent the office boy out for sandwiches and upon his return he shared your lunch with you. Since you and he are now equivalent cells, he cannot, however, eat it for you. The amoebocytes see to it that everybody has a chance to eat, but the digestive process itself takes place inside the separate cells. The amoebocytes also store reserve food, such as carbohydrates. In the sponges, excretion is a simple intracellular business, the carbon dioxide and soluble wastes being dumped in the canal system which networks the sponge body.

In the extremely degraded phylum Pogonophora, discovered recently at the bottom of the deep seas, there is no internal digestion system. The pogonophores are like parasites without a host. The outer surface of the animal has microscopic hairlets or processes resembling those in the intestines of vertebrate animals. Apparently the pogonophores have reverted to the most archaic of feeding systems—simply taking in any already decomposed organic matter that they find in the ocean's bottom sluice. In this respect they are not nearly as advanced as the single-celled predators, such as *Amoeba*.

UNINVITED DINNER GUESTS

Among certain kinds of flatworms we find another way of making a living without working for it—of literally eating high on the hog. These are the parasite worms—one of the worst curses of mankind and of its mammalian companions. Parasitism by worms is unquestionably a rather modern form of degeneracy, since the flatworm is probably the oldest multicelled animal on earth, and the perverted life habits involving much younger phyla, such as mammals must necessarily be adaptations. The free-living turbellarian (primitive flatworm) three billion years ago of course had nothing to parasitize. Probably he fed in much the same fashion as his present-day counterpart. The common planarian worm, for example, has a three-branched gut channeled to a mouth located in the middle of the worm's body. Behind the mouth is a pharynx which is a sort of retractable soft beak. In feeding, the pharynx is protruded from the mouth and sucks up miscellaneous particles of food, including small animals. The raw food goes to a simple gut cavity which is branched extensively enough to assure that food, after digestion by special cells in the gut lining, gets around the whole circuit. There is no anus. Wastes are eliminated by a system of tubules containing so-called "flame cells" which are flickering tufts of ciliae. The ciliary "flame" pushes water down the tubule and creates a slight vacuum within it. As a result, water from the surrounding tissues is drawn into the tubules. The prime function of this rather unintelligently planned system is the elimination of excess water rather than body wastes. The flame cell is analogous to the amoeba's contractile vacuole. Since there is no positive circulation, the tubule water-control system depends on gas diffusion and this limits the size of the animal. This is why flatworms are flat.

The notoriety of the flatworm is not associated with this harm-less and unfathomably stupid free-living creature but with the other two classes which evolved from it: the trematodes or flukes and the cestodes or tapeworms and, through a more speculative line of descent, the terrible nematodes, which are no longer flat.

However, before we vent our spleen on the wormlike parasites, we must go back a billion years or so and take a look at a parasitic habit adopted by an especially vicious class of protozoans—the Sporozoa. They have no cilia, no flagellas, no pseudopods. They usually pass from one host to another in armored capsules called spores which enclose the juvenile stage. Once inside the host animal, they feed on specialized cell contents, or in the gut, multiplying by rather complicated tricks, sexually or asexually. If it is fair to assess the evolutionary age of a parasite by its place in phylogenetic chronology, then the sporozoan *Monocystis* is by far the most ancient of them all since it makes a living by invading the sperm cells in the sex organs of the earthworms. A member of the same order, gregarines, enters the gut lining of a grasshopper.

What the sporozoans lack in independent means of locomotion and ability to digest raw animals, they make up for in exceedingly complex reproductive techniques. One cannot regard them as among the oldest of protozoans classes, since before there are parasites there must be hosts. Yet it is charitable to assume that at first they may have played a part in developing and integrating the host. Perhaps they started out as something rather like the choanocytes or amoe-bocytes of sponges. One day the office boy didn't come back. He went out and formed a cyst around himself and returned to claim food rather than bring it. Consider, on the other hand, the role of the wood-digesting flagellates in the gut of the termite, one of the oldest insects known. No colony of the venerable termites would be able to exist in its odd ecological niche if it were not for the special chemical enzymes that the flagellates excrete. This sort of kindly parasitism is called symbiosis. Experimentally the termite's gut population of protozoans can be eliminated. The termites keep on eating but produce fecal pellets of undigested wood and eventually starve.

We know more about the villainous sporozoans, chiefly because one genus, *Plasmodium*, is involved in a disease that has caused more human suffering than any other and was probably responsible for the decline and fall of Greece and Rome—malaria. Here we see the incredible complications of sporozoan reproduction. To define and describe in detail the stages in its life cycles in the mosquito and in man would take a whole book in itself. Suffice it to say that the logical beginning of the gloomy cycle is not when the *Anopheles* mosquito introduces the plasmodium into the blood stream of a man, but when the infected human blood cells are sucked up by the mosquito. At this stage the fatal protozoans are ready to develop into sperm and egg cells. Sexual fertilization takes place in the mosquito's stomach and yields a perverted baby which crawls through the stomach wall and forms a round cyst in which it divides into thousands of rodlike *sporozoites*. The sporozoites break out of the cysts, collect in the mosquito's salivary glands and are ready for inoculation into a man in the tropics on his way in the evening to the officers' club for a scotch on the rocks.

Within a few hours, before the same man has digested his dinner, the sporozoites in his blood stream have all entered fixed cells in the blood passages of the liver, the spleen and other organs. Here each sporozoite grows into an active feeding stage, the *trophozoite*. While chewing up liver cells and the like from within them, it becomes a little monster with as many as thirty-two nuclei. The multinuclear creature, being unstable, divides into as many offspring as it has nuclei, these being the *merozoites*, which are the most vicious stage of the cycle. They break out of the fixed cells and enter the blood stream, attacking the man's red blood cells. Another feeding stage ensues, followed by another asexual production of merozoites. Since the staging is such that the breakouts are simultaneous, a good fraction of the man's blood-cell population is assaulted at the same time and the patient suffers paroxysms. The cycle begins again when, for some mysterious reason, the trophozoites start to form potential sex cells and are sucked up by another mosquito.

It is important to note that the intermediate host need not be a human being nor even a warm-blooded vertebrate. Birds and lizards are subject to malaria. Probably *Plasmodium* dates back to the first time land vertebrates and insects lived together in the middle Paleozoic. (It is even conceivable that just as human malaria may have caused the fall of Rome, reptilian malaria may have toppled the dinosaurs.)

The subclass Coccidia consists of an appalling smear of sporozoans which cause highly contagious, extremely fatal diarrhea in many vertebrates, including chickens, turkeys, cattle, sheep, pigs, goats, cats, dogs and even pet white mice. Like *Plasmodium*, the Coccidia have both sexual and asexual life cycles but do not need the funny business with the mosquito. Some of the more recondite species, such as *Eineria schubergi*, infect very unexpected species, such as the centipedes. The infection is spread in cyst form from the host animal's feces. This is the reason for keeping poultry off the ground on wire meshes.

The fact that the habit or art of parasitism occurs in the two oldest phyla, protozoans and flatworms, indicates a deep schism in the life process itself. It would be easy to draw a mystical distinction between the outgoing, adventurous animal on one hand and the introverted, dependent parasite on the other. Actually the parasite may be the more adventurous. The first parasites may even have invented polymorphism. The parasite is a crook, but a very brilliant one. In order to understand how fortuitous the many lives of an advanced parasite may be, we must return to our consideration of the flukes and the tapeworms and then consider still another, even more sinister, wormlike phylum, the nematodes.

The natural history of parasites like the trematodes (flukes) is a tightrope act between oblivion of the host and oblivion of the parasite. The parasite dies, if the host dies; hence it is in the parasite's interest to hedge his bets and to pour out statistical torrents of offspring who can catch a ride on the right *intermediate* host at the right time. As an example of the convoluted lives led by a trematode, consider the *Clonorchis sineusis*, the Oriental liver fluke which afflicts human beings.

As an adult, *Clonorchis* feeds in the bile passages of the human liver. When it has a mind to, it produces thousands of eggs (and fertilizes them itself) which consist of a single germ cell surrounded by yolk and a shell. These eggs in vast number pass through the bile duct into the intestine and are eliminated with the feces. Although embryonic development is completed with the shell, the resulting larva (the *miracidium*) does not hatch until the egg has been swallowed by a particular kind of snail. (It has to be one of a small number of species belonging to a single family of snails.) Within the snail's body, the hairy miracidium hatches out and makes its way into various snail tissues where it transforms itself into a second larval form, the *sporocyst*. Ths is a thin-walled saclike mass of germinal tissue from which is produced in great numbers a third generation of larvae, known as the *redia* (from the Italian microscopist Redi). The rediae migrate to the blood sinuses of the snail's liver where each redia produces internally a mass of germ balls, each of which develops into a microscopic tadpolelike larval stage, the *cercaria*. The cercariae burst out of the walls of the redia "mother" in great numbers, make their way outside the snail and swim around freely in water. When a cercaria meets up with any one of several kinds of fresh-water fishes, it bores through its skin, sheds its tail and becomes encysted in the fish's flesh. At this stage it becomes a *metacercaria*. The live cysts may be eaten by humans who do not cook their fish sufficiently or at all. In the stomach of the final human host the metacercaria emerges from the cyst, makes its way to the liver where it becomes a fully adult fluke, ready to start the cycle over again.

Note that in this weird history, there have been three stages of frantic multiplication. *Clonorchis* relies on numbers but it also relies on the Oriental habits of leaving human excrement around where snails can get at it and on an Oriental liking for uncooked (raw, pickled, smoked) fish.

It is possible that if these habits were reformed, *Clonorchis* would disappear from the Chinese liver, but this fluke or one of its cousins might adapt to the liver of some other vertebrate that eats raw fish.

The flukes vary in their choice of intermediate and *definitive* hosts (the latter being the host in which they achieve sexual maturity). In the course of evolution the nervous system of the adult fluke has been almost eliminated; it is blind, deaf, and what brain is left is attached behind the mouth or sucker, with a few nerves extending out along the animal. Nevertheless it has memorized a life sequence of unvarying if unpleasant complexity. It knows what it is about. The sheep-liver fluke, the flukes that specialize in inhabiting the lungs of frogs, the gills of fish, the intestines and blood of man—all seem to have been specialized descendants of the simple free-living flatworm. The schistosomes or blood flukes have made life precarious for men who live in the Nile Valley, in the irrigated lowlands of Pakistan and over much of Africa, Asia and South America. They require a snail as intermediate host and in man live chiefly in the small blood vessels of the lower intestine. The three species of *Schistosoma* (*Bilharzia*) infecting man differ only slightly in life history and symptoms of the disease, schistosomiasis or bilharziasis, that they cause. One of the noxious skills of these flukes is that they do not have to be eaten. In the *cercaria* stage, they leave the snail and, when they encounter people bathing or wading, they are able to enter the body through the pores of the human skin.

I cannot resist telling one fluke story which borders on the dizzy horrors of science fiction. This concerns the sheep-liver fluke, *Fasciola hepatica.* Until 1963 it was generally accepted that this animal used only the mud snails as intermediate host. However, it was discovered that the fluke as a cercarian form does not willingly leave the snail's body. It is ejected. The snail imbeds the cercariae in balls of mucus and expels them. These balls of mucus are devoured by another intermediate host, the ant. In this insect they encapsulate in the abdominal cavity and mature to the form that is so dangerous to the sheep's liver. The question is, how do they get from an ant's stomach to a sheep's liver?

By a very strange process indeed. A single cercaria works its way to the brain of the ant and "takes over." Henceforth the ant is an automaton of a kind that it was not intended to be. Under the direction of the primitive creature dominating its nerve center, the ant is compelled to do things it would never dream of doing. It climbs to the very tips of grasses and weeds and waits there. Clustered together, the infected ants hang for hours, offering themselves to be eaten by sheep or cattle, who of course oblige. The rest is routine for the fluke.

One needs to know more about the process of how a single larval trematode is able thus to physically hypnotize an insect as sophisticated or as occupied with its own deep instincts as an ant, since it introduces a new dimension in entomology as well as parasitology. It also offers perhaps the ultimate in puzzles as to the workings of instinctive behavior. I cannot to my own satisfaction attribute such intricate behavioral patterns to the fluke's DNA molecules. But we shall later multiply such instances and argue more fully our case against the mere physical inheritance of behavior.

The tapeworms or cestodes are flatworms which lack any external locomotive hairs and even lack a digestive system. They have heads (solex) with hooks, suckers or other adhesive organs, but these are used mainly for hanging on, since they absorb nourishment through the walls of their bodies. The sexually mature adult always lives in the intestine of a vertebrate—*any* vertebrate from fish to man. From the fact that this worm has no digestive system but must live on food predigested by its host and from the fact that its hosts (vertebrates) are young on the planet, it is assumed that the cestodes are degraded forms of the trematodes or flukes.

In the adult form, the tapeworm lives in an atmosphere (the vertebrate intestine) where there is no oxygen. It has thus had to go to a form of respiration which is anaerobic in nature, like that of the normal intestinal bacteria with which it shares the host's bowels.

Tapeworms are highly sexed, although hermaphrodite, since they have little to do except hang on, grow and reproduce. The immature larval or cysticercus stage is found, not in the intestines, but in the muscles, livers, brains and other organs of cattle, pigs, rabbits, men, etc., being developed there as the result of the contamination of food with feces from the primary host. It is thus quite a different animal from its parent, since it has access to the blood of the host and is not forced into the unnatural habit of anaerobic respiration. It is in the form of the juvenile stage that the tapeworm is transferred from one host to another, in man by eating improperly cooked beef, pork or fish. From beef to tapeworm, maturing in man's intestines, it may reach a length of twenty feet or more. The common tapeworm of the southeastern United States, the dwarf tapeworm, long celebrated as a sort of native of Tobacco Road country, actually does not require an intermediate host. A child with filthy habits is the only host. The eggs of the worm return via feces-contaminated food or hands to the child's digestive tract, go through a brief bladder worm stage there, and then add to the intestinal population of adult tapeworms. When you see tapeworm-infested children in the South, you are seeing not the results of dirty, badly cooked food but of family toilet regimes so rottenly managed that the feces of the children become a stable part of their diet.

We come now to a parasite that until recently has been so little understood that it has under cover of a night of ignorance come to threaten the health and existence of all vertebrate animals, including man, and has invaded even crustaceans, mollusks, insects and centipedes. This is the nematode or roundworm. It is a member of a phylum wholly separate from that of the other worms we have considered. It has only recently been realized that the *Aschel-*

minthes (*asucs*, sac+*helminthos*, worm) is an absolutely colossal one. Many zoologists believe that as a subphylum, the nematodes alone will eventually be found to include *more species than all other kinds of animals combined, including the arthropods.* If this proves to be true, we must conclude that almost unknown to most of us, our time has become the "Age of Nematodes." Nematology has suddenly become as important as entomology. This animal does not prey only on other members of the animal kingdom. The United States Department of Agriculture now estimates the annual nematode damage to our agriculture as about two billion dollars. Some 300 million nematodes of a single kind have been estimated to occur per acre in sugar-beet fields of Utah and Idaho. Among the plants it damages are beets, carrots, chrysanthemums, cotton, mushrooms, peanuts, potatoes, rice, tobacco, tomatoes, wheat—and countless others. At least three million people in the United States alone suffer with nematode (ascaris) infections. The phylum is insatiable and ubiquitous. It may live in an alpine pool or a desert; around the roots of a plant or within the human eye. Although a very large proportion of their incalculably vast population is *not* parasitic, we have only recently discovered this. It is the parasitic nematode that has rung our alarm bell and made us reach for our microscopes. Over the past few decades, it is as if we had realized that we were being invaded by astronomically vast colonies of malign little beings from outer space. And yet it is an ancient animal that probably evolved, perhaps by neoteny,* from something like the trochophore or larval stage of the annelid worms.

Fundamentally the nematode is much more complicated than any flatworm. It bears certain superficial resemblances to the arthropods, since it has a hard skin of keratin, which must be shed every time it goes through a growth stage, and in fact the stage between molts is called, as in insects, an *instar.* The body is constructed on the tube-within-a-tube plan, a construction which allows a wide variation from the semimicroscopic size of most soil- and water-living species to the *Ascaris,* which inhabits the intestines of man and many of his favorite animals and grows to be a foot long.

The nematodes insist on bisexuality, the females being larger than the males. Reproduction is efficient, to say the least. A female

---

* Neoteny exists when the adult form of one animal develops from the larval or juvenile form of another. It is thought, for example, that insects originated from the juvenile form of millipedes.

Ascaris lays about 200,000 eggs every day. Perhaps partly because of bisexuality or for some other more bodeful reason, the nematode has an astonishingly disproportionate part of its body devoted to nerves. More than 50 per cent of the cells of the entire animal are nerve cells. Most of the nerves and muscles, the excretory organs, the outer skeleton are all built into the body wall. The sense organs include the mysterious *amphids*, situated like ears on either side. The space between the simple cylindrical gut and the body wall is occupied only by sexual organs. Depending on diet, the mouth may have smooth lips and merely suck in food; it may be provided with chitinous jaws or it may have sharp spears with muscles to push into plant or animal tissue. Perhaps very significantly, nematodes have no circulatory or respiratory system.

We need to know more about this extraordinarily successful animal. How does it get by without blood or respiration? What is it doing with all those nerves? What is the function of the heavily nerved amphid organs? So little do we know of the creature that the amphids have been loosely called "glandular sense organs," which is the kind of language anatomists use when they are up a tree. (In another class, analogous organs called *phasmids* are located in the tail rather than the head.)

Perhaps it is the overgrown nervous system that has contributed to the remarkable adaptability of even single species of the nematodes. Anatomically indistinguishable races of the same species may flourish from ponds in northern Siberia to jungle lakes in tropical Africa. There is only one other creature on earth that has this *racial* adaptability: that is man. Perhaps we see in the nematodes the primacy of the nerves which we pride ourselves on having first demonstrated to the planet.

In addition to the parasitic habit, nematodes show a variety of diets. Many are carnivorous, eating protozoans, small annelids, rotifers and even other nematodes. (The cannibalistic genus *Mononchus* eats other nematodes which infest root plants, and so should be encouraged in the same manner as we sic ladybird beetles on aphids.)

The human parasites are naturally the ones that nematodologists most often study—the pork-muscle worm *Trichinella*, the intestinal whipworm, the giant kidney worm, most of all the hookworm. Three hookworm species infect mankind. (According to a United Nations report, 600 million cases of hookworm disease occur throughout the world, which is nearly one out of five living people.) Other species invade various other mammals. The hookworms live in the intestine, biting on to the villi of the bowel lining and eating blood. They secrete a poison that causes anemia and general weakness. The eggs already contain embryos when laid and pass out in the host's feces. The larvae are hatched in the dirt and molt twice before becoming infective. A hot, moist soil and absence of direct sunlight favors the development of the final so-called bilariform larvae. They penetrate the skin of the feet or hands and make their way first, curiously, to the lungs, which they may damage. Eventually they come back up the windpipe and return to their true home, the bowels. Everywhere in the world that people refuse to treat their sewage and go without shoes, there will be cases of hookworm.

Trichinosis comes from nematodes that have lodged mainly in pigs but has also come from eating the poorly cooked meat of any omnivorous animal—bears, for example, or men. (The habit of some human cannibals of eating the raw brains of an enemy chief is sure to lead to trichinosis, sooner or later. They should be admonished to at least heat the brains in boiling water.) *Trichinella* has the evil instinct of migrating through the blood stream and encysting in the muscles, brain or heart.

The ancient disease of elephantiasis, in which the legs or genital organs swell to enormous proportions, is caused by the exceedingly minute microfilarial form of a nematode that multiplies in the lymph spaces of the human body and is transmitted by the night-biting mosquito, *Culex fatigans.*

In an animal so versatile as the nematode, it is not surprising that one genus specializes in infecting the lungs of frogs and garter snakes. This particular worm has developed such an astounding reproductive trick that I cannot resist mentioning it here. The young worms in the frog's lungs pass through a transient male stage. Their sperms are stored in a seminal receptacle and are then used to fertilize eggs which are produced by the same worm when it later turns into a female. Such ingenuity impresses us with the fearful suspicion that perhaps eventually it will be found that anything we can do, the nematode will be able to do better.

VORACIOUS JELLIES

Let us return to the eating processes of less alarming animals. We are still starting up the ladder of evolution and must consider the coelenterates (jellyfish, corals, hydroids, sea anemones, etc.). Even the simplest coelenterates, such as *Hydra*, which looks like a water flower, possess a complex weapon which enables them to defend themselves and kill other animals for food. This is one of the strangest and most sophisticated weapons in the world of animals. It is the *nematocyst* (*nema*, thread+*cyst*, vesicle). There are three widely different-appearing classes of coelenterates: the Hydrozoa, which include most of the very small jellyfish and the familiar hydroids seen growing on wharf pilings; the Scyphozoa, a large jellyfish (but not including the notorious Portuguese man-of-war, which is a special kind of hydrozoan); and the Anthozoa, including sea anemones, the corals and the sea fans. Every single one of them is armed with nematocysts. The nematocysts vary from lassoes that coil around the victim, glutinants that trap him and penetrants that go at him like a harpoon. All are poisonous.

The nature of the stimulus necessary for discharge of these weapons is simply not known for sure. It may be chemical, mechanical or even psychological. The poison sometimes contains serotonin (as does wasp venom), which is a powerful histamine releaser and an important neural chemical in many animals, including man; there are two other ingredients which have much the same effect as "nerve gas" (an ultimate chemical warfare agent, the formula for which is still classified as "Secret"). We shall have more to say about such poisons later, but suffice it to say that the coelenterate would never have been the successful animal it is without this weapon.

Hydra only opens its mouth after the prey has been punctured.

The puncture is believed to release a chemical, reduced glutathione, into the water from the body juices of the small animals that coelenterates prey on, such as crustaceans and worms. *Hydra* does not eat animals which lack this chemical (such as other hydras). However, if the water is dosed with reduced glutathione, the hydra will open its mouth so wide it will literally turn itself inside out and will then turn cannibal and try to eat other hydras. The process of digestion is partly in the gut, which is lined with enzyme-producing cells, and partly intracellular, as in protozoans.

Coelenterates have been subjected to more biological research than any other animal, with the possible exception of fruit flies and earthworms. Although the belief was once general that as a phylum they were the first multicelled animals, this is no longer a popular theory and that honor is given to the primitive flatworm.

Most coelenterates are distinctly polymorphic. They undergo various stages of asexual and sexual reproduction. There is, for example, a polyp stage which sticks to one spot, like a rooted plant. It buds off a medusa stage, which is usually sexual (except for deep-sea jellyfish) and gives rise to a ciliated larva—the planula—which after a brief period of wandering about, squats down on some object and returns to the polyp or hydroid habit. There are many fundamental problems, not only in this alteration of generations but in the differentiation of cells. (How, for example, does a coelenterate, in its growth from an egg, know which cells shall become germ cells? It appears that in such a creature the germ cells develop from rather generalized embryonic tissue and not from a special line of segregated reproductive cells.) The regeneration capabilities of the coelenterates have been a continuing source of amazement and investigation. As with certain worms, when a hydra is cut in two pieces, a new lower body appears on the piece which has tentacles and new tentacles form on the lower body piece. The only section which will not regenerate into a new complete animal is the extreme basal region—an interesting exception, since this is a sort of home for all the old and decrepit cells of the body. They migrate here and gather, like old people in Florida, just before being sloughed off entirely. (This is an efficient technique for staying young and it is a pity that the human animal has become too complicated to use it.)

In the hydroid stage one can watch a fascinating food struggle between parent and asexual child. The youngsters swell under the adults' skins and burst out as miniature hydras. Although they stay attached to their parents, they have the hunting instinct. A water flea, for example, will be caught by both parent and child and struggled over. The child may win and swallow the prey. Since the young hydra is too immature to have his own digestive system, the flea will pass through him into the body of the parent to be processed.

The larger coelenterates, such as the great, exquisitely colored jellyfish (some of them over seven feet in diameter) and the Portuguese man-of-war, are extremely vicious predatory animals. They feed mostly on fish, but some of them have pet fish species, which they do not sting, and which attract other fish and seem to offer them other obscure comfort and service.

The Anthozoa (anthos, flower+zoa, animals) were for centuries regarded as plants. This was especially true of the corals. However, all the Anthozoa, from the simplest sea anemone to the most complex coral or gorgonian, have nematocysts and, although they do not go through a medusa stage, their eggs develop into planulas that return to the hydroid form. The reef-forming corals get some additional help from plants (calcareous algae) which they incorporate in their tissues. The carbon dioxide produced in the respiration phase of the imbedded algae is believed to affect chemically the equilibrium between calcium bicarbonate (water soluble) and calcium carbonate (insoluble), so that the reef material can be produced from the latter. At any rate, corals which do not have symbiotic algae do not build reefs.

RAPACIOUS STARS

Let us look at the echinoderms. As we have previously noted, this phylum has certain properties, mainly embryological and chemical, in common with vertebrates. However, the starfish does not eat clams as a man would. In fact, we don't know how he does it. In some mysterious way he is able to cause the bivalves of a mollusk to gape open. When even a small crack has been produced, the starfish pokes out his pouchlike stomach from his mouth, which is in the middle of the belly side, and inserts it into the mantle cavity of the bivalve. He then releases a digestive enzyme so immensely powerful that it causes the soft parts of the mollusk almost instantly to liquefy and disintegrate. A starfish has been seen to devour fifty-six clams over a six-day period of good hunting. He is also a connoisseur of oysters. In fact the whole mollusk phylum, except the cephalopods (octopus, squids) has reason to dread him. The starfish is not, however, a compulsive eater. He can survive several months in the absence of food.

The echinoderm is a true sea creature. The coelomic fluid, which circulates in the cavity which is analogous to our own body cavity between our flesh and internal organs, is almost indistinguishable in background composition from sea water. It performs the functions of a blood-circulating system, and contains many phagocytes and amoeboid cells and, like the hemocoelic blood of an insect or crustacean, bathes all the tissues of the body. There is no heart or system of blood vessels. The coelomic circulation is managed by the team action of flagella on the cells of the internal lining. The digested food from the notably acrobatic stomach passes into the coelomic fluid. Oxygen passes into this all-important liquid through thin-walled specialized cells of the body wall and is carried in simple solution rather than by blood cells. (For this reason it would be impossible to kill a starfish with carbon monoxide, which works on vertebrates by displacing oxygen from the hemoglobin of the blood cells.) There are exceptions to these rules, in that *Thyone*, a mud-living species, does have hemoglobin-containing blood cells and the holothurians (sea cucumbers) have a pulsating heart and an extensive system of blood vessels. As usually happens with animals, however, the unexpected prevails and the life habits of these more vascular creatures are much less lively than those of the starfish.

One of the most spectacular feeding organs in the whole animal kingdom is commonly possessed by echinoderms. This is the jaw apparatus which Aristotle described as resembling a "horn lantern with the panes of horn left out." Each of the five white calcareous teeth of "Aristotle's lantern" looks like the incisor of a rat. In sea urchins it can be seen curving inward over the top of the lantern. Each tooth is imbedded in a pyramid of bone. The five pyramids are firmly held together in the five-sided lantern by strong muscle fibers. The strength of this system can be appreciated by anybody who has seen the pits chewed in steel wharf piles by sea urchins nibbling at the algae crusts.

The starfish and certain other echinoderms probably owe most of their success to the fact that few other animals want to eat them.

FROM OYSTER TO OCTOPUS

From the consideration of one of its chief predators, it is natural to proceed now to the mollusk phylum (*molluscus*, soft), a fantastically varied one, when one considers the difference between an oyster and an octopus. Man's acquaintance with mollusks is very ancient. Along San Francisco Bay there are enormous mounds of shells, estimated to have accumulated over a period of 3000 years. And the kitchen middens or garbage piles of many Stone Age peoples in Europe are made up mainly of shells.

As a model for an animal, the mollusk's body can be divided into four parts (1) viscera, containing digestive and reproductive organs (2) a muscular foot, (3) a head and mouth in which there is a muscular tongue, called the *radula*, bearing long rows of teeth, and (4) a *mantle*, a sort of cloak of skin which enfolds the animal and on its outer surface secretes the shell. As usual, there are exceptions. In bivalves like clams, there is no head and no radula. In oysters, even the foot is missing.

The Class Gastropoda (*gaster*, belly+*podos*, foot) includes snails and their relatives which vary from a small species of tree snail found only in one valley of one island of the Hawaiians, to the common garden snail that everybody, more or less, has seen and most people in France, Japan and China have eaten. There is an immense variety of diet among snails. There are fruit-eating species in semitropical regions and cannibal snails who eat the fruit eaters. There is a small carnivorous snail (the oyster drill) which is an unsolved headache for oystermen. Some gastropods are parasitic on sea cucumbers. In the more primitive snails the intestine is fairly straight and the anus and gills are at the back. In most gastropods, however, the larva goes through a torsion stage of development and in the end the anus and gills wind up on the front of the body. Most of the marine snails are carnivorous and they will come gliding from all corners of a tide pool, tentacles waving, for a piece of crushed clam. The big conches like *Strombus* and *Busycon* are used as bait in the codfishing industry and are often ground up to make chowder for human stomachs.

The gastropod teeth are remarkable. Of all the mouths in the animal kingdom, this is the most efficient, and if human beings could find out how to develop the denture of snails, they would live longer and enjoy their meals more and pay no dentist bills. The snail's radula, considered from the standpoint of a mechanical engineer, is a perfect grinding device. This organ lies upon a thick muscular cushion situated on the floor of the snail's mouth. A tough membrane covers the under surface and bears many parallel rows of fine teeth. (Depending on the species, the number of teeth may be as many as 750,000.) Somewhat like a cat's tongue, the radula does not bite food but rasps it to pieces as a file rasps iron. This impeccable organ is enclosed at the hind end in the radular sheath, and in this sheath *new* rows of teeth are constantly growing and moving forward to replace the worn-out teeth at the front end. It is a pity that such a dental system (a kind of constantly renewed assembly line of splendid teeth) should be wasted on so modest a class of animal. In the world of the mammals, especially the carnivores, an animal ages and retires to die as his teeth wear out. For example, the sea otter's teeth are full of jagged cavities because he wears them down chewing on sea urchins. In their sleep, anxious men (usually old bachelors) grind their teeth almost to the gum line by gnashing them during the long lonely night.*

Some gastropods have very capricious, perhaps almost perverted appetites. The great black slug *Arion ater* normally feeds on fruit (frugivorous is the word), but he is not above eating flesh even when it is alive, in the form of small crabs. One specimen kept two days in captivity was turned out on a copy of the New York *Times* and began to devour it. During a twelve-month period in a London publishing house, slugs were observed to have fed nightly on the coloring matter in certain book covers. (One would like to know *which* books.)

---

* It is true that men are able to replace their teeth with embarrassing and extremely costly substitutes, but the gastropod's solution is better both aesthetically and functionally.

When we come to the bivalves (clams, mussels, oysters, etc.), the feeding character of the animals is less colorful. An oyster works hard to feed himself, but all he can do is pump his gills and see what turns up. It is amazing what *does* turn up. In working these gills eighteen hours a day, the oyster strains eighteen gallons of sea water during this time, which corresponds to 75 million microscopic organisms (algae, etc.) every day. Where oysters congregate, in a so-called "oyster bar," the water is thick with life, mostly with malevolent design on the poor bivalves, but some who simply like to eat with him. Starfish and oyster drill snails attack them. A species of miniature crab lives within the mantle cavity, while around, on, and boring into the shells are many kinds of protozoans, the yellow boring sponge *Cliona*, a smear of hydroids and other coelenterates, flatworms, nematodes, bryozoans, annelids, a vast throng of crustaceans from tiny copepods to large crabs and even representatives of the chordates, the sea squirts or tunicates. Over the oyster bar the waters swirl with ctenophores and teleost fish. An oyster bar is a sort of natural marine zoo. Since bivalves, such as the clam, oyster and mussel represent money in the bank, there have been numerous researches carried out and campaigns to protect them. As usual, it turns out that the insatiable appetite of man himself is the most fearsome disaster that the oyster faces.

The bivalve body is keyed on its gills. Respiration, digestion, circulation and, in many species, reproduction involve the gill system. Some digestion of food by white corpuscles of the blood actually takes place in the gills. A clam pulls in water containing oxygen and food particles through its inward siphon by waving the cilia on the gills. The food is entangled in cilia and mucus, passes down the gill filaments to the lower edge of the gill and then streams forward to the mouth and into the stomach and intestine which makes a loop or two before ending near the outward siphon. Near the stomach is the liver and a long blind tube opening into the stomach. This tube secretes a glistening rod of protein which is slowly pushed into the stomach and breaks up, releasing a starch-digesting enzyme. One of the rather startling peculiarities of the clam's intestine is that it passes directly through the ventricle of the heart. Blood returning from the viscera passes through the kidneys, then the gills (to get oxygen) and finally to the heart. The blood of most mollusks contains a blue, oxygen-carrying protein compound, hemocyanin, with copper taking the place of the usual iron. However, the clam can afford two blood pigments. The red in the muscles of the radula is due to hemoglobin. The kidneys of the bivalves have received curiously little attention, but it is a striking lesson in the convergence of biochemical evolution to note that terrestrial pulmonate snails (who have a kind of lung), the marine snails who live mostly above the high-tide line and all the birds (who as an animal class left the water, as amphibians, some 325 million years ago) excrete their nitrogen wastes in the form of uric acid.

The class Cephalopoda (*keptale*, head+*podos*, foot) includes the octopuses and squids and is the mysterious crowning glory of the mollusk phylum. Unfortunately this can be said only in a qualitative sense. It is one of the great puzzles of animal life that the cephalopods, with so much going for them, represent a small class of only about 400 living species, though there are some 10,000 fossil ones. They are the only invertebrate group which contains large, dangerous animals on the vertebrate scale. The giant squid of the North Atlantic attains a body length of twenty feet, has a pair of grasping tentacles over thirty feet long and eight shorter ones of about ten feet.

There is no doubt that cephalopods are mollusks. When rationally examined, the adult anatomy is entirely molluscan. The mantle cavity has gills, the siphons are formed from the mantle edge; it has a radula, even the ink sac is a peculiarly molluscan invention. When we look at the proudly shelled nautilus group of cephalopods, mostly extinct (the "pearly nautilus" of song and myth), we are convinced. One can understand the body plan by imagining a snail in which the mouth with the radula has been moved back into the center of the foot, and the foot itself draws out around the mouth and into tentacles. The visceral mass in the squids has an *internal shell*, while in an octopus the body is a mere bag. In squids and octopuses, the mouth is armed with a beak like a parrot's, except that it curves inward, and the tongue is a radula. The saliva is rich in *serotonin*, a potent chemical which we mentioned in connection with jellyfish.

In some cephalopods, *Eledone*, at least, the stomach has a muscular grinding organ like a bird's gizzard. It is interesting to watch a cuttlefish stalk a prawn, much as a cat stalks a bird or a mouse. When he catches it, with cold unvarying technique he tears off the legs, lifts the carapace and dips his beak into the soft belly side. The common, small octopus (*Octopus vulgaris*) feeds mostly on mussels. He will collect fifteen to twenty of them in his nest hole before sitting down to dinner.

All in all, the cephalopods are formidable fish- and crab-eating hunters. They have eyes very similar in construction to the vertebrate eye. Although the eye of the nautilus functions like a pinhole camera, the other cephalopods have developed the crystalline lens.

The possession of very fast-conducting giant nerve fibers to the muscle of the mantle results in instantaneous escape and attack reactions. Anyone who has ever seen a pack of squids methodically and swiftly running down big fishes must wonder why the squids did not permanently take over as the master large animals of the sea. And why did the octopuses never invade the land, as did the molluscan second cousins, the snails?

In his famous novel of our invasion from Mars, *The War of the Worlds*, H. G. Wells, a very percipient student of biology, pictured the Martians as, in effect, giant octopuses. There are biologists today who believe that a land invasion by the cephalopods would have been an inevitable step in evolution and may still be. I think it is too late. Even now they may be on their way out, not entirely because of man's activities (although men have regarded them as special food delicacies since ancient Greek and Roman days, when they cut off the tentacles, filled the body with spices and baked it in a kind of pie, and I have myself taken part in the capture and eating of small octopuses*). More likely the larger species are too easily caught and eaten by killer whales and large sharks. And yet that cannot be the whole story. Somehow this promising animal, which has with its strong yet delicately poised nervous system, its splendid eyesight, its suction-cup tentacles, the potential ability to handle and contrive (as did the anthropoids with their hands), failed to make it. If they had really made it, they would have been better animals than we. It is a pity, not only because an intelligent

---

* In Balboa Bay, California, at low tide one could, at least in the old days, readily get enough for an octopus-chowder feast by pouring salt in their holes and grabbing their heads when they scrambled up. The Balboa way of preparing them for dinner was quite the opposite of the Greco-Roman technique. After removing the viscera and brain, the highly nervous tentacles and mantle must be pounded on the sidewalk until they cease crawling away. It is essentially the tentacles that the Balboans eat.

species with ten arms would have been able obviously to get more done and to develop the brain faster, but because of the much more graceful sex actions, so free from the basic sordidness of mammalian copulation.

7

EATING DIRT

It may appear as a comedown (after contemplating the tragic failure of the cephalopods) to get back to ground, namely, to the earthworms (annelids) and their relatives. Although actually they now represent a phylum of modest size (about 8000 species, mostly of earthworms and leeches), we have seen that they were at one time intermediates in evolution to the arthropods and mollusks. Their most prominent characteristic is the segmented body, the segments of which are called metameres or somites.

The phylum is divided into five classes: Archiannelids (tiny marine worms), polychaetes (marine bristle worms), oligochaetes (earthworms and their fresh-water relatives), leeches (predominantly fresh-water creatures), and myzostomes (parasites on starfish and sea lilies). Since the earthworm's feeding habits are those chiefly of interest to us, we shall confine most of our discussion to this animal. The earthworm's body is covered by a thin skin and is armed with a few bristles called *setae* (in contrast to the luxuriant bristle forest of his polychaete cousins in the sea). Nevertheless, there are eight setae per segment and any robin can tell you how firmly they hold a worm in the ground.

The earthworm is surprisingly well nerved and in certain parts of the skin there are sensory cells of various types, some of whose functions are not well understood. They do have eyes or at least light receptors which allow the worm to tell the difference between light and darkness.

The digestive canal begins with a muscular pharynx which secretes mucus and which is also the main digging and eating organ. The gut narrows to a straight tube, the esophagus, which carries the food past the five pairs of hearts and the reproductive organs.

In the esophagus we confront a mystery that has puzzled every biologist since Darwin—the so-called calciferous glands. These appear frequently to form calcium carbonate crystals. The best guess is that this is a kind of "Alka-Seltzer" gland to neutralize the acidity of much of the worm's diet. His favorite leaf mold, for example, is extremely acidic.

Actually the diet of earthworms varies with the species. Some eat fallen leaves and are particularly fond of lettuce. Others make their living on organic matter contained in the soil. In times of drought, the leaf eater will take refuge underground.

The plasma or fluid of the blood is red from dissolved hemoglobin, iron-containing but not identical, however, with vertebrate hemoglobin.

The excretory system, the *nephridium*, is amazingly similar to the vertebrate kidney. In native American earthworms there is a pair of nephridia in every segment except the first two or three and last one or two. In the dry regions of India there are species in which the nephridia empty their wastes into the intestine, where all of the available water can be absorbed back into the body. This is an adaptation made also by birds and by certain desert insects.

In loose soil the earthworm burrows by forcing its pointed head between pieces of earth. In harder soil the worm literally eats its way. The earth is passed through the digestive tract and deposited on the surface of the ground as "castings," often seen in small piles where earthworms are thriving. Darwin was especially interested in the beneficial effect that earthworms have on the soil, by aerating it, changing it chemically and bringing subsoil up to the top, like very deep plows. An earthworm will go down six or more feet in the winter and a foot or two in summer. By drying and weighing the castings collected, Darwin estimated that the worms bring up to the surface from seven to eighteen tons of soil per acre per year. This is enought to make a "cultivated" soil layer up to about two inches in depth every ten years. Later studies have proved that in certain tropical regions, the "soil-surfacing" by worms may be up to one hundred tons per acre per year.

The ability of earthworms to regenerate lost parts has fascinated people since it was first recognized in the eighteenth century. It seems incredible that it would have taken man so long to learn this fact, since he has used this harmless little friend as bait for fishing in fresh-water lakes and rivers for unnumbered centuries; but one must recall again that the Greeks and Romans and the Chinese were not experiment-minded and that the black, suffocating cloud that descended on the Western mind during the years from about A.D 400 to 1450 strangled not only experimental but even charitable interest in the world of animals. Indeed, it is from this time cavity in the Western spirit that we inherit even until this stage of the twentieth century the curious ideas of the "simple" that such things as earthworms are not even animals, but are vague wiggly blobs more akin to the moist soil from which we pluck them than representing, as they do, an incalculably vast step in evolution from the beginning of life.

Yet once it was found that if you cut an earthworm into two pieces, it would start to regenerate a brain or a tailpiece, such men as Spallanzani were justly inspired with the thought that we might learn something from the gentle creatures—perhaps, the annelids would teach us how to regrow a leg or an arm or even a head. In spite of the immense number of able scientists in Europe, America and Asia who have studied the process of regeneration since Spallanzani's day in the late eighteenth century, we have no more solved the problem than we have been able to cope with the very similar puzzle of the differentiation of organs in the growing egg cells of any animal or plant.

We have learned some remarkable things to add further to our puzzlement. The earthworm, being a vastly more complicated animal than a planarian flatworm, cannot be simply cut in two and then be expected to grow into two perfect annelids. If any number of segments up to ten is cut off the head of the American earthworm, a new head of four of five segments will form. If more than fifteen segments are amputated, no head will reappear; the wound will barely heal, and one has a headless little monster. On the other hand, regeneration of a new tail can occur at any level from the thirty-fifth segment back to the hind end. But the tail-amputated worm has a terrifyingly accurate memory. Every time the level of amputation is moved ten segments farther from the head, the average number of segments regenerated declines by ten.

Let us make this clear. The worm (say, *Eisenia foetida*) you are going to cut up originally has ninety-five segments. Suppose you cut at the eightieth segment. The regeneration process results then in exactly fifteen segments. If you cut at the fiftieth segment, the regeneration process will give back a new tail of exactly forty-five segments. How does the head end of the worm know when to stop adding segments? Of course this is precisely comparable to the development of the newly hatched juvenile worm which is born with exactly ninety-five segments. In its most naked form we are at the heart of the awful mystery of development and growth.

We shall find this regenerative ability, at least in separate limbs, echoed in some of the species to be put now in the spotlight, for we must now face up to the habits of the terrific phylum Arthropoda, which possibly (aside from that dark horse, the nematodes) must be regarded as including the most successful animals in the earth's history. Frankly the job is beyond me. Among the arthropods are animals which do anything imaginable and eat everything conceivably edible—each other, their mothers, all organic life and all the garbage from organic life.

8

A TRILLION TINY JAWS AND CLAWS

After some generalizations, we shall content ourselves with a few selected crustacean and insect scenarios—those we believe most instructive in telling the human race how to feed itself.

The segmented-body-plan relation of the arthropod phylum to annelid worms is quite obvious and, in fact, the arthropods have been described as annelids that knew what to do with their segments. The evolutionary gap is lost in the fog of pre-Cambrian time since some of the earliest fossils are those of the crustacean trilobites who ruled the oceans for several hundred million years.

Arthropods (*arthron*, joint+*pod*, foot) are conveniently divided according to their natural feeding tools into chelicerates, in which a pair of clawlike appendages (*chelicerae*, claws) takes the place of a jaw, and the mandibulate or jawed arthropods. The chelicerates have no antennae and none of them is capable of winged flight.

The spider nevertheless has been a constant source of edification or mild horror to mankind, while their cousins the ticks and mites have proved damnable nuisances. All these animals suck their food.

One of the earliest spiderlike creatures was *Limulus* who still thrives modestly on our beaches, being known as the horseshoe crab. It is not a crab. It is a "living fossil" and has been around these beaches with no change whatsoever for 175 million years. Although it has a shell and gills on its belly, it has claws instead of a jaw and lacks antennae. Its close relatives and contemporaries were the still older sea scorpions known as euryptids. Now extinct, for over 30 million years these terrifying animals sometimes grew to nine feet long.

(One need not fear the evolutionary emergence of any such formidable arthropod on earth for the simple reason that the molting habit of all arthropods entails an automatic limitation by gravity. When you are big and you shed your skeleton, as arthropods do, you are too weak to stand up and get around without the beneficent buoyancy that water provides.)

As a hunter and trapper, the spiders have lamentable deficiencies. Their eyes are usually weak and instead of the nimble antennae of the insect and crabs they have had to make do merely with palps as feelers. Yet so cunningly has evolution rewarded them compensation in the development of silk-making organs and the incredibly complex instincts for using this silk for flying through the air as spiderlings and for trapping food, that they will probably be around as long as there are small insects to feed upon. This is not to insist that spiders can eat only insects. A spider will eat anything live that is within certain size limits, which means small enough for it to catch. The fisher spiders, such as *Dolomedes*, catch trout fry, prize fishes in aquaria and tadpoles. A two-inch fish is no more formidable and tastes as good to a fishing spider as a robust grasshopper. The only requirement is that the fish must be brought to land (frequently after a considerable struggle) because the predigestive juices of the spider would be diluted in the water.

This is an urgent point. Although all spiders are predatory carnivores, they cannot eat solid food because thay have no chewing parts. Instead, they suck their victims dry, and thus may be likened to vampires. When we talk of spiders eating, we really mean clawing, chemical softening and sucking. The pharynx and stomach are blueprinted for this kind of dietary regime. The tubular pharynx and esophagus have heavy reinforced walls which prevent their collapse when the internal pressure is reduced. Powerful muscles attach the plated stomach walls to the thoracic skeleton, so that the walls can be pulled apart, creating a vacuum to suck in the juices of the victim. Surrounding the intestine is an organ for providing digestive enzymes, similar to that in crustaceans, which is a sort of combination of liver and pancreas.

The orb weavers are meticulous housekeepers. Bodies of insects, drained of their juices, are dumped off the top of the web; and their toilet habits are relatively dainty. They are careful to void their milky excrement in a sudden jet several inches from the web. (This habit is also common in certain nesting birds.)

Spiders have a double breathing system, the tracheae of insects and the peculiar "book lungs" (a series of platelets something like the leaves of a book), resembling the gill flaps of related marine arachnids, such as *Limulus*. In the more advanced spiders, such as the web spinners, the book lungs appropriately tend to become vestigials. The spider of the future, like the insect of the future, is likely to be smaller, since the tracheal system of respiration favors tiny animals.*

The large spiders, such as the tarantula, are relicts of an ancient past and may be on their way to extinction. They are pitifully unprepared to cope with such deadly enemies as the mud wasp or "tarantula hawk."

The spider's kidney system is double. It has Malpighian tubules, like those of insects in the abdomen, while in the forepart (cephalothora) it has a pair of coxal glands, similar to the "green glands" of the crayfish. This peculiar kind of kidney shows unmistakable relationship to the nephridia of earthworms and other annelids. It is highly probable that other glands in the body, originally excretory in nature, evolved into the spider's glandular masterpiece, her silk-manufacturing mechanism.

There is reason to believe that the spinning tools derived from double-branched abdominal appendages of ancient spiders probably were used as swimming organs. Associated with each of the "swimmerets" (as the present coxal glands are associated with forelegs) were organs that voided excretory products through a pore or some part of the swimming paddle. Silk is a protein and doubtless started out as a waste product. When evolution persuaded the spider that she could use these filaments in trapping and hunting, the primordial kidney became an exquisitely tuned factory for turning out different kinds and textures of silk on demand. The two pairs of double-branched swimming paddles of the third and fourth segments of the ancient spiders became the four pairs of spinnerets of the modern spiders. These organs retreated into the body, and it is only among the most primitive of today's spiders that the eight spinnerets can still be seen as fingerlike projections, like teats on a cow.

---

* Miniaturization may be a good stratagem for any animal, provided that the animal is highly *social*. It is not recommended for man since he has not attained truly social rapport and his brain must therefore remain large enough to provide the individual intelligence required of intrinsically solitary animals. Nearly all spiders are even more solitary than man and the success of their miniaturization must therefore depend on a corresponding miniaturization of their natural prey.

Since the spider's silk is also a food product (It is thriftily devoured by most orb spinners, who construct a new web every twenty-four hours), we are further interested in the goings on at the silk plant. The original kidney that dribbled waste over a swimming paddle has become a sort of industrial complex. Two large flasklike glands secrete the dragline that webmaking spiders spin out behind them wherever they go. It is used also to construct the frame, the lines and the spokes of an orb web. It is not sticky.* There are up to 200 small pear-shaped glands which secrete a silk protein that acts as a glue. It is used to anchor the dry dragline when a spider drops from the ceiling to the floor, and to cement together the web framework. There are many small, round organs called aciniform glands, which secrete silk for the elastic spiral line of the web and also swathing bands which the spider throws around a struggling insect caught in her web. There are also cylindrical glands that make a special silk used in wrapping the eggs in a cocoon. In the web weavers and several other spiders, tree-shaped glands secrete still another type of silk that does not harden upon contact with air but remains as sticky blobs along the lines of the web. Spiders that have a comblike tool, called a cribellum, for spreading out swathing bands of silk have special glands to supply the cribellum.

If we try to imagine the instinctive foremanship required by the spider in stopping and starting all these silk-producing machines synchronously as the instant occasion demands, we are again placing a shattering burden on the DNA molecule as a purveyor of inherited behavior. For it should be noted that spiders have no chance to be taught. When they hatch as spiderlings they crawl up a blade of grass or a fence post, turn into the wind and spin out their first pathetic little silk thread. As it becomes long enough and as the breeze strengthens, they are carried away, perhaps for many miles, even across bodies of water, as a storybook boy would be carried away by a big kite. Henceforth the chances are, with their weak eyesight, they will never see another spider until mating time. In many species this may also be eating time—for the female. In considering the diet of the arthropods, one should never leave the

---

* That spiders produce a non-sticky line could have been easily discovered by the ancient Greeks (who claimed a great interest in spiders) since the observation does not require a microscope. That it was not discovered by them demonstrates a certain fatal lack of practicality in their natural science.

husband off the menu. Spiders very commonly lose a leg at an
appropriate joint, where the blood flow will stop, in which case
they immediately suck it dry, for no spider will let food go to
waste. Bleeding, incidentally, is a very serious matter for spiders as
for all arthropods, since, instead of having the elaborate capillaries
of vertebrates, the whole return system to the heart is through
sinuses—interconnected internal pools of blood which can be quickly
drained if a break in the integument occurs. (Of course, this is
what makes any arthropod, including its own species, such desirable
food for the chelicerates. The sucking process then becomes very
efficient.)

Some mites make silk, although in thread so fine they are in-
visible to the naked eye. Men have often dreamed of making for-
tunes out of spider's silk. It is still used occasionally in optical
instruments like transits because of strength, fineness and uniformity.
A reel of spider silk fifty feet long sells for about $20. It is
possible that the fineness of spider's silk could be reduced to the
diameter of a protein molecule, if there were any incentive for the
spider. Spider webs and gossamer (the remnants of the flying lines
of spiderlings often blown together in masses by a March storm)
have been used by European peasants in stanching the flow of
blood from wounds. Yet the taming of spiders to produce commercial silk, which would be greatly superior to the silkworm's
product, has always turned out to be a losing proposition. The
silkworm is the larva of a moth and can be easily fed and tended.
Its silk derives from modified salivary glands in the head and
comes out in a single line which is usually between 400 and 700
yards long, representing the total lifework of the larva. The spider
on the other hand makes silk for many purposes. She is a solitary,
predatory animal, completely unco-operative, and is not about to
be milked. Spiders feed only on small living creatures and each
spinner has to be segregated, because when larger spiders are put
together, cannibalism immediately results. Discouraged by these implacable habits, man has always returned to the silkworm and to
the artificial spinnerets and to artificial fiber. And yet . . . would it
not be wonderful to know exactly how a spider can do the required
job instantaneously? Make a fiber unequalled by human synthetic
organic chemists in any property you can name? Not only that but
to card it, cut it, adjust it, put it together about a thousand times
as fast as the best Hong Kong tailor? A hundred million years or so

of inherited memory have gone into the perfection of this un-explained craft. It is the burden of several of my books that the learning of such crafts as these, the breaking of the code of crea-tivity in animals, the comprehension of entirely *all* of the physical and metaphysical tricks involved, will make man, through self-submergence in the animal kingdom, truly superman.

In studying the orb-weaving spiders, all men have been inspired as were such wildly diverse personalities as Fabre and Nietzsche. Question after question occurs to an observer. How, for example, does a spider keep from being caught in its own web? An answer comes simply from studying the creature's activities closely. It is very careful to step only on the dry radii, not the sticky and elastic spirals.

Although the orb-weaving spider has attracted men's aesthetic attention, it is another arachnid order (Acariniformes), including mites and ticks, that have caused him the most anxiety. Here the head, thorax and abdomen are fused into one. Some ticks and mites transmit diseases and many species of mites are themselves pestif-erous parasites of plants, animals and man. There is even a par-ticular mite that ruins cheese. They can all be identified as arach-nids by their eight legs and, like all arachnids, they eat by sucking.

The discovery that Texas cattle fever is tick-borne was made in 1893 by Theobald Smith and was the first time an arthropod had been found to transmit a disease. After Smith's work, Ronald Ross showed that malaria was transmitted by the bite of the *Anopheles* mosquito and soon thereafter Walter Reed and his team proved the role of mosquitoes in yellow fever.

The cattle tick carries a sporozoan that lives in red blood cells and is something like the organism responsible for malaria. A more peculiar transmission is involved in ticks whose sucking habits infect man with the viruslike Rickettsia that causes Rocky Mountain spotted fever. Scrub typhus, also a rickettsial disease, is transmitted by chiggers (the larvae of mites of the *Trombicula* group), while the bacterium-causing rabbit fever of tularemia is carried not only by ticks but by fleas, lice and horseflies. The virus of St. Louis encephalitis has been isolated in mites that are skin parasites on pigeons and chicks.

Aside from acting as carriers of disease organisms, mites can take the fun out of life in many ways. It has never been deter-mined why some people appear immune to the bite of chiggers, while in most people it causes red welts and excruciating itching. Mange in dogs and cats and other animals is caused by fertilized female mites who burrow into the skin and lay their eggs. Poultry mites are queer animals, whose habits have been closely studied, since it is possible to take advantage of the fact that they attack only at night. During the day they desert the host and hide in cracks and crevices where they can be smothered with oil. (An essential weakness of all trachea-breathing animals is that they are born suckers for oil-water mixtures which clog the respiratory apparatus. This is why mosquito larvae are wiped out by oiling stagnant ponds.) A fantastic case was reported in which mites in one household infested the baby but also liked to congregate in an electric clock, presumably on account of its warmth.

The case of the poultry mites who desert the chicken or another bird in the daytime is so curious that it has been attributed to the fact that birds often take daily dust baths. Evolution has taught the mites to avoid the dust-off treatment by invading the host only during roosting hours.

There are special mites that infest the inside of dogs' ears, parasitize horseflies, live on potato beetles, and attack leather and other materials of animal origin. An almost innumerable variety of mites attack plants. Especially noteworthy is *Tetranychus* and other so-called spider mites (or "bagworms") who spin silk from an opening near the mouth. A heavily infested plant may have its leaves covered with cobwebs from mites.

The water mites (hydrachnids) have the distinction of being the only members of the spider class that have colonized fresh water. They are predacious and parasitic, attacking small crustaceans, the larvae of aquatic insects and aquatic worms. They are active the year round even under the ice.

The life history of a typical tick consists mostly of waiting and molting. Ticks carry some kind of sensing device (Haller's organ) on the first pair of legs. In the case of the common dog tick *Dermacentor variabilia*, the egg hatches into the usual six-legged larva (common to all ticks and mites) which feeds on small mammals, such as field mice. When its belly is full of blood it drops off and molts into a nymph with eight legs. After some feeding on another mammal, it drops off in turn and molts into the adult. The adult tick climbs high up on a shrub, holds on with its third pair of legs and holds out its first pair with the Haller's organs, to sense the passing of a large mammal. It may wait indefinitely, for like many animals of the arachnid class it has a very patient stomach and a slow metabolism. That ticks are not very choosy about what they grab onto is shown by the standard field technique of collecting ticks—just drag a white woolen blanket slowly over grass and bushes. This trick has been disillusioning to those who were fond of believing in a sort of tick mystique, operating through the mysterious Haller's organs and zeroing in on your favorite dog. Ticks and mites have become so important and the number of species so large that their study has been given a special name, acarology.

The tick, although generally larger than the mite, is not in the same ball league. The mite, like the insect and the nematode, must be regarded as one of the world's most successful animals. It thrives in every little ecological nook from the reindeer moss of the polar regions to the tropical rain forest, under the bark of a tree, in the miller's flour barrel, between the gills of a mushroom, on the rancher's cattle as well as on the tulip bulbs nurtured by the rancher's wife. Mainly it is sucking or parasitizing some larger animal or plant. It can never in itself be regarded as a substantial food source.

This is quite contrary to the status of the marine arthropods which, among the mandibulates or jawed creatures, pile up into incredible living pools of sea food for fishes and whales and other citizens of the ocean.

The crustaceans (*crusta*, shell) are most simply defined as gill-breathing mandibulates, with two pairs of antennae and, generally, double-branched appendages. In the course of evolution from annelids, they converted the front two legs to a jaw. They vary in size from microscopic "fish lice" to the giant spider crab of Japan which measures twelve feet from tip to tip of its outstretched arms. There is no doubt of the close relationship between annelid worms and crustaceans, except that again the crustaceans have done something creative with their segments. Of the nineteen segments of a crayfish, for example, only three of the appendage pairs of their segments are alike. The appendages are specialized for feeling out the environment, handling food, fighting, breathing, walking, reproduction, swimming or escaping from enemies.

All the crustaceans live in water, except a few land crabs and pill bugs (the ones you find under rocks). The class is divided vaguely according to the nature of the feet. If one bears in mind the food economy of the oceans, the copepods (*kope*, oar+*poda*, foot) are by far the most important. They form the crucial link between the floating microscopic plant life, the phytoplankton or algae, which they eat, and everything in the ocean which eats them or which eats larger organisms which eat them. Without copepods, whose total numbers in all the salt water and fresh waters of the earth, run into very large powers of ten, like the number of inches between the sun and the star Betelgeuse, there would be no complex marine life as we know it. A baleen whale's breakfast, for instance, may consist of several tons of "krill" (copepods).

Under the microscope, the free-living copepod of the whale's breakfast is seen to be elongate with a shell covering the forepart. The forepart narrows to a segmented region and again to form a segmented abdomen ending in a pair of branched spikes. In some species the second antennae are very long and are used for swimming in quick little jerks. Those copepods who have degenerated into parasites are hardly recognizable as crustaceans; they look like tiny bugs. The procreative habit betrays them, because like respectable free-living copepods, the typical nauplius larva develops from the eggs.

The nauplius betrays the identity of other dubious crustaceans. It was only a little over a hundred years ago that another crustacean, the barnacle, escaped the classification of mollusk, to which it had been assigned because of its shell. Actually one should think of a barnacle as a small shrimplike animal standing on its head in a little house, kicking food into its mouth with its feet. It belongs to the subclass of cirripedes (*cirrus*, curl+*pedis*, of the foot) and, indeed, its most interesting feature is the jointed, curly legs. As a nauplius larva, it swims freely for a while, then latches onto a rock or a ship's bottom and undergoes metamorphosis into the shell-bearing adult. Various species of barnacles have become parasitic, since the nauplius decided to attach itself to a live fish or crab or a whale. In the course of evolution, holdfasts developed which penetrated the host's flesh. Perhaps the barnacle's chief claim to fame is the fact that it was the first animal to inspire Charles Darwin's specialized interest. He worked for eight years on barnacles, becoming a real professional biologist a full decade before the *Origin of Species*.

Another subclass is the branchiopods (*branchia*, gills+*poda*, feet) in which the leaflike appendages serve both as gills and as swimming organs. *Cladocera*, a common water flea, occurs in such great numbers in the Great Lakes that it displaces the copepods as the staple fish food. Its offspring are nourished not only by the usual yolk but by supplementary secretions from the walls of the brood chamber. The fairy shrimps are the most primitive of the branchiopods because they have no shell, each segment being free as in the earthworm. These fragile and glasslike little creatures feed only in the nauplius form since the adults last only long enough to procreate.* Many of the fairy shrimps can live only in ice-cold water. They disappear with the late spring. Another branchiopod is the water flea *Daphnia*. It is a common prey of other small carnivorous animals, such as hydras, tropical fishes and tadpoles. Nevertheless this water flea is a complicated little beast. Its exoskeleton is molted seventeen times. Growth occurs right after each molt before the new exoskeleton has had a chance to harden. The segmentation is not very obvious, but its five pairs of leafy legs produce a respiratory current of water that also brings in food particles (algae, small copepods). Its second antennae have branched into antlerlike forms that are used for swimming. An important point about *Daphnia* is that, in spite of its relative complexity (glandular digestive system, rapidly pulsing heart, compound eyes, sensory bristles), it is all female. Normally it produces unfertilized eggs which develop only into females. It is significant that males, when they occur rarely, do so under what might be called depression conditions. This is not an uncommon state of affairs. The male is a kind of accident, deriving from bad water or semi-starvation. When in various arthropod species he is regularly present, he is more than likely to be eaten by the female as part of the nuptial proceedings, or when tolerated, he gets cuffed around or spends his life as a degraded parasite on the fat female person.

Among the ostracod crustaceans (*ostrakodes*, having a shell), sometimes called seed shrimps, males are absolutely unknown in many species. The ostracod has also simplified its small body. It has no heart and the number of appendages is reduced. It eats plankton and pond weeds and is evidently a degenerate form, although not parasitic. There is something of enduring pathos about the ostracods. They are careful not to offend anybody, even in dying. Their

---

* This is an evolutionary stratagem which we shall see repeated in such arthropods as the ant lion. Although it does not make much sense to a life-greedy animal, such as man, its efficiency in passing on the germ plasm with an adult phase which requires no food, is obvious.

delicate little bodies dry up within their own organic coffins. They remind one of the romantic land of Indian fable where the old women shriveled up but could be revived by steeping in water to share their wisdom with a tribe in trouble.

We go now to fiercer creatures. The very large group of malacostracans contains all the bigger crustacean forms with which we are familiar but also some remarkable small creatures. For example, the amphipods or beach fleas show the famous "sun compass" response. If they are moved from a beach facing the ocean on the east and placed in a dish from which they can see only the sky, when they begin to dry up they will move eastward. But if their native beach has faced the sea on the south, then under the same open-sky laboratory conditions they will move southward. Since this orientation takes place regardless of the time of day, they must have a biological clock which allows them to compensate for the motion of the sun.

The isopods include the pill bugs and sow bugs which most people assume are related to other "bugs" rather than the crabs. (The fact is, the word "bug" has no zoological meaning.)

The mysids are small shrimplike animals found along the shores of most oceans. They have double-branched legs, a very primitive trait going back to the oldest fossils known. However, their family place among the malacostracans is clear from the fact that as adults they resemble the larval stages of lobsters and shrimps.

Another small food-providing member of the malacostracan subclass is the euphausiid. These tiny creatures have very large eyes and there are luminous areas on the eyestalks, the leg bases and the underside of the abdomen. They occur in such huge population explosions that in many regions of the ocean they form a layer dense enough to reflect sound. It is they who have received publicity for producing false depth readings on modern marine-sonar instruments. In the antarctic they displace the copepods as the favorite food of the baleen whales. The gigantic blue whale is especially fond of them.

The decapods are the crustaceans with which we ourselves are on best eating terms. They have ten feet (*deko*, ten+*poda*, feet), although the first pair is usually a greatly enlarged pair of fierce claws. Included are such famous names as *Homarus*, the northern lobster; *Panulires*, the southern or spiny lobster; *Cambarus*, the crayfish; *Cancer*, the rock crab (also a sign of the zodiac); *Callinectes*, the blue crab; *Uca*, the fiddler crab; *Palaemonetes*, the fresh-water shrimp; and *Pagurus*, the hermit crab.

Because of its cheapness and availability, more anatomical and biochemical research has been expended on the crayfish than on any other crustacean. Although there are some 130 species in the United States alone, they are so much alike and so similar to the northern lobster that a single crayfish serves well as a model decapod.

The digestive system consists of a fore-gut (including an esophagus and two-part stomach), a mid-gut to which the combination liver-pancreas is attached, and a hind-gut comprising the rest of the intestine. The cardiac part of the double stomach is outfitted with a so-called "gastric mill," three complex teethlike organs that grind up food. Thus the decapod is well designed to digest everything he can catch, which includes other shelled creatures. After being chewed in the gastric mill, food passes into the smaller pyloric stomach where it meets enzymes from the liver-pancreas. Like the vertebrate liver, this organ is a priceless chemical Jack-of-all-trades. In addition to secreting digestive enzymes, it stores food, regulates the sugar concentration in the blood and reduces the waste nitrogen compounds to simple ammonia, which being almost infinitely soluble in water is easily thrown overboard by an aquatic animal. The excretory system consists of a pair of "green glands" located in the head at the bases of the second antennae, and in fact the attached bladder opens to the outside by a pore in these antennae. This is much as if we urinated through our ears. Decapods, of course, have an anus in the usual rear position at the end of the hind-gut.

The molting process is very serious in all arthropods, since it is only by periodically shedding of the whole exoskeleton, including part of the intestinal tract and the stomach lining, that these animals can grow. In decapods, it is a time not only of physical danger but of chemical crisis—how to get enough calcium to form a new skeleton? First of all, decapods eat this discarded exoskeleton right after molting. Furthermore, in the actual process of molting, calcium is absorbed from the softening exoskeleton and is deposited in the pancreas-liver for further use. When about to molt, the animal seeks a sheltered nook, arches itself and pulls out of the old skeleton

by extraordinary acrobatic maneuvers that we can best compare
with a man trying to get out of an old suit of winter underwear
through the flap in the seat.

Adult crayfish usually molt twice a year, once in the spring
and once in the fall. The molting process is controlled by hormones,
which are molt-inducing and molt-preventing. The organs that
secrete the preventing hormone (X organs) are located in the eyestalk; thus molting takes place within about fifteen days after the eyestalks are removed. The so-called Y organs, located near the base
of the jaw muscles, secrete the molt-inducing hormone which is
similar to the "ecdysone" hormone of insects. The crabbing industry
is understandably interested in these phenomena. Soft crabs (that
is, any crab that has just molted) bring the highest prices, but
they are very shy and hard to bait. A practical technique for inducing molting in crabs that have been caught and placed in
enclosures is wanted by the crabbers. It is noteworthy that extracts of a mammal's pituitary gland, when injected into crustaceans,
produce the same results as crab-eyestalk extracts.

Like spiders, crustaceans have sinus-type blood-return systems
and a wound in a leg could quickly drain the whole body. A crab
will break off an injured leg at a special breaking point by the
action of a muscle designed explicitly for this purpose. At the
breaking points there are located preformed membranes that lessen
hemorrhage.

Crustaceans by no means have the regenerative versatility of
their forefathers, the annelid worms. There are some peculiar limitations. If the end of an eye is amputated, a new eye will regenerate.
If, however, the entire eyestalk is cut off, not an eye but an antenna
is formed. This must mean something, but so far crustaceologists
have not found out what. If the big claw of a crab or lobster
is removed, in subsequent molts the remaining smaller claw will
become the big one and the amputated great claw will be replaced
by a small one, thus reversing the symmetry. Since problems of
regeneration are very close to the essential mysteries of tissue
differentiation in embryonic growth, these curious happenings are
trying to tell us something, but as yet we have not learned to
communicate—the medium remains the message. . . . The Andalu-
sians are content with the medium, in the case of fiddler crabs. They
pick the claws and let the animal live and molt to produce another
big claw from the other side later. This enormous claw is comparable

to a lobster tail in content of delicious meat. Male fiddler crabs in fighting concentrate on trying to snatch off the opponent's big claw.

We have mentioned the stubbornness of robber crabs in refusing to eat anything except coconuts. The really astonishing thing is that this is the only animal known that can open a coconut, unaided. The South Sea Islanders know how to catch him. The crab climbs the tree to cut the coconut, then climbs down backward. The natives climb up part way and fasten a girdle of grass to the tree. When the crab crawls down, he feels the grass and thinks he's reached the ground. He tumbles down, stunned, and the natives fall upon him.

The structure of the compound eye is strikingly similar in crustaceans and insects, hence apparently these extraordinarily complicated organs have arisen twice in the course of evolution. The great neurologist Ramon y Cajal admitted that the complexity of the nerve-fiber tracks behind a compound eye "staggers the imagination." It should be mentioned that some ancient arthropods such as *Limulus*, are able, like bees, to analyze polarized light. Since light reflecting off the sea is polarized (some of the directions of vibration of a light wave being canceled out), it has long been suspected that the ability of an animal to get around and find its way to the water and even to navigate in the water may be connected with an ability (which we humans do not have) of detecting light polarization.

Crustaceans have an organ, consisting of a cavity in the basal segment of each first antenna, opening to the outside by a small pore and containing many sensory hairs and sand grains. These so-called "statocysts" are organs of equilibration. They tell the animal when he is right side up and moving in a sober manner. If a crayfish is allowed to molt in an aquarium containing iron filings, some iron filings instead of sand will deposit in the renewed statocysts. This crayfish will make patterned movements in response to a magnet.

The migratory habits of some of the larger crustaceans reflect the pull of old evolutionary forces. Since salt water is where the crustaceans were first evolved, the blue crab moves down Chesapeake Bay to the Virginia capes into saltier water every year to breed, returning several hundred miles up the bay to feed during the rest of the year. All land crabs migrate to the sea to breed. The spring lobster forgets its fear of light and crawls over the bottom in broad daylight on its way to deeper water at breeding season.

In the stupendous arthropod class of Insecta, we see feeding at its most artful, even horrible levels. And we see a new thing in feeding—where the larval form of the animal is a savage, crafty predator, while the adult may be a gentle vegetarian or may not even eat at all. We see societies of animals, where the gathering of a particular food is highly practiced and societies where a specialized agriculture has been carried on for millions of years before man grew wheat or corn.

In a technical sense, insects are easily defined as mandibulate arthropods which have three pairs of legs when adult. The body is divided into head, thorax and abdomen. The thorax bears both the three pairs of legs and the two pairs of wings.

The damage done to man and his works by insects is so incalculable that an impartial observer of the planet might have concluded early in our history that if the fight for dominance of the land was to be fought between mammals and insects, the issue was all too clear. In a few million years, mammals would be exterminated. They may yet be, for the explosive evolutionary drive of the insects has by no means been permanently paralyzed. Mosquitoes, for example, develop mutational resistance to insecticides nearly as fast as we can learn to synthesize new ones, and in our panic we strew poisons upon the land and in the water which kill friendly animals as well as ourselves. As will be pointed out later, we may have to take lessons from the coniferous trees that have learned to resist insect attacks by a method of such subtlety that it could have only arisen by evolution over many hundreds of millions of years.

The insect, as evolved from millipedelike ancestors by the ploys of neoteny, is really not very old, at least compared with its crustacean relatives which we have just reviewed. This is because living on the land depended first on the plants colonizing the lands, for otherwise there would be nothing to eat. Thus the first insects were vegetarians and, as the plants grew higher, insects learned to fly to reach the foliage. It was at that stage, long before the age of flowering plants, that the insects developed wings. It was natural selection in its most critical form, for the insects had to chase their food upward. And it was also at this stage that certain plants, such as the conifers, learned their subtle trick. Otherwise, so madly, unthinkingly voracious are insect swarms, one would guess that both trees and insects would have perished together and perhaps life on land would have come to an end a hundred million years before the time of the dinosaurs.

The earliest fossil insects are found in Carboniferous strata laid down some 300 million years ago. They are cockroaches. The intimate relationship between insect and ancient tree are seen in the fact that the best preserved fossils are those found enclosed in amber (the fossil resin of conifers).

The first thing we ask in classifying an insect is whether it has wings or not. The most primitive kinds, such as springtails, silverfish and firebrats, are not only wingless, and thus close to the ancestral millipede, but have no metamorphosis (distinct change in form from juvenile or larval form to adult form) and also have no jaws. The silverfish and the firebrats are old enemies of librarians, since they have the ability to digest cellulose and like to inhabit seldom-disturbed books, such as the collected works of Anthony Trollope.

The winged insects are divided mostly according to the mechanics of metamorphosis. In one division (evolutionally the oldest) the egg hatches into a form that looks like a miniature adult with small wing pads. The larvae are called nymphs and molt successively until the adult or imago is reached. One order is the orthopterans (*orthos*, straight+*pteron*, wing) which includes grasshoppers, crickets, cockroaches, walking sticks, praying mantises, etc. The chewing parts are all-purpose and unspecialized. The cockroaches, being very ancient, eat anything, including clothing. The grasshoppers (or locusts, as they are called in Europe) are destructive vegetarians, while the praying mantis is a fierce carnivore, feeding on other insects, but in the tropics some large species can capture small birds, lizards and frogs. It is very beneficial to man because of its appetite for insect pests. In some American states for this reason the mantis is a protected animal. The female usually devours the male in the act of copulation, and Fabre in his typical florid and high-octane prose has given a very pathetic account of the poor husband, with head and upper body chewed away, still managing to get through the final spasms of the sex act. For carnivores, such as the mantis and spiders, this is a perfectly logical course of events. The main object of the adult phase of such animals is to produce surviving young and if the male can supplement his contribution of sperm by the gift of his body as food for the pregnant female, he has doubly donated and is a sacrificial hero. (It must be remembered that in the vast majority of insects the parents die shortly after egg laying.)

One order of the primitive (gradual metamorphosis) division consists only of the termites. Termites are at least as different from ants as elephants are from giraffes. The ants are a modern animal, deriving from primitive wasps, while the termite is perhaps as old as the cockroach. Because it smells of such antiquity and its mode of metamorphosis is so old-fashioned and simple, it has been customary for entomologists to look down their noses at the termite, but this seems undeserved and haughty discrimination. The termite has managed, in the first place, to make a remarkable deal with certain flagellated protozoans who live in its gut and digest wood for it. Secondly, the termites have adopted social practices of such unbelievable co-operative delicacy and nuance that some people have regarded a termite colony as a single animal, held together in its parts perhaps by some unknowable extrasensory drive. Termites have castes and subcastes: winged reproductives, wingless productives, workers, soldiers, nurses and bottle washers. Unlike ants and bees, where all workers are underdeveloped females, with termites there are males and females in every caste. There is not only a queen, there is a king. Simply because they eat our houses and are as old as the cockroach does not justify our failure to afford them respect as one of the most remarkable animals ever developed.

The Odonantiformes (*odontos*, tooth) are the dragonflies and damsel flies. Their larvae develop in the water, and both nymph and adult are extraordinarily skillful carnivores. The dragonfly nymph has a strange "mask"—a kind of superstructure on the jaw for seizing small insect prey. The adult is a splendid, though primitive animal. It will dart through a swarm of gnats, engulfing dozens of them in the scoop formed by its hairy front legs and chewing impassively as it flies on to more interesting prey. Fossils of giant dragonflies have been found, but unlike the dinosaurs, it was able to stay on earth by miniaturization. The tracheal system of insect breathing does not favor large organisms, and the archaic dragonflies were evidently slow fliers—otherwise they would not have been able to keep up the pace, because of lack of oxygen. Perhaps their relatively simple, unspecialized body plan allowed them to shrink in size and increase in wing speed, whereas the dinosaur was too far gone in gigantism to withstand the countless rain of eons of geologic time and climatic change.

Another order includes the aphides, cicadas, tree hoppers, plant lice and scale insects. These are mostly destructive pests, their mouth parts and digestive systems being designed to suck up the sap from plants. The fluid finally discharged from the intestine sometimes contains sugars. This is the origin of the "honeydew" produced by plant lice or aphids.

The order of Hemipteriformes (*hemo*, half+*pteron*, wing) consists of the insects we commonly call bugs (stinkbugs, bedbugs, water striders and water bugs). Half of each forewing is leathery, the other half membranous. Piercing and sucking parts are essential tools of their sometimes infamous trade. The notorious chinch bug destroys grain in the Mississippi Valley. Many of the bug order destroy garden crops. The so-called "kissing bug" is held responsible for transmitting the trypanosome of Chagas' disease in South America, while the bedbug is not the housewife's favorite insect nor does it find favor with the fitfully snoozing skid-row bum.

There are some fierce animals in this order. The "assassin bug" entices ants by an irresistible secretion. Ants are suckers for chemically pleasing materials, but the bug's lure is a Mickey Finn. It contains a paralyzing narcotic and while under its influence the ant is sucked dry. The "wheel bug" injects into its prey a venom which has the power to digest and liquefy the inner tissues. Thus this creature actually digests its food outside its own body, pumping the dissolved innards of the prey into its own stomach. How can an enzyme juice so powerful and instantaneous be stored by the assassin bug without harm to its own tissues? This is a problem analogous to the perennial one of why our digestive juices do not eat out our stomach linings. Sometimes, of course, they do and we have ulcers. The answer probably lies in special anti-enzymes or special chemically resistant cells. For its size, the giant water bug is probably the most powerful of all hunters. Its venom can subdue small snakes and fishes and even birds.

The blood-sucking lice constitute a separate wingless order, regarded, however, as having degenerated from a winged insect of more noble habits. It is of course the carrier of typhus and of relapsing and other fevers. Remote cousins are the wingless chewing lice and bird lice. They also have degenerated from a winged ancestor. They eat hair, feathers or the dermal scales of birds' feet and legs.

The thrips constitute another order of gradual metamorphosis. They have two pairs of wings like little toothpicks covered with microscopic bristles. With their piercing and sucking mouth parts, they can ruin many crops, especially onions, strawberries and pears. A few species are carnivorous, feeding on aphids. Obviously, they should be encouraged, as are ladybugs.

When we consider now those insects that have a complete metamorphosis, in which the wings, for example, develop within the larval body, entomologists believe we are dealing with a recent kind of animal. Since metamorphosis, either of the gradual or the complete type, is nearly universal among insects, one asks oneself, what is it good for? Although the crustaceans and many other invertebrate marine animals undergo larval stages, it would seem in a general way that the purposes on land and in the sea are different. In the sea the larval stage is usually a traveling stage. It is dispersed as widely as possible. The nauplius of a crustacean gets around. The spider travels as the spiderling over meadow and river, unfed and able to go for weeks without feeding. But in the insect, the roles are reversed. The larva is pre-eminently the feeding stage, immobile or crawling. It is the adult who by its powers of flight can disseminate the species. It is the adult who is a sort of flying machine for reproduction. Very often the two bodies are fantastically different (as in insects which undergo complete metamorphosis). The larva may live in the water or under the bark of a tree or even in the nose of a sheep, while the adult flies in the air, looking for enough food to allow it to continue flying to seek a mate or, in some cases, for food on which its eggs can grow. In the meantime it is also achieving wide geographical dispersal of its genes.

This system of dividing up one's life into two entirely separate existences—separate both in form and function—must be a good one. Its tremendous success is illustrated by the zoological fact that no insect family—in the taxonomic sense of the word—has ever been known to become extinct. That, of course, is the ultimate criterion of animal success. The individual lifetime of the adult is only as long as it takes to "do the job." In the spiders we have seen that it is the most modern and successful ones that live the shortest lives. (Orb weavers average a year, while the obsolescent tarantula may live as long as the wasps allow her.) The one-year generation is also popular with insects. The modern style, so to speak, in arthropod life is to be small and to die young, having made full nutritional precautions for the next larval generation. This great scheme of life can only be achieved, of course, with the establishment of the absolute primacy of instinct. When you die before your young are hatched, you cannot teach them anything. They have to learn by the principle of transcendental or metaphysical memory, which, as I hope to convince the reader, is by no means as rhetorical a process as it sounds. It is simply a memory that does not depend on the *physical* continuity of the living structures that are doing the "remembering." It is the pragmatic resolution of the otherwise flabbergasting and sense-shattering dualism between mind and matter—between life and the non-living universe. Perhaps it is appropriate that this pragmatic resolution should be made most plain in a creature as inhuman and intrinsically alien to us as the insect.

This central theme will continue to engage us, but let us return to the process of metamorphosis. The changes that take place during complete metamorphosis (as when a caterpillar becomes a butterfly) are biochemically drastic in the extreme. In the quiescent pupa certain organs are broken down, digested by phagocytic white blood cells and used to build new ones. The wings, legs, eyes and mouth parts of the adult (imago) are formed from the so-called "imaginal disks," groups of new cells. These disks can, in fact, be removed from one larva and implanted into the body of another, where they will develop into extra organs.

The stimulus to metamorphosis arises from hormones that are located in the brain. Nothing so well demonstrates the evolutionary relationship between the nerves and the glands as the fact that these brain-derived hormones act (as do the pituitary hormones, from glands in the base of the brain in vertebrates) by triggering off other glands in the insect. The hormone of the prothoracic glands, ecdysone, acts on the skin and other structures, inducing them to grow and molt. Thus ecdysone seems to correspond to the hormone of the Y organ in crustaceans. Another, so-called "juvenile hormone," *prevents* metamorphosis. (As we shall learn later, it was the secret of the ancient conifers to learn how to synthesize this chemical and, by offering it to the insect larvae who harassed them, to paralyze this development.)

We do not know for sure how these various hormones that induce or retard metamorphosis are balanced, but the equilibrium seems definitely to depend on the glands in the brain. It has been shown in the case of the American silkworm (a larva) that the brain must be chilled for about two weeks before it will release the hormone that triggers the prothoracic gland. This makes sense for the insect, because it prevents the larva from metamorphosis and hatching in the late summer or fall, which would not allow the adult moth time enough to do the job of breeding and hatching before it perished in the cold of winter.

The Neuropteriformes (*neuron*, nerve+*pteron*, wings) are the dobson flies and the ant lions. The aquatic larva of the former is a favorite bait of fishermen. The ant lion is one of the oddest examples of huntsman. As an adult it looks something like a modest dragonfly but is actually a poor flier and for good reasons. The adults do not eat. Their flying is purely for mating approaches—so that boy can meet girl. The larva (sometimes known as the "doodle-bug") is something else again. It excavates small pitfalls in sandy locations and hides in the bottom of the pit on the shady side. When an ant or other pedestrian insect comes to pause, antennae flickering, on the brink of the pit, the ant lion goes to work madly tossing sand in the air, causing little landslides. The ant slides down toward his predator and is stabbed with a deadly venom.

The Coleopteriformes (*koleos*, sheath+*petron*, wing) are the beetles—an enormous order, including probably more species than any other group of insects. The forewings are horny sheaths not used in flying, which is accomplished solely by the membranous hindwings. All the beetles chew and may be carnivorous or vegetarian. Among the carnivores are tiger beetles, water beetles, various ground beetles, the glowworms and fireflies and the much-admired ladybirds which eat aphids. The herbivorous species include the cotton boll weevil and other weevils in which the mouth is at the end of a long snout. Some sly tricks have been developed by the predator beetles. There are, for example, the "trash carriers," who disguise themselves for capturing game by carrying the waste garbage from previous meals on their backs, so that they look like slowly moving hunks of dirt.

The diving water beetle (*Dytiscus*) is a ferocious animal and its larva carries ferocity to an actually absurd degree. Its venom is an exceedingly powerful digestive enzyme, as in the case of the wheel

bug. Two equal-sized Dytiscus larvae may seize each other simultaneously and both will die a quick death by inner dissolution. There
are very few animals, even when starving, which will attack an equal-
sized animal of its own species in order to devour it. Yet Dytiscus
larvae will attack and consume each other, even when there is other
food at hand. This is perhaps unique in the animal world and
requires more study. Conceivably it is a disease associated with
overpopulation.

On the other hand, the ambrosia beetles cultivate fungi as
food crops, an agricultural achievement which is shared by some
African termites and some ants and which will be discussed more
fully from the ant point of view.

The Lepidoteriformes (lepis, scale+pteron, wing) include the
butterflies and moths, which to the delight and wonder of every
schoolchild, demonstrate complete metamorphosis in its most theatrical aspects. The pupal instar is commonly called the chrysalis. The
chrysalis of a moth is usually enclosed within a silver cocoon, while
the butterfly in this stage is merely supported around the waist by a
silken thread spun by the caterpillar just before it molts.

Moths are generally nocturnal with threadlike antennae, while
butterflies are creatures of the day and have antennae with a knob
or swelling at the end.

Both adult moths and butterflies are nectar and pollen eaters,
hence the order is probably no older than the flowering plants
(Cenozoic era).

It is only during the caterpillar or worm stage that actual
growth occurs. As it stores food and grows, the number of cells does
not increase; the cells merely become larger.

Moths and butterflies, being preyed upon rather than preying,
are provided with exquisite defensive tricks as well as methods for
detecting the opposite sex. A male gypsy moth can detect the odor
of the female at a distance of two miles. The wings of many
butterflies are distinctively colored and patterned, according to sex
and species. There are cases of edible butterflies (edible for birds)
coming through evolutionary change in wing color and pattern to
resemble an unrelated but bird-displeasing species of butterfly. Certain species of moths that are eaten by bats have learned to detect
the ultrasonic signals which the bats send out to locate their prey
by echo and when the (to us inaudible) beeps occur the moths
dive to the ground.

The relation between plants and insects, especially as exemplified by the lepidoptera, is one of the most significant on earth. For one thing, insects are by far the most important herbivores; they consume more tonnage of plant tissue than any other kind of animal. The butterflies and moths eat their healthy share—*but only in the larval form.* The prickly-pear cactus, which once covered thousands of square miles in Australia, is now rare, having been all but wiped out by the cactus moth from South America—but the wiping out was done by the caterpillar. Many plants have developed defenses. Certain caterpillars normally do not feed on holly leaves but will gobble them up if the sharp points are cut away. Plant chemicals act both as poisons and as attractants. Plants of the citrus and parsley family, although unrelated, have in common certain essential oils that are wonderfully attractive to the caterpillars of the black swallowtail buterfly family. They will even eat filter paper soaked in these oils. Caterpillars of the cabbage white butterfly are attracted by mustard oil and will eat plants on which they normally do not feed when these are treated with mustard oil glucosides. On the other hand, the very large coffee family of plants, with 10,000 species, is rarely touched by caterpillars, probably because of the bitter quinine-type alkaloids developed by these plants, undoubtedly as insect repellants.

Butterflies that are distasteful to birds are generally those that have developed immunity to the alkaloids in such plants and therefore eat them. As a consequence, when a bird swallows such a caterpillar, it is like swallowing a quinine pill. The larvae of the monarch butterfly like to feed on plants of the milkweed family which is rich in cardiac glycosides, such as digitalis. Birds won't eat these caterpillars. They will feed with relish, however, on a generation of monarch butterflies raised on cabbage.

Butterflies evolved from the nocturnal moth and owe their success largely to their decision to feed during the day. Because of their choice of food plants, all butterflies are somewhat distasteful as compared with moths.

For some creatures in this order, life is short in the adult stage. The Polyphemus moths, almost as big as bats, fly low hunting only for love. They are too vulnerable to try to hunt for food. They eat nothing. Their brief moonlit nights are for mating and for oblivion.

Next to the beetles, the most successful order of insects by number of species is the Dipteriformes (*di-*, two+*pteron*, wing), comprising flies, mosquitoes and gnats. As the name indicates, they have only two wings, the hindwings having been reduced to a curious pair of structures called halteres—short rods with knobs on the ends. The Dipteriformes have sucking mouths and the larva is generally a legless maggot. They have an ancient history, dating back into the Paleozoic. There is no animal that has so plagued human beings by transmitting diseases and also merely by its ugly presence. In the far north of Canada and Siberia, almost microscopic biting gnats and midges, called "no-see-ums," can make life almost unbearable. Although mostly bloodsuckers, garbage collectors and occasionally carnivores, the Hessian fly is an exception, since it feeds on wheat stems and is extremely destructive.

The robber fly has taken to catching and eating other insects with much the same swift implacability as the totally unrelated dragonfly. He has a chitinous cutting tool, which has the virtue of continuous regenerative sharpness. He can cut through a hundred beetle backs and still be effective. Mosquitoes also use chitinous cutters to pierce the skin of their prey and drink their blood.

Although fleas have no wings, they are advanced insects, belonging to the order Siphonapteriformes (*siphon*, tube+*apteron*, no wings), which undergoes complete metamorphosis. The wings are modified for piercing and sucking. Next to the mosquitoes, they have been man's most terrible insect enemy, since they are specific carriers of the bubonic plague. The flea is not a notably successful animal, numbering only about a thousand species, each with an attachment for a certain kind of mammal. However, as we know to our displeasure, some of these are not too proud to change hosts. The human flea, *Pulex irritans*, will readily attack cats, dogs and rats. The same is true for *Ctenocephalus felis*, the cat flea, and *C. canis*, the dog flea. The maggots live obscurely in cracks in the floor, among straw or dirt, living on organic debris.

9

THE SOCIAL STOMACHS

Let us skip hurriedly from such a miserable animal to the magnificent order of Hymenopteriformes (*hymen*, membrane+ *pteron*, wing) which includes the bees, wasps, ants and ichneumons. Here we are in a brave new world of insects, undoubtedly the most modern and highly developed of any of the phylum of arthropods.

Although it is the highly complex but highly rigorous societies of the hymenoptera that have infinitely fascinated observant men, one must not overlook their individual capabilities. A worker honeybee is a marvel of specialized equipment. She approaches a flower as a plumber would approach a leaky toilet with his kit. She has a sucking tube within which a furry tongue moves up and down; a pair of claws to hold onto rough surfaces and between them a flaplike pulvillus to stick to flat surfaces. The front legs are outfitted with a semicircular brush and a hinged scraper which work together as an antenna cleaner. The middle leg has a spur used to pick off the scales of wax secreted between the abdominal segments. The hind legs carry pollen baskets composed of the concave broad side of the leg, plus long bristles. Her "honey stomach" is designed for storage of the nectar collected on the daily round, but it can also provide her with flight fuel. Poor thing, her egg-laying organ, at the biochemical command of her queen, has been transformed into a stinger and she will never become a mother (unless perchance the queen dies). So instinctual is her patriotism for hive and species that she will unhesitatingly drive her weapon into an enemy, dying of self-evisceration in the process.

Let all who believe that the natural animal will never commit an act lethal to itself mark well this kamikaze act. Its international effectiveness is borne out by the fact that a toad, once stung, will even avoid harmless flylike creatures whom evolution has taught to look and buzz like bees.

Since we shall examine in another place many aspects of the social structure of the bees as well as their controversial means of communication, we confine ourselves at present to their food habits, which nonetheless concern their techniques of reproduction, since as in all metamorphizing insects the eating generation is primarily the larval generation. In social insects, however, the eggs are not laid in a nest of food and left. Solitary wasps will go to incredible lengths to stalk and paralyze spiders and other prey, lay eggs in this live food, and trust to baby's instinct to eat his way to maturity and freedom. In the hives or hills of social instincts there is on the contrary an interminable parade of frantically busy nurses.

The only adult reproductive individual in a hymenopterous colony is one fertilized female. Males (or drones) are produced parthenogenetically (i.e., without fertilization of the egg). Workers are underdeveloped females to which the queen gives birth by portioning out a few of the sperms that she accumulated in receptacles in the abdomen from the nuptial flight perhaps the year before. (This discovery was made over a century ago by a German beekeeper who was alarmed by the fact that in one of his hives all the brood was hatching into drones. The queen was so old she had run out of sperm.

Consider now, after the rites of spring have begun, the literally killing job of the worker bees. Each insistent little larva, after hatching, must be fed about 1300 times a day or 10,000 times during its period of growth. In its first six days out of the egg it increases in size by a factor of 1500. The flying worker delivers a load of nectar to the younger workers or "house nurses." This package is passed back and forth and certain enzymes are added to digest the natural sugars. But baby must also have protein, which it gets from pollen. Some workers gather pollen in the morning and nectar in the afternoon. Others devote their lives to collecting one or the other. No worker collects both nectar and pollen on the same trip. During a normal summer, a worker in a single day may collect nectar from 250,000 flowers and make 37,000 trips to fetch a pound of nectar, involving a combined flight distance of 300,000 miles. The average hive will also consume 100 pounds of pollen during the summer.

The wing loading that the home-coming worker achieves in flight is fantastic. When "empty" she weighs about 80 milligrams, but she will carry 70 milligrams of nectar. For the backbreaking work she herself needs 40 milligrams of sugar per hour. She is expected to make wax for building the comb, which the young workers do while hanging from the top of the nest site and secreting wax scales from certain glands. This is a tough job and the wax-making bees consume eight pounds of honey for every pound of wax deposited. It is not only a tough job; it is a perfect job. Mathematicians have determined that the shape of wax cells is such as to hold the largest amount of honey with the smallest amount of building material. (So great is the uniformity that in the eighteenth century Réamur suggested that the diameter of beeswax cells be used as an international unit of measurement.) The worker has other jobs. She makes "bee glue" from resins (propolis) gathered in trees which is applied in making the hive watertight, encasing dead mice that might have intruded into the hive, etc.

Moreover, workers also make the honey. When the enzyme-treated nectar is placed in the cells, the workers fan it with their wings so that it evaporates and solidifies.* When weather becomes

---

* When fermented, honey becomes the Teutonic drink, mead. The word "honey-moon" comes from the old German custom for drinking mead for thirty days after a wedding. If you weren't drunk by then, you were dead. Anthony Ludovici, an English Nietzschean of the Edwardian era, complained bitterly that Britain had lost its virility since it gave up the mead drinking of Anglo-Saxon times and took to sissified beverages such as Scotch whiskey, gin, beer and port wine.

Honey was used by the ancient Egyptians, since they had no sugar plants. Even with the development of sugar cane and sugar beets, man has in later, less leisurely years come to fall in love with honey, which may vary, as wines vary, from the nearly water-white product from alfalfa blossoms, through the amber from goldenrod, to the almost coal-black nectar from buckwheat or privet. By moving his hives a beekeeper can vary his honey as a vintner varies his wine. The strong flavor of wild-thyme honey may be smoothly diluted when the mild-flavored alfalfa nectar is gathered simultaneously. Basswood, a light honey used by packers to make more ethereal the final blend, has a minty taste and is more common today, because as farms are abandoned in northeastern America many of the fields have changed into woods containing basswood trees.

In the case of appleblossom honey, bees collect almost no surplus, making it a rare commodity. This is because in the United States apples flower during May when the incoming nectar is used for feeding the young almost as fast as it is collected.

There is an important nutritional advantage of honey. Sucrose (common table sugar) has been under suspicion, as have saturated animal fats, for

unfavorable the workers swarm to the rescue. If the outside temperature drops below 57 degrees Fahrenheit, they will cluster closely and maintain a temperature of 90 degrees Fahrenheit by fanning their wings, creating heat by muscular activity. In less intimate swarms they will air-condition the hive if it gets excessively hot, by the wing-circulated air.

With all these chores, it is not surprising that, while the queen and the drones remain at home, she laying eggs, they waiting in a kind of stupor to contribute their sperm in some vague future nuptial flight, the poor worker lives a short life. No matter; in the well-nursed younger generation, the queen has seen to it that the supply of future semifemale drudges is sufficient to get through the season.

The living habits of the wasps and hornets, close relatives to honeybees, vary widely. While some of them are social, many are solitary carnivores. Social organization in insects may have arisen many times in evolutionary history and does not necessarily depend on food habits, for many ant colonies are carnivorous. The solitary wasps represent another example of supreme concentration on the feeding child. The common mud dauber plasters its nests in deserted parts of buildings everywhere. The females are creatures of strength and slim elegance. They catch spiders, paralyze them with a sting and fly off with them to their nests and lay eggs on them. After hatching, the wasp grub will consume one paralyzed spider after another, very rapidly, because he does not like dead flesh. The mother has chosen well, because a spider can live a long time without starving to death. The grub grows with great rapidity, as well it should with all this food.

The *Pepsis* wasp or "tarantula hawk" is the largest of the wasp family and appropriately its special prey is the largest spider. As is quite a commonplace in the animal kingdom, it is the female that hunts and she hunts solely for her future children. *Pepsis* flies with a deep-toned hum accompanied by ticking sounds. Her wings are orange and her fiery-red tail is armed with a poison sting.

---

predisposing toward atherosclerosis and heart disease, and this is what you would get if you went around drinking the nectar from flowers. However, in the hive the bees, who want their little sisters to have sound hearts, add an enzyme, invertase, to the nectar which converts sucrose to the innocuous smaller sugar molecules, levulose and dextrose. Honey can thus not only be pleasant but positively therapeutic.

Each species of *Pepsis* prefers a different species of tarantula as prey. When about to attack, they give off a pungent odor.

This encounter of a wasp with a larger animal has been studied as carefully as the art of bullfighting and, like a bullfight, the end is theatrical and inevitably the same. The wasp has good eyes, the spider poor ones. The wasp stands in front of the tarantula, touches it lightly in a feint, tricking the spider to stand on its "toes," then dives under it and touches it from behind (the "picador" phase). Some students believe the wasp has given the tarantula false mating signals. At any rate the huge beast is confused and takes the final venomous stab in the soft under parts with strange fatalism. Paralyzed, she is dragged away to the wasp's burrow and used as live food for the larvae that will hatch on her.*

Some wasps catch spiders by deliberately flying into the web. If the web owner doesn't come running, the wasp will yank at the strands until she does come. The wasp quickly paralyzes her and carries her off live to be larva food.

Many wasps and hornets prefer insects. The cicada-killing wasp is small and in a successful hunt has paralyzed quite a load. It is too much to take off with from ground level so she hauls it up a tree and gets the benefit of an air lift in flying it back to her nest.

Another solitary wasp is *Eumenes fraternus*, the potter wasp. She makes a spherical mud flask about the size of a small cherry, with a short flanged neck. The flasks are attached to small twigs. The potter wasp fills them with caterpillars on which she lays her eggs. *Perionyx* seizes a grasshopper by the antennae and, sitting astride the poor paralyzed creature, flies home with it grasped between the legs. Wasps and hornets are great builders. Some of them made a good grade of paper by chewing the fiber from weathered trees. Some paper wasps apply water to the walls of their nest to cool it by evaporation.

As I have mentioned, there is a close family relationship between the wasp and the ant. The wasp is the older animal, but as insects go the ant has made the most rapid progress. The ant society is so implacably communistic that it even shares the

---

* This astonishing apathy and helplessness of so fierce an animal as a tarantula have always puzzled observers. It is almost as if the spider were hypnotized (and perhaps she is). She does not put on the gallant show that a bull does against the matador.

vices of human communism—every ant colony will fight to the death every other ant colony, even of the same species.

The wise heads during ancient human history have always been impressed by the ant. King Solomon advised us to "go to the ant" (a clever admonition on the part of an absolute monarch), while Hesiod, Aesop, Plutarch, Horace, Virgil and Pliny were all ant fanciers (in the curiously amateurish way of the classic world so strangely reflected in the more modern and grandiloquent arthropod science fiction of Maurice Maeterlinck).

Social evolution in feeding habits is clearly evident in the harvester ant. They now collect, store and eat plant seeds. The "kitchen midden" of seed chaff around a harvester nest sometimes contained a sprouting seed, so the idea got around that the harvester ants planted vegetable gardens. They are still in the collector stage but given a million years or so they might graduate to planters. That they were once hunters is indicated by the existence of a large-headed caste probably descended from the ancient soldier caste before the species took to eating grain. These big heads don't do anything particularly useful, but their oversized jaws are capable of cutting up flinty seeds, so perhaps they are the beginning of a "miller caste." (How nice it would be if a transition from soldiers to millers were possible in a human society!) If the larvae are fed a high-protein diet (e.g., captured insects), they grow into soldiers. The worst nuisance the harvesters endure is the thief ant. They dig holes into the granaries of the harvesters and steal seeds. They are so small that the harvesters cannot pursue them through their burglarious holes, so perhaps evolution will find a clever way for the frugal harvesters to deal with the thieves, as men try to deal with rats.

Several steps upward in sophistication are the *Atta* ants and their relatives who are true farmers. They make a compost of leaves upon which they cultivate fungus or mushrooms. There is a small-sized "minim" caste which specializes in keeping up the fungus garden. They weed out the foreign fungi spores from the spores which the foraging caste brings in, for it is a very special kind of crop that *Atta* grows. This fungus has been cultivated by the ants so long that it has lost the ability to produce true fruiting bodies. For this reason plant taxonomists are not even able to classify it. It is wholly dependent on the ant in an unparalleled sort of symbiosis. The fungi cultivated by certain other agricultural ants are found to be the mycelium stage of mushrooms, but this is not the case with *Atta's* crop. (The other farmer ants do not feed on the mycelium but on small clumps formed on it by something mysterious the ants do to it.)

This whole matter of fungus cultivation by ants is still full of puzzles. Yet it is evident that not so many millions of years ago, these Atta ants and their cousins made a tremendous break-through. On an insect scale it is fully comparable with the transition from hunting and food gathering to food growing in human history. One assumes as ever that this complicated gardening technique is wholly instinctual; that if *Atta* larvae were brought up as orphans, they would still differentiate into the usual castes and start foraging for fungi spores and cultivating them. That difficult experiment has not been carried out, to my knowledge, but I should be greatly surprised if it did not turn out that way. One is asked therefore to assume that something in the chemistry of the *Atta* ants' DNA molecules instructs them to make a compost, forage for fungi spores, select only one particular spore, purify it from all the wild spores, cultivate it in the compost and live on it. I cannot believe that all the millions of years of ant evolution can produce so miraculous a molecule or, indeed, that *any* molecule can achieve the inheritance of explicit *behavior* of this sort. The *Atta* ants are using metaphysical memory.

10

FISHES, MEEK AND TERRIBLE

In further pursuing the eating story, we now must jump once more over the great divide between the protostomes and deuterostomes and consider the fishes. The only living representatives of the very primitive jawless fishes are the cyclostomes (*cyclos*, circle+ *stoma*, mouth)—the lampreys and hagfishes. Instead of jaws, they have round, sucking mouths. In the lamprey this jaw looks and acts like a plumber's suction cup. The lamprey latches onto a fish, rasps a hole in its flesh with its filelike tongue and sucks blood.

Lampreys must not be mistaken for true eels, which are highly modified bony fishes, as if one slimmed down a codfish and pulled it out into a snakelike form. Although parasitic and a great nuisance, the lamprey goes through a noteworthy two-stage life history. All lampreys, whether they live in the ocean or lakes, go up rivers and streams to spawn, like the salmon family, and after spawning they die, as do the Pacific (but not the Atlantic) salmon. The spawning habit has proved to be their Achilles heel in a great campaign to eliminate them from the Great Lakes, where they had managed to reduce the population of lake trout to an almost negligible level by 1949. Killing the larvae in their upstream mud beds is accomplished with specific poisons which do not harm the troutlings, which are also produced by upstream spawning, since the trout is a member of the anadromous salmon group. (*ana*, up+*dromos*, running). The campaign against the lampreys has been so successful that the lake trout fishing industry recovered its health, at least temporarily, before DDT ruined it again.

The lamprey larva was once believed to be a separate animal and was called Ammocoetes. It lies buried in the sand, feeding by sieving tiny fresh-water organisms into its mouth, the water stream exiting through ten pairs of gill slits. It stays the remarkably long time of four years in this condition, before it develops a thyroid gland and changes to an adult lamprey. A detailed study of the thyroid mechanism in such a primitive fish makes it probable that this gland, common to all vertebrates, originated in connection with the process of feeding.

Where does the lamprey fit in the evolutionary tree? We have noted previously that the jawless ostracoderm fishes were the oldest known vertebrates. Several years ago a fossil named *Jamoytius* was discovered in very ancient Silurian rocks. This seems to be intermediate between the still more primitive chordate *Amphioxus* and the ostracoderms. In fact, the lamprey larva is strikingly similar in nearly all respects to *Amphioxus*. It appears that the lampreys and hagfishes were the first to branch off the family tree, just before the sharks and rays. The parasitic habit would not, of course, have developed before there were other fishes to parasitize. Parasites cannot make a living by sucking each other's blood.

One can sum up by stating that, although no cyclostomes like those of today can have been the ancestors of the rest of the vertebrates, cyclostomes were closely related to the ostracoderms which probably started the great vertebrate subphylum. A lamprey is therefore the nearest thing we have to a living vertebrate fossil dating back some 450 million years. Such phylogenetic age deserves reverence, but the lamprey (although eaten with gusto by gourmets) has been too unfriendly to the kind of fishes most of us prefer, to allow him his freedom of the lakes.

The first fishes lived in fresh water and they had problems. The most serious was water balance, since the osmotic difference between their body juices and the water outside them was so drastic that, without a bilge pump, they would absorb so much water their tissues would swell up and burst. We have seen that single-celled animals solved this problem with a pulsing vacuole. Something fancier was needed in so large and complicated an animal as a fish. Evolution put together a rather slapdash primitive kidney with tubules to separate excess water and a funnel-shaped opening to the outside. A second trip to the drawing board evolved a tuft of capillaries (the glomerulus), carrying blood under high pressures so that the filtration process could be more efficient. In the primitive fresh-water fishes, the capillaries of the glomerulus exude a filtrate of the blood into tubules. These reabsorb food and let the water go outside via the gills. The kidneys later took on the additional function of elimination of nitrogenous wastes. Even today fresh-water fishes eliminate nitrogen in the form of ammonia via their gills.

As fish evolution went on, some of these animals decided that the ocean was the place to be. Unfortunately, by this time the seas had become very salty. The water-balance problem completely reversed itself. The sea around them had more osmotic concentration than the fishes' blood and it was not the swelling up but the drying out of their cells that they had to prevent. The sharks and other elasmobranches solved the problem by a clever chemical expedient which somehow did not occur to the bony fishes. The elasmobranch livers started manufacturing urea from ammonia and carbon dioxide. Urea is water soluble and relatively harmless, and a high concentration in the shark's blood balances off the high concentration of inorganic salts in the ocean.

What the teleost or bony fishes did was to soft-pedal the glomerulus and to swallow more salt water, so that intestinal water absorption was increased. However, since their systems could not stand such a high concentration of sodium and potassium, they developed a method for desalting part of the blood and excreting the salt through their gills. (Such a process requires considerable chemical energy, as does any chemical separation, and this is apparently provided by adenosine triphosphate in the gill system.*) Salt-water fishes excrete nitrogenous kidney wastes as urea, rather than the ammonia of their fresh-water forefathers, but they do not maintain a high concentration of urea in their blood, as do elasmobranches.

In spite of this difficult beginning, teleost fishes are the dominant form of ocean life today (some 20,000 species compared with about 3000 species of elasmobranches) and one wonders why. Their explosive development has filled the seas, from top to bottom, with all imaginable forms and habits. In view of their food importance to man, one would expect that the personalities of migrating fish, such as herring, halibut, tuna, etc. and their strange pulsations in population would be thoroughly predictable, but, in spite of pro-

---

* Methods of desalting sea water for human use are being laboriously worked out by the expenditure of much research money. As in so many other cases of chemical technology, this problem has been solved by evolution through processes that operate under mild conditions. Sea gulls have a perfect process for desalting sea water, but we cannot understand how it works.

longed research, the fishing industries of all nations operate on a
basis of guesswork modulated by a sort of scouting and intelligence
service. Commercial fishermen are always in trouble and squawling
for government help.

The teleosts are characterized by their scales, which are thin
and flexible and overlap like shingles. The scales of all fishes are
formed within the mesoderm in the embryo and hence are covered
with a layer of living tissue. This makes them moist (unlike the
dry scales of reptiles) and responsive in some way that we do not
thoroughly understand to the hydrodynamic job of swimming fast.
The water resistance of a live fish is much less than that of a dead
one. The scales of the teleost may be the secret of his success,
and yet it does not explain how he has been able to adapt to
the gloomy depths (with a luminescent light of his own to see
his way around) to become a sea horse, a flounder, a flying fish
or an electric eel with enough electrical condensing apparatus to
stun a mule and drown it. It is true the teleost has been around
a very long time but so has the shark. Perhaps the elasmobranches
outsmarted themselves in developing cells that were resistant to
high internal concentrations of urea. In achieving their one great
specialization early in the career of the subclass, conceivably they
gave up the dazzling possibilities of radiative adaptation that has
been the trademark of teleosts.

One teleost specialty is the swim bladder which sharks lack.
This regulates the buoyancy of the fish so that it can remain at
any particular depth without effort. These organs develop in much
the same way as lungs, but the arteries which feed them come
from the aorta, whereas true lungs always receive their arterial
blood supply from the right pair of gill arteries. The gas for
expanding the swim bladder and thus increasing the buoyancy in
shallow water is provided by special glands and the same glands
also absorb gas when the fish descends into deep water. The whole
apparatus is controlled by the autonomic nervous system, as is the
heart in all vertebrates.

The variety of appetites among fishes is, of course, as vast
as the number of things to eat in the ocean and in all the
fresh waters of the world. Smaller fishes usually live mostly on
copepods (crustaceans). Bottom fishes, like rays, nose around for
mollusks in the slime. Although vegetarians are exceedingly rare,
the saupe (found in the Mediterranean) is one of them.

There is a general rule about the feeding of fishes, which may apply in a general way throughout the animal kingdom. Fishes that find their food everywhere are gregarious and travel in schools, just as grass-eating cattle move in herds. This is true of herring, gray mullet and scores of others. The family of Sparidae fishes have teeth not dissimilar to those of humans; they are heterodont (teeth of varying kinds), a rare fish trait. In contrast the teeth of the bass are small, very numerous, covering both jaws, part of the palate and even part of the tongue. The bass swallows its victims whole like a boa constrictor. The piranhas of South America have triangular teeth which above an undershot jaw close over each other like the blades of pruning shears and are so sharp that the Indians of Guiana use them mounted as knives or arrow points. Like sharks, piranhas go wild at the scent of any blood, including that of their own species. A wounded piranha will be torn instantly to death by his companions. Quite recently the piranhas have moved into Argentine waters and this invasion has been blamed on the ceaseless slaughter of crocodiles who used to eat vast quantities of them. Piranhas are very good eating for man, in spite of their boniness. The natives of eastern Peru net them after stunning them with dynamite or *barbasco* poison.

Other fishes, plectognaths, to which the puffers, trunk and porcupine fish belong, specialize in cracking hard-shelled mollusks, crabs and sea urchins. Angelfishes are expert in snatching the exquisite but edible feather crowns that certain feather worms thrust out of their limey tubes.

In a fresh-water lake the food cycle is quite implacable. A given lake or even a large pond will support a fixed *poundage* of fishes; this can consist of a lot of little ones or a few big ones. As lake managers have found, once the equilibrium is tilted toward small fishes, by overfishing on the part of anglers (especially northern American anglers who seldom are satisfied with the "pan fish" as Southerners are), it is very hard to re-establish a good balance. If the smaller fish are allowed to multiply, overpopulation makes them still smaller. This "stunting" phenomenon, which used to be idiotically attributed to excessive inbreeding, is merely one of the symptoms of a population explosion.

In eastern lakes, the extremely carnivorous lake trout is at the top of the food chain, just as is the muskellunge in northern Canada and just as, among mammals, the tiger is king of the Indian jungle. The brown trout can thrive mightily if given a suitable prey such as the herringlike little alewife. The rainbow trout feeds on microscopic plankton and crustaceans, but in a managed lake its peculiar spawning habits must be taken into account. Being a member of the salmon family, it must have access to the streams that feed the lakes since it will spawn only in moving water.

Among fishes that will eat humans, the sharks are of course outstanding, but, for some curious reason, there is a faction among the fishy equivalent of the Audubon Society that stubbornly maintains that no sharks ever attacked a *live* human being. It is perhaps a matter of geography. The late Herman Oelrichs once offered five hundred dollars for an authentic case of a shark attacking humans along the Atlantic Coast north of Cape Hatteras. No reward was ever claimed. On the other hand Australian ichthyologists have listed over two hundred shark casualties in the tropical and temperate waters off that continent. However, there is confusion in the popular mind as to which sharks are man-eating. The two largest species, the whale shark and basking shark, are harmless to man. Sharks that *do* attack men are the great white shark, the blue pointer or mako, the gray nurse or sand shark, the tiger shark, the whaler shark and the hammerhead shark (whose expanded head acts as a forward rudder and enables it to maneuver with vicious skill). If in doubt, one should assume that any shark approaching one is doing so in a mood of voracity rather than pure research. Many South Sea islanders are more afraid of large groupers or sea bass because some of them have mouths big enough to take in a broad-shouldered man at one gulp. The twenty species of barracuda all are ferocious carnivores and the bigger ones are very pleased to snap off a human leg and eat it. Specimens two feet long have been taken off Liberia. Their monstrous mouths gape back to the level of their eyes and the jaws are full of long teeth. In the rivers, the gar pike is a tooth-happy carnivore, and practically all the casualties attributed to alligators in the United States have been traced actually to bitings by gar.

Peculiar ways of earning a living have been found among fishes. The archer fish, for example, hunts insects by means of an improbable weapon—a drop of water. *Toxotes* has a groove that runs lengthwise along the roof of its mouth with a funnel-like opening at the rear. When the fish presses its tongue against the roof of its mouth, tongue and groove form a tube like a peashooter.

Near the shores of a stream, gliding up toward a tree hopper or some other succulent insect prey on an overhanging twig, the archer fish compresses its gill covers, and the paper-thin tip of the tongue serves as a valve that keeps the water under pressure. As the tip is lowered (the valve released), out shoots a drop of water from the mouth of the tube. The accuracy of aim is extraordinary because of the fish's remarkable aerial vision. The insect is approached from the surface if the water is muddy and from just beneath the surface if the water is clear. All it has to do is point its head at the insect. The prey falls as if hit with a bullet.

Lophius piscatorius, variously called the angler, goosefish or frogfish, lives on the bottom of the North Atlantic. It has a fishing rod modified from the dorsal fin spines. From the tip of this organ, placed just over the large, sharp-toothed mouth, dangles a permanent "bait"—fleshy, wormlike tentacles that can be expanded and contracted. The prey (smaller fishes or crustaceans) that find this false worm irresistible are drawn into the predator's mouth by a swift ingoing current created by the angler's gill-muscle action.

Although such eccentric specializations are proof of the great plasticity of the class of fishes, they are no more important to the main line of evolution than are parlor magicians and sword swallowers to the progress of man. The archer and angler fishes have most cunningly exploited tiny ecological niches but it was the lungfishes that led to the revolution that put vertebrates for the first time on the land. It was a chancy existence, for the earth was not only subject to tectonic changes that resulted in the alternate flooding and drying up of whole continents but the changes of the seasons on land involved much greater physiological shocks than they did under the bland and inertial sea. Life in the water is provided with automatic compensations. As the water gets colder oxygen becomes more soluble in it, so cold-blooded life can move around more briskly. Because one is in a medium in which it is impossible to fall down, getting around and doing one's business are easy. How easy can be seen from the ratio of carbon-dioxide production by the animal to the animal's weight, since carbon dioxide is a measure of the rate at which fuel is being burned to conduct one's affairs. In the average fish this is 0.10 per cent, in man it is 6.50 per cent and in birds it reaches 27.0 per cent. Because of high specific heat, great bodies of water change their temperature only with reluctance, and even when the surface is whiplashed by the cruel sun of summer, it is cool not many fathoms deep. (It is quite probable that this mildness, this bounteous life insurance provided by the oceans, prevented the emergence of any better brain than that of a squid. Except for predators, life was too easy. Intelligences of a higher order, such as those of porpoises and killer whales and seals, had to come back to water after the mammalian plan was put through the meat chopper of millions of years of adventurous life on land.)

In order to meet the immediate hazards of dry spells, the land-exploring fishes were quick to develop the habit of estivation. This is the opposite of hibernation and refers to a period of dormancy when it is too hot to breathe fast or to find food. Scorpion fish in hot surface sea water grimace convulsively—the equivalent of a dog's panting, but the lungfishes in their mudholes just go to sleep. *Pseudocrytes*, one of the gobies common in the Ganges River, has developed a habit of seasonal burrowing. During the rainy season it is busy constructing a nest and when the droughts of February and March arrive, it lies tail down, snug in its burrow, breathing air at such long intervals that respiration can hardly be detected. The gobies of the Ganges are in so profound a sleep that they can be handled without awakening. So tightly do they fit the burrow, however, that there is no room even for waste products of the body which therefore must be internally stored. For the lungfishes, the nature of the mud in which they choose to estivate is critical and they have developed into soil experts. The South American lungfish selects an impervious clay so adhesive that his skin can lose no moisture, for if it did he would die from dehydration in a few hours. During the big sleep of estivation, the clay surrounding his body remains moist. His African relatives, however, instead of packing themselves in gloves of clay, surround their bodies with the equivalent of temporary skins of wax paper.

Some true fresh-water fishes undergo hibernation during winter. A fish freezes at a temperature slightly below the freezing point of water, hence it can be encased in ice and still not be frozen—merely in a state of hibernation. When winter sets in, whole schools of carp will retire to the bottom of lakes or ponds and spend months dormant, partly buried in mud. When hibernating, a fish's metabolism becomes so slow that it can live on stored energy, but it must have a little oxygen. The curious nature of water has made this problem less serious than it might have been. In lakes and ponds when the temperature gets down to 39 degrees Fahrenheit, it so happens that this is the temperature at which water is heaviest. Thus the oxygen-rich upper layer sinks to the bottom, bringing its oxygen with it—enough to keep the carp and other hibernators alive through the winter. As winter comes on and the water gets below 37 degrees Fahrenheit, it becomes lighter; the ice forms at the top and floats, while underneath there remains a layer of heavier, warmer water. Water is unique in this respect. In places in the universe where life exists possibly in liquid ammonia as the planetary fluid, there is no such easy hiding place from the cold since ammonia ice sinks and, moreover, the specific heat of liquid ammonia is so much lower that widespread and embarrassing changes in temperature would harass the living organisms.*

* Perhaps for this very reason (because of the greater challenge of the environment), inhabitants of a large planet immersed in liquid ammonia might be expected to develop faster into warm-blooded beings and to conquer their environment with greater brain power than we observe in our sea life.

11

THE POOR FROG AND HIS COUSINS

The evolution of amphibians from lungfish has been mentioned, but one point in the body chemistry of lungfish must be emphasized. Being fresh-water fishes, their normal kidney product would be ammonia. However, since the excretion of ammonia while caked in mud would be fatal (Try taking a steam bath in ammonia some time), the lungfish had to redevelop the salt-water-fish habit of excreting urea. The amphibian egg, like the salt-water-fish egg, diffuses urea out into the water. However, the primitive amphibians are not quite sure whether they want to make urea or ammonia—a demonstration of their linkage to fresh-water fish. The South African clawed frog *Xenckus laevis* undergoes metamorphosis (from tadpole to frog), but it refuses to get out of the water. During metamorphosis it makes a halfhearted gesture toward making urea but returns to ammonia excretion by the time it is a young frog, and yet if the adult frog is forcibly taken out of the water, it immediately changes to urea excretion.

In a more normal kind of frog (or salamander) there is a frantic mobilization of enzymatic machinery in the metamorphosizing tadpole in order to switch from ammonia to urea. Moreover, the blood chemistry must be changed. The hemoglobin in the tadpole is structured to bind oxygen very firmly, since there is so little of it in water. It must change to the frog's hemoglobin, in order to operate in air where oxygen is plentiful; the "unloading" capacity of the blood must be increased. Metamorphosis in the frog has been studied very intensely, since it is a closer relative to us than an insect, and it might tell us something about embryology in general. It is pretty widely accepted that the thyroid hormone initiates the process of metamorphosis, but a key question is, why does it affect different tissues in such different ways? Over thirty-five years ago, Schwind of Cornell University successfully transplanted the eye of a tadpole into the tail of another tadpole, expecting the eye to disappear with the tail in the process of metamorphosis. But the transplanted eye fooled him. As the tail began to wither away, the eye stubbornly resisted the degenerative process. It migrated forward and finally came to rest in the sacral region, metamorphosis thus yielding a young frog with an eye in its lower back.

The amphibian has always been a rather vague and unstable creature. The immense pull of the water has never quite let go of him. He developed legs and lungs and eggs that could be laid on land (so the fossil record shows), but our familiar north-temperate-zone amphibians lay small aquatic eggs. The earliest amphibians (the stegocephalians) laid much larger reptilelike eggs with protective coats, a type of egg still found in some tropical species.

The fossil record also shows that the first Amphibia were scaly and so were those that led to the reptiles. Since our present Amphibia are scaleless, they are highly specialized creatures that have taken a detour from the main road of evolution and have found a precarious ecological niche that is safe, only because they do us no harm and are economically neutral (except perhaps in frog-eating countries).

Externally frogs show a common vertebrate trick of adaptation, that of "countershading," a device often used in military camouflage. The back surface is dark, the belly surface light, a combination which makes the frog swimming near the surface hard to see by its enemies both above and below. Frogs have webbed feet, while toads and salamanders show countershading but lack the webbed feet.

Amphibians are carnivorous and their whole musculature, body plan and especially their remarkably specialized eyes are designed for capturing arthropods. The typically large mouth leads directly into the stomach through an almost non-existent esophagus. The liver and pancreas play much the same role in amphibians as in all vertebrates. Blood from the intestine carries digested food to the liver, where it is processed and stored as glycogen, or animal starch.

Samples of food taken from the stomach of a mud puppy (a salamander that lives in rivers or ponds) show mostly crayfish while similar analysis of a frog's stomach would show about 75 per cent insects. On the other hand the tadpoles of each are mainly vegetarians, though quick to act as scavengers. Like all herbivorous animals, they have long digestive tracts which, during metamorphosis, are greatly shortened.

Because of the generally similar character and diet of amphibians (who, however, range in size from the spring peepers, who can comfortably perch on a pencil, to tropical toads as big as a beer mug), the evolutionary principle of *competitive exclusion* is well demonstrated. According to the rule, no two similar species that live in the same region can make a living by precisely the same job. They cannot compete in all aspects of their lives because this represents an unstable equilibrium. If they *do* thus compete, the result is invariably the extinction of one or the other of the species.

The ways by which frogs manage their lives in order to escape the penalties of this law are various. For example, they occupy different habitats within the same range. The wood frog (*Rana sylvatica*) spends all of its time in the forest except when it comes to the ponds to breed. The leopard frog (*R. pipiens*) stays in meadows and low fields. Its close relative, the pickerel frog (*R. palustris*) sticks to a marsh. *R. clamitans*, the green frog, and *R. catesbeiana*, the bullfrog live, respectively, in small and large ponds. Another method of avoiding collisions and extinctions of species is for the frogs of different species to be of greatly different size. Thus the bullfrog and green frog, although they both like ponds, are so far apart in size that they catch and eat prey of different kinds. Still another way is to breed at distinct times, so that the hungry young do not compete. In a region containing the frog species mentioned, the wood frog is always the first to breed, followed by the leopard frog, with the bullfrog waiting until early July, long after the wood frog tadpoles have grown into adult animals.

In regions of severe winter cold, all amphibians must hibernate. Most frogs migrate to ponds in the fall and hibernate under mud at the bottom, like fish. They still live as long as the ice does not reach their hearts. In this condition the oxygen is obtained by breathing through the skin. People who collect frogs as commercial food make good use of the hibernating habit. Toads, who are not so dependent on water, bury themselves in the earth.

The silver cord that binds most amphibians to water can be weakened to some extent by an amphibian invention—the large urinary bladder, which was not present in the fishes but which persists in all four-legged land vertebrates. Water transfer back into the blood from the bladder is under hormone control by the nerved part of the pituitary gland system—another amphibian first. Moreover, the frog and his relatives have appropriated from the shark family the ability to tolerate large concentrations of urea in the blood. This trick was lost in subsequent evolution to mammals, and one is again tempted to put part of the blame for the lowly standing of amphibians and the small number of their species on this cellular peculiarity. Like the elasmobranch fishes, they have gained in biochemical safety but have lost in evolutionary drive. Perhaps the frogs and salamanders are pathetic, harmless and nocturnal precisely for this reason.

12

THE REPTILE MENU

It is ironic that, while the whole reptile class is now of practically no importance to human beings, it once ruled the planet and started the evolution of birds and mammals. We shall review later the probable reasons for the decline and fall of the great reptiles, but we must first clarify the improvements that they made over amphibians.

First of all, the scales were a lot better covering than the leaky, moist amphibian skin. For land purposes, they were also much better than fish scales, because the latter are covered with a living membrane that is a streamlining asset in water but an embarrassingly vulnerable bunch of mucus on dry land.

The reptilian scales constituted a chemical invention of high order, since they are composed of keratin, a tough proteinous plastic similar to that found on birds' legs and on the tails of a few mammals, such as the rat and the beaver. The scales of fishes are made of other materials, often a leathery, degenerate type of bone. This important chemical difference coupled with the entirely distinct embryological formation of reptilian and fish scales may indicate that the amphibian which gave rise to the reptiles had passed through a stage of scalelessness. Scales of the true reptile kind then proceeded to evolve simply by the hardening or keratinization of the outermost layer of the skin. In some reptiles, such as snakes and lizards, this ectodermal covering can be shed. Turtles, however, merely keep adding new layers of keratin under the old ones. This produces the parallel lines around the "diamonds" on a terrapin's back.

Other improvements included changing of the inner ear to become much like that in mammals. The circulation of blood was made better by a more clean-cut separation of arterial and venous blood. Reptiles also engineered a more positive breathing pattern. A backward movement of the ribs allows the lungs to expand and suck in air, and a reversal of the process expels air.

There is left on earth one species of an ancient order of reptiles known as Rhynchocephaliformes (*rhynches*, snout+*cephale*, head), the tuatara, found on a few New Zealand islands. It looks like a lizard but is millions of years more primitive. Its closest relatives lived 135 million years ago and probably took a boat to New Zealand to escape the competition of the mammals on the mainland. For reasons of geologic catastrophe, the mammals never caught this boat. When the tuatara was first discovered, zoologists felt nearly as thrilled as if a live dinosaur had been found for, indeed, the tuatara's ancestors reached their highest development before the reign of the dinosaurs. When Europeans first arrived, tuataras were living on the main island, but the introduction of dogs and rats promptly extinguished them there. They maintain a tenuous hold in the few islands where rodents and dogs have not taken over. One can see why such creatures had no chance in the evolutionary race with mammals by watching a tuatura's way of life at a temperature of about 50 degrees Fahrenheit. He will go for a whole hour without taking a breath. This may well have been standard performance for reptiles in the later Mesozoic era when such temperatures must have been by no means unusual.

The development of the amnion membrane around the embryo made it possible for large eggs, with leathery shells, to be laid on land—even in desert sands. This membrane is shared by the reptilian descendants—birds and mammals.*

There was no lack of evolutionary drive in the reptiles. Some developed the ability to fly. (The bones became hollow, the tail became short and in some forms even the teeth were lost. But in place of feathers, the flying reptiles had a skin membrane more like the covering of a bat's wing.) Others went back to the sea and looked rather like sharks. They became extinct, but highly modified forms, such as turtles, took their place. On the land there flourished a host of different species, carnivorous and herbivorous, large and small. This enormous host of creatures has now been cut down to four latter-day orders, only one of which has a reasonable chance of long-term survival.

* Very stubborn old wives' lore insists to this day that a human baby born with a piece of the amnion on its head—a "caul"—will be lucky and prosperous.

The order of Cheloniformes (*chelone*, turtle) is made up of both land and marine turtles and, except for the tuatara, is probably the most primitive of living reptiles. It has specialized itself out of serious contention by forming a carapace on its back out of fused ribs and a plastron under its belly from bony plates formed in the body wall. Teeth are lacking and the jaws are covered with horny, often formidable beaks. Some zoologists use the word turtle for aquatic species, tortoise for land animals and the Algonquin Indian word terrapin for all edible species except sea turtles.

Not all turtles have rock-hard shells. The family Trionychidae, without a shell, which probably represents the earliest of the order and has remained unchanged for some 100 million years, is still reasonably successful, since about 10 per cent of all living turtles belong to this family. It is not slow. It strikes like a snake, while it swims and moves like a mammal.

Except for some vegetarian tortoises on the Galápagos Islands, a turtle will eat any animal it can readily capture. In general plan, the digestive tract is much like a man's, except that it ends in a cloaca which also serves as a vagina in the female and as a housing for the penis in the male. In the stomachs of big leatherback turtles are usually found pieces of the very large cold-water jellyfish. That this may be a favorite diet is indicated by the array of flexible, backward-facing spines that line a leatherback's esophagus—good dining tools for helping to swallow soft, slippery prey. The leatherback shares his liking for this food with the ocean sunfish.

Unfortunately for most of the marine turtles, their eating habits are not so interesting to men as are they themselves or their eggs as food. Whalers, stopping at the Galápagos, made the convenient discovery that a large turtle when caught and turned on its back would live patiently on deck for months without attention, thus providing a supply of fresh meat, like paralyzed spiders for wasp larvae. Aside from the diamondback terrapin of our eastern estuaries and the hawksbill turtle (for tortoise shell), the only reptile of appreciable economic interest to man is the great green turtle, and it may be justly said that the exploration of the Caribbean was inspired mostly by men in search of this amiable 500-pound creature. In order that Winston Churchill could have his invariable green turtle soup every evening of his adult life in England, thousands of green turtles must have given up their lives for this noble cause alone. The green turtle is now on the way to absolutely certain extinction, not solely because of Churchillean epicurean tastes but because the Mexican peasants believe her eggs are infallible aphrodisiacs. We shall later present further aspects of this typical tragicomedy of extinction.

Since all marine turtles must return to the shore to lay their eggs, they would be advised to be sure that their eggs do not taste good to big birds, raccoons, dogs, coyotes and people. The loggerhead turtle's meat tastes like oil-soaked rags, but the eggs are such a delicacy that they are sold in the markets of Georgia.

Although the remarkable field researches of Archie Carr have clarified a lot of problems about the marine turtles, we still do not know where the little turtles go after they hatch and make their run for the water. Thus the adolescent years of a green turtle are a complete blank. We do not know what they feed on or where they eat. We do know that they are born with an amazing mastery of directional navigation, for the parents in Brazil can infallibly find the tiny dot of Ascension Island to breed and the young after hatching can make the long trip back to coastal waters, without instruction and without fail.

One rather ironical reason for scientific interest in the order of turtles is their unusual longevity. If the previously mentioned trend in other instinctual animals toward shorter lives, smaller size but more elaborate behavior is universal, then the turtle is out of step here too. There seems to be little doubt that the Galápagos turtle can live well over a century. Even the little box turtle, found over most of the United States, grows very slowly. When it is three inches long, it is about five years old; at five inches it may be a twenty-year old (having reached sexual maturity at about the same age as a human female) and it continues to grow slowly throughout its span, which could be fifty years or more. The chances are very great, however, in these days that as a pregnant female it will end its life prematurely squashed under the wheels of an automobile.

The order Squamatiformes (*squamatus*, scaly) includes close relatives, since a snake is hardly more than a lizard that has lost its legs (and in some of the oldest snake families vestigial legs or bone girdles for attaching them can be found by the anatomist). Both animals have a bone structure peculiarity that is very important to them: they have movable quadrate bones connecting the lower jaw to the rest of the skull. This invention allows them to open their mouths very wide. This is especially necessary for snakes, for as a general rule they swallow their prey whole.

Another first for some snakes and lizards is the transformation of salivary glands into poison glands. Both the hemotoxins of rattlesnakes (blood-destroying) and the neurotoxins of cobras (nerve-paralyzing) were originally designed to begin digestion of the victim from within itself before it was swallowed. Thus snake poison is analogous to the potent enzymes that various carnivorous arthropods use (e.g., the *Dytiscus* larva) to predigest the prey or at least to immobilize it. When a venomous snake bites you on the ankle, it appears as an act of desperate self-defense or perhaps of insulting aggression, but it may be of some comfort to realize, as you strive to recover your cool, that if you had been a smaller animal he would have eaten you in a partly digested form.

There are absolutely no vegetarian snakes. The teeth are curved backward and exceedingly sharp, so that the more the victim squirms, the farther back into the throat it slides. Moreover, the teeth on the upper jaw are arranged in two parallel rows on each side. There is one row along the maxillary bones at the edges of the mouth plus an inner row on each side of the roof of the mouth, on the pterygoid bone. These bones are movable and by working them alternately, a snake can, so to speak, *walk* his head over his prey. Lacking limbs, a snake cannot hold its food while tearing it to pieces. The swallowing mechanism has some limitations but more in the lower direction of the size of its prey. If the food is too small, the "walking" jaw mechanism fails and one may see the embarrassing sight of a small animal escaping as fast as it is swallowed. The tongue plays no part in the eating process. This strange and valuable organ, which is sensory rather than digestive, rests in a sheath of the lower jaw, when the snake is eating. To avoid suffocation, the snake pauses and pushes its windpipe forward far enough to take a few deep breaths.

In the case of a snake with poisonous fangs, the same bone structure by a peculiar rotational movement allows the snake to strike and inject venom as though from a hypodermic needle, without having to close the jaws.

One does not have to have fangs to be a successful snake. One of the best friends a man in California can have is a king snake, because it will eat practically any animal it can get in its mouth, including gophers and rattlesnakes. In fact, snakes are heartily eaten by other snakes, because they are easy to swallow, but there is no known case of cannibalism, that is, of snakes of the same species eating each other. Snakes often eat lizards, but the converse is not true. The constant war between snakes and small mammals is about a stalemate. In addition to the famous mongoose, the hedgehog, although normally an insect eater, will take advantage of its spiny armor to make a leisurely repast of a venomous snake, not even bothering to kill it. Other snake predators are opossums, armadillos, skunks, badgers, raccoons, dogs, cats, hogs and even rats.

There are some absurd but tenacious superstitions concerning snakes. The idea seems to be ineradicable in certain parts of the Middle West that snakes will milk a cow dry. Snakes cannot suck. The hoop snake, that grabs its own tail and rolls lickety-split like a spare tire on the loose, is from the same garden of imagination as the unicorn. Rural people will soberly swear they have observed such a phenomenon, but the snake coyly refuses to perform before herpetologists who have spent their lives in the field.*

Snakes evolved in the Cretaceous epoch about 100 million years ago. Their ancestors were a type of lizard known today as the monitor (Varanidae) and they can be justly regarded as the last great specialization of the reptiles, just as they and the lizards appear to be the only living reptilian order with a fairly good chance of continued survival. Snakes make poor fossils, partly because of their slender teeth and delicate skull with many of its bones only loosely joined to the rest. A snake lacks eyelids (hence the famous "hypnotic" stare) and also lacks ears. Its tongue is as complex, versatile and poorly understood a sensory organ as the remarkable heat-radiation sense, once thought to be nervously localized in the facial pits of the pit-viper family (rattlesnakes, etc.) but now known to be widely distributed throughout the suborder of snakes. The value of this sensing ability is obvious, especially for locating bird's eggs or any warm-blooded prey.

The snaky habit of locomotion is rather a tricky engineering feat. However, it should be pointed out that a snake can bend

* Stories of this kind have been significantly more common in those sections of the country, like the southern Mississippi Valley, where haunted houses were familiar staples and ghosts were as common as bill collectors. Except for some settlements which television had left virginal, such as the Pine Barrens of New Jersey, the hoop snake and the ghost have vanished along with the Model T and the six-day working week.

easily not because his bones are loosely joined but because there are so many bones to take part in the act of bending. (If a giraffe had as many bones in its neck, it would be a horrible creature indeed, half snake and half mammal.)

The blood-circulation system of all reptiles is very good, the heart especially being a sturdy foolproof organ. The extraordinary durability of the snake's heart is probably the basis of the myth that a snake, no matter how mangled by a man's hoe, will not die until sundown.

Some of the snakes, but by no means all, have gone further than the typical reptile and bear their young alive. In most of these cases, the reproduction technique is a compromise; the eggs are formed, shell and all, but are hatched internally (garter snake, rattlesnake). The sea snakes and some cobras, however, have gone all the way toward being truly viviparous. The embryos are nourished in the mother's uterus by means of a placenta. As a demonstration that the details of reproduction are curiously capricious and optional, even within closely related families and genera, the king cobra lays eggs which hatch outside, just as do the eggs of a turtle.

The food instincts of the newborn or newly hatched snakes are dramatically specific, illustrating the power of transcendental memory. If the water extract of the skin substance of some animal that the species is accustomed to feed upon is placed before the little snake, it will respond with tongue-flicking and aggressive coiling. It will turn up its nose at the skin extract of an animal that is eaten by another, even closely related snake species. Its mother and father and remote ancestors did not eat, say, kangaroo mice, so it is not interested in the chemical evidence before it of a kangaroo mouse.

Among living reptiles, snakes and turtles are best suited to the hibernating habit, so they are the only reptiles that are not confined south of the ground-frost line. With their modest tool equipment, snakes are not very good at making burrows or nests, but, like human hippies or tramps, they are very nimble at taking over somebody else's abandoned homes. They also take refuge in holes under boulders, under stone walls, deep holes in banks or those left by the decay of tree roots. Snakes that live outside the tropics have a remarkable habit, also strangely hippie in manner, of spending the winter entwined in a ball of several (up to thirty or more) individuals. These clusters are similar to the balls of earthworms found during a dry season and for much the same purpose, to conserve heat or (in the earthworms) moisture. Usually all of the snakes in a single hibernaculum or den (perhaps an old badger burrow) are of the same species, but sometimes the winter sees the sleepy entwining of snakes, one of which normally eats the other. Among snakes that practice that kind of "sleep-in" are the garter snake, the black snake, the copperhead and the rattlesnake.

As might be expected, water snakes like to eat fish. *Natrix*, not to be confused with the venomous water moccasin, is especially fond of catfish, which it swallows whole, spiny fins and all. The spines often pierce not only the gut but the body wall of the snakes, but he seems immune in some way to peritonitis, and eventually the spines drop off.

Many snakes, considered to be of the more advanced types, have lost one of their lungs in the course of evolution. Pythons and boas (of the family Boidae) are, on the other hand, very primitive. Not only do they retain two lungs but they have vestigial hind legs, visible as spurs near the base of the tail. They are non-venomous and kill their prey by constriction. Since this method of predation is, however, quite normal in many snakes, the term "constrictor" is quite ambiguous. (A king snake, for example, is a powerful constrictor). A mammal or a bird seized by a snake is thrown into a panic and struggles violently, hence his greatest need is for oxygen. The constrictor takes advantage of this by throwing its coils about the throat, resulting in suffocation. Certain African peoples have worshiped the python, and death by horrid torture is the penalty for killing one. Even for an accidental killing, the criminal is buried alive. The python is symbolized in West Africa as the god of war, the god of wisdom and is sometimes even credited with making women pregnant.

The garter snake (*Thamnophis*) must be regarded as statistically the most successful genus. It contains by far the most species and is the most widely distributed; above all it has succeeded best in the most necessary and difficult job that modern wild animals face—making himself at home near man. The pretty but shy green snake (*Opheadrys*) is another absolutely harmless snake, attractive enough to make a pet.

The young of a few pit vipers, among them the American copperhead, have evolved a very cute habit: They entice prey (especially birds) by wriggling a brightly colored tail tip that looks like a worm. Probably the rattlesnake's rattle started out as a lure rather than a warning. Rattlesnakes are born with one rattle, the so-called button. Young snakes ready to enter hibernation at the end of their second summer usually have a string of four buttons. The following autumn they have six or seven. Thereafter they add an average of slightly more than one a year.

As in so many animals, there are things about snakes we do not understand. Aside from their mysterious sensory abilities, often the zoologist is faced with less occult but more exasperating puzzles. In the shieldtail snakes (family Uropeltidae) the tail ends farcically in a kind of disk set at an angle to the axis of the body. What in the world is this for? A stopper to the burrow? But the snake does not use it as a stopper to the burrow. That would be a most unsnakelike thing to do anyway. It seems to us men that this appurtenance is about as useful as a clubfoot. But the snake in his 100-million-year-old wisdom must have attributed some inexplicable value to his disk. He knows something about his environs that we do not know.

The snake's ancestors, the lizards, go back 150 million years to the Jurassic era, long after the dinosaurs had reached their prime. The earliest lizardlike creatures were the marine mosasaurs, who reached a length of twenty feet. The mosasaurs disappeared with their land counterparts, the dinosaurs, when evolution suddenly frowned fatally on all really big reptiles. The monitors of today are the closest to the fossil ocean-going lizards. As a suborder, the lizards today are obviously not sure whether they want to be lizards or change into snakes. There is an incredible variation in leg development, from four good legs down to many kinds with degenerate stubs, some without any vestige of a leg and a few in which even the girdle bones have disappeared entirely.

Probably as a throwback to days of greater glory, many lizards have small bones called osteoderms imbedded in the skin. When all of a lizard's snakelike scales are underlain by these baffles, he is truly armor-plated and is a tough little ruffian, such as the skink.

Although a lizard has more in common in most ways with a snake than with an alligator, he has the crocodilian's skillful defensive use of the tail. This is not all to his advantage, because a predator may be attracted by the contortions of this member and grab onto it, with tooth or claw, whereupon it proceeds to break off and the predator is left with a tail but no lizard. The split may be in the middle of the vertebrae or near one end. The muscles also separate neatly, leaving on the stump a series of cone-shaped depressions that do not bleed. A new tail grows quite rapidly.

Lizards have much the same food preferences as snakes, although many of the small ones are insectivorous. There are very few vegetarians known, the marine iguana of Galápagos, who eats only seaweed, being a notable exception. Lizards usually capture their prey with their teeth, although a few, like the true chameleon, put on a dramatic production by the use of a lightning-fast eversible tongue. This family has other gifts. The big Mediterranean chameleon is the only well-known vertebrate that can move each of its eyes separately. The right eye can look up and to the right while the left eye moves to look down and to the left. Since in mammals both eyes are invariably co-ordinated, this reptile's nervous mechanism of sight must be quite different than anything we are familiar with. Although to my knowledge no one has tried to disentangle the complex optic-fiber arrangement in this particular case, it would obviously be useful to know how it works and whether it has enough merit to warrant copying for man. All the chameleons can rotate their eyes through a wide arc. The true chameleon has a blunt head, turret eyes, a curling tail that grips like tweezers. In some cases the head has huge, odd-shaped casques or helmets, horns, forks, etc., remindful of prehistoric reptiles. The sticky tip of its tongue can be projected farther than the length of its body, like a muscular popgun. The American chameleon has the nervous ability to change its color from brown to bright bluish-green, depending on the background and its own emotional state. Among its prides is a brilliant orange dewlap which is suddenly thrown out from under the throat when courting a female, challenging a male for territory, or trying to scare off a boy or a dog. Many tropical species have even more dazzling displays.

A reptilian specialty, particularly prominent among lizards, is the so-called "median eye" or "third eye" on the top of the head. It is an outgrowth of the parietal organ of the brain in lizards, but in some primitive animals it is an extension of the pineal organ. In cyclostomes (lampreys and hagfish) both the parietal and pineal bodies form "eyes." A median eye on top of the head is found in the oldest known fossil vertebrates (ostracoderms) and was generally present in the ancient amphibians and Paleozoic reptiles. Actually the parietal or pineal organ, or both (although not forming eyes), is found in birds and mammals. It now appears that the pineal body is an endocrine gland that is affected by the relative lengths of day and night experienced by the animal. It tells him, in other words, when to think about spring and breeding or of winter and finding protection. In most lizards the parietal organ actually develops into an eyelike structure with lens, retina and nerve. It is not much of a sight organ, since the cornea is thick and clouded, yet it is certainly enough of an eye to tell the length of the daytime and hence to guide some of his endocrine-controlled behavior. Whether this is its sole purpose is not known. It would seem a rather useless tissue elaboration if meant solely to tell a lizard how long the sun is in the sky, when plants can deduce this without any sensory organs at all.

There are some weirdos in the suborder of lizards. The scary gila monster, although mildly venomous, is easy to tame and has been exhibited in zoos for a century and a half. Although it is well satisfied with a diet of raw eggs and chopped raw meat, nobody knew for sure until recently how it made a living in the wild until some zoologist was patient enough to follow it around and find that it lives mostly on birds' eggs and hatchlings, with an occasional meal consisting of the young of small mammals, such as field mice.

The horned toad (a lizard, not a toad) is very fond of eating ants. At about the time it is changing its skin, this little animal develops a strange and spectacular ability, which does not seem to have any clearly defined purpose. It throws blood from its eyes to a distance of seven feet. This trick is made possible by the temporary capability of increasing the blood pressure in the head and a specialized nictating membrane that acts like a fast gate valve. The little jet of blood contains no venom and is perfectly harmless, but in the skin-shedding condition all reptiles are shaky and irritable and this demonstration may be designed to confuse or frighten a predator.

Some of the lizards are regarded as good food for man. The iguana is carried usually in the rural markets of Mexico and the chuckwalla has been a favorite morsel for certain American Indian tribes, especially in wintertime when game is scarce. For hibernation the chuckwalla crawls into a crevice, then inflates himself with air, so that he feels that in this condition he cannot be dislodged and it is safe to fall asleep. All the Indian lizard gourmet needs is a sharp stick to deflate the unconscious chuckwalla and he wakes up to find himself roasting on a spit.

Small lizards have been used in a noted study to determine the reptilian life expectancy. The Caribbean chameleon *Anolis* was tagged in great numbers and the results of a subsequent body count showed that 95 per cent of these little creatures live less than one year in the wild, but they live to be at least four years old if kept in protected cages. This is a common actuarial statistic throughout the wild-animal kingdom and shows how formidable the pressure is to develop some small evolutionary advantage. Without his little trick of protective coloration, the chameleon's life expectancy would long ago have dipped below the equilibrium level and the family would be extinct.

The order of crocodilians (crocodiles and alligators) is composed of naturally long-lived and formidable animals, but they are undergoing extremely rapid extermination at the hands of man, because female human beings like shoes and handbags made out of their skins. The crocodilians are the most advanced of all reptiles and share many mammalian features. Regarded by some as a sort of living fossil, the crocodile has developed a clever, modern breathing process, although it can stay under water for five hours without drowning. In the first place the nostrils are on the top of the snout, instead of the front. The inspired air, instead of entering the mouth cavity only a short distance behind the front teeth, as in frogs and lizards, is conducted in a closed passage above the hard palate to the back of the throat, which can be kept shut by a flap of mucous. This makes it possible for a crocodile or alligator to breathe while it is chewing up a prey in the water. The heart has four chambers as in mammals, although the ventricles are not entirely separate. The teeth are all in separate sockets—a modern arrangement.

Although crocodilians are confined to tropical or semitropical places because they have no convenient way of hibernating, they would be savage and successful animals if it were not for man's perverse interest in their hides. In southern China the alligator is believed to have been the model for the "dragon," a sort of universal folk symbol. In distinguishing between alligator and crocodile, the most obvious difference is in width of snout, the alligator's being much broader. Also the fourth tooth of the lower jaw of the crocodile fits into a groove in the upper jaw, while in the alligator it slips into a kind of pocket. Colombia is probably the crocodilian headquarters of the world with eight species. The Nilotic or salt-water crocodile in Africa has attained great spiritual significance for the native human. Not only are the contents of its musk highly valued, but, in the discipline of youth, it takes the place of the goblin or the bogeyman that'll get you if you don't watch out. To the adults of certain Nilotic tribes, it serves as a totem brother (members of the crocodile totem will presumably not have a leg bitten off by their spiritual brother) and also as a lie detector. A woman suspected of adultery is tossed into a crocodile-infested river to prove her innocence.

Crocodilians have developed to a high extent the peculiar biting habit noticed in some lizards—the twist and gulp. The alligator is, however, not always eating. His substitute for hibernation is simply not to eat from early October to late March. He is not sleeping but might as well be. He is living on the gorges of summer. Crocodiles who have killed large animals often hide them and eat them later when the flesh has putrefied enough to be soft. Among the twenty-five crocodilian species, the Nilotic or salt-water ones not only are the man-eating champions but, among tribes who do not revere them for religious reasons, they are the most prized food. The people of the Irrawaddy delta catch this crocodile by using hook and line with a puppy or a duck for bait. In ferocity the mugger or marsh crocodile of Ceylon is not far behind. His savagery is said to be increased by the accidental taste of a human bather. One might expect the muggers of the mainland to have acquired a taste for human flesh for they sometimes snatch corpses off burning ghats in the rivers.

American alligators have a peculiar interest in dogs. While the sight of a dog will infuriate a bull buffalo so much that he will charge into an automobile containing one, the Florida alligator's interest is apparently more on the menu side. A barking dog in a boat will attract alligators from miles around.

Alligators are great roarers. In the southern part of the United States the bellowing of male alligators during the breeding season can be heard for long distances. It is not known for certain whether this is to attract females or to impress other males or both. Male alligators will give a roaring response to any challenging loud sound, such as a gunshot or thunder. Experimentally it is found that they respond most fiercely to sounds having a frequency of about fifty-seven vibrations per second, such as the B flat two octaves below middle C played on the French horn.

13

WINGS TO FIND FOOD

What bird watcher would define a bird as a "feathered bipedal, homoiothermic amniote"? Birds are so fascinating to so many people and such a tradition of tender nonsense has grown up about them that it is hard for a writer to steer prudently between brutal realism and gush. I shall try to stick to realism, since it seems to me that the class Aves represents the most vivid example of behavior (sometimes complicated beyond belief) that is controlled almost completely by transcendental memory (instinct).

I have discussed previously the evolution of birds from reptiles, as proved in the beautifully preserved fossil birds of the Mesozoic, who had some feathers, clawed fingers on each wing, solid bones, a reptilian tail and a complete set of teeth. Other fossil birds have been found in later rocks that are transitional between the long-tailed *Archaeopteryx* and the stub-tailed modern birds. Although birds will probably be around in some form or other for a long time, if only as pets, we must admit that the great period of bird evolution—of multiplication of bird species—has come to an end. For animals who are still on their way up in evolutionary drive (notably insects and nematodes) every large new collection turns up many species new to science. This is not true of birds. The last new species discovered in North America was in 1918. One does not have to put on one's sob-sister cap to belabor the point that species are disappearing, especially in the Pacific islands and that during the lifetime of ornithologists still drawing a paycheck, such colossal disappearances as that of the passenger pigeon in the United States have taken place. There are now about 8500 clearly distinguished bird species in the world. Twenty-seven orders of living birds are recognized varying from such ancient forms as the grebe and penguin to the only recently evolved perching birds (sparrows, wrens, thrushes, robins, crows and a host of others. There are about seventy families, and this kind of bird so took the world by storm that the order of Passeriformes—literally sparrowlike—contains nearly half of the total number of bird species on earth.)

We do not know how or when either birds or mammals developed warm-bloodedness, but the thermostat center is nervous and located in the thalamus or hypothalamus of the brain. The rate of metabolism or fuel burning is much higher in birds than in any other animal, and by this process the blood temperature is maintained constant at 104° Fahrenheit or higher. In other words birds commonly live in a state which in a man would be regarded as one of delirious fever. This high rate of chemical living requires a lot of food and it is no secret that birds are great eaters. They will eat up to 30 per cent of their weight every day compared with 2 per cent for an elephant, 4 per cent for a hog and only 0.7 per cent for a crocodile. When not occupied with the tension of breeding and nesting, the bird is eating or looking for food, and the great seasonal flights of migrating birds are simply organized periodic food hunts.

The kind of things birds eat is, of course, almost illimitable. All birds have two kinds of stomachs, whether they use them both or not: a glandular stomach (crop) in which hurriedly eaten food can be stored and digested and a muscular stomach (gizzard) in which more thorough grinding action takes place. The two-step process is analogous to the digestion of ruminant mammals, such as a cow, where the cud can be regurgitated for more reflective chewing, but since birds have no teeth, the gizzard does the same job or a better one. Grain-eating birds, such as domestic fowl, need grit in their gizzards to supplement the intense muscular action of food-chewing in that organ. (The crop is an innovation, since the ancestral reptiles had only the gizzard.) Yet some grain-eating fowls use the grit only as a supplement to powerful natural millstones. The mucous lining of the gizzard secretes a keratinous fluid that hardens into horny plates or ridges. A turkey can grind in its gizzard twenty-four walnuts in the shell, also steel needles and surgical lancets. After being in a turkey's muscular stomach, a tube of sheet iron was found to be flattened and partly rolled up.

A remarkable adaptation of the gut in birds is found in pigeons and various members of the parrot family. In pigeons the crop becomes a large double sac which not only stores grain but also secretes "pigeon milk" for feeding the squabs. Both males and females have these milk-secreting glands and it is true milk formed by the breakdown of cells, just as in mammals. Prolactin, the hormone immediately responsible for stimulating milk secretion, is identical in birds and mammals and was, in fact, first discovered in pigeons. Pigeon milk, like the milk of sea lions, is extremely high in fat content.

The brilliant success of the two-stomach plan is shown by certain gulls. When eating fish, the glandular stomach does most of the job, but in the autumn when the gulls move inland for grains, the muscular stomach comes into its own. Among the fish eaters, there are some who make hogs of themselves. Sea birds are often seen flying around for hours with the tails of fish still protruding from their beaks. Boobies often swallow so many fishes that they are too heavy to take off in flight and find it necessary to disgorge part of the load. Grebes often pluck their own feathers and eat enough to fill their stomachs as a protection against sharp fishbone. The Adelie penguin, like a guest at an ancient Roman banquet, sometimes resorts to an emetic to provide room for still more delicious fish food. Some sea birds are bullies and thieves. Jaegers and frigate birds force weaker birds, such as terns, to disgorge, and the laughing gull shamelessly robs the pelican.

The digestive process naturally depends on the food habit. In fruit eaters, such as young cedar waxwings, the food goes through the entire digestive tract in sixteen minutes. The digestion of a seed eater will be much slower. European hawkfinches, who specialize in such hard foods as cherry and olive pits, take several days to masticate and absorb them. In general, the intestines of the bird depend on its size, the bigger the bird, the longer and narrower the intestine. (This is an instance of a general law of nature, in which the smaller the object the higher the ratio of surface to volume. The narrow intestine of the big bird has more surface for a given volume.)

Certain birds, especially the domestic chicken, have an auxiliary organ, the caecum, which (as in ruminants) is populated with bacteria capable of digesting cellulose. The indigestible residue is dark and moist and is discharged independently of the whitish, drier intestinal feces. This is a marvelous bird, the chicken—

Gallus. Their wing system, however, is not designed for extended flying. The "white meat" of the breast of a chicken or turkey indicates too few blood vessels to energize the muscles for the kind of flying carried out by pigeons and wild ducks. The dark meat of their legs shows, on the other hand, that they are very active runners. (Some wild fowl, such as the ruffed grouse, are also poorly muscled for flying. If the grouse is flushed four times, its breast muscles get so tired that it can be picked up by hand.) No one knows precisely how or when *Gallus* was domesticated. Although it is not mentioned, either in the Old Testament or in Homer, it was known in the age of Pericles as the Persian fowl. According to Chinese legend, the chicken was introduced into that culture about 1400 B.C. from the West. Today jungle fowl quite like the chickens of millions of barnyards in the civilized world can be found in small flocks in the forests and thickets of the Malay Peninsula. The roosters crow their immemorial song of territory and the hens lay eight to twelve creamy white eggs on the ground and proceed at once to the condition that farmers call "broodiness." There is no one to steal their eggs from them, except snakes and weasels. With its matchless digestion, *Gallus* may well outlive its present masters and the cock's crow may be heard long after the bugle has sounded its last taps. (The chicken is an "indeterminate" layer. Some female birds lay a clutch of eggs, according to the quota system. If the eggs are stolen or eaten, she is unable to do anything about it.) But the barnyard hen—or the practically robotized hen in the modern egg factory—will keep on laying as long as you keep on stealing her eggs.*

For its continual eating and the active life for which it was designed, any bird needs powerful body glands. Its double-lobed liver is much larger than the liver of a mammal of the same size, and the pancreas is also a big gland. The excretory system is well adapted for a flying animal. Instead of urea, the liver produces

---

* Somewhat the same basic indecency pervades our relationship with the cow or nanny goat. She is kept in a perpetual condition of lactation for calves or kids that do not drink her milk. The perversion of the reproductive patterns of animals is one of man's great specialties. His breeding experiments with animals, for example, usually follow the pattern of hybridizing two different races, then selecting from the progeny likely males and females for a continuous program of incestuous matings—politely called inbreeding—until the desired genes are promoted from recessive to dominant—or, in the familiar phrase, until the strain breeds true.

nitrogen wastes as uric acid which is not very soluble in water, hence the kidneys may excrete directly to the cloaca without a heavy water-holding bladder. In dry climates the feces of sea birds sometimes accumulate in great deposits over their nesting sites. This guano, being rich in nitrates and phosphates, is valuable as fertilizer. In the past, before nitrogen fixation became a standard process, the entire expenses of the Peruvian government were paid from the sale of guano which was shipped all over the world.

Some birds, being continually victimized by lice and various parasites, are careful to keep their nests clean. Certain young hawks flip their tails at the moment of a bowel movement to toss the feces out of the nest. The parents of perching hatchlings are as fussy about carrying away the excrement as human mothers are about a change in diapers.

The problem of maintaining the temperature of a warm-blooded animal such as a bird is not simply the matter of getting enough food but of the rate of heat loss. Here again we encounter the law of the surface-to-volume ratio. The smaller the animal, the larger its surface for a given body weight and thus the faster it loses heat. A mouse has far more surface in proportion to its weight than a man, and hence must feed itself more fuel in proportion to body weight and burn the fuel with oxygen faster than a man. This inexorable law has almost caught up with the hummingbird. He is at the lower limit of size where it is possible to exist as a warm-blooded creature. His heart is as big as he can afford (2.37 per cent of total body weight, compared with 0.42 per cent in a man) and it beats at the alarming rate of 615 times per minute. He has learned one desperate expedient: *he hibernates every night.* In this condition of dormancy his body temperature goes down almost to that of the environment and his oxygen need dips correspondingly. If he had not learned this trick, he would starve to death overnight.

When food is scarce, some other birds can also become temporarily cold-blooded and dormant. The poorwill can go several months without eating in this condition and the immediate cause is not temperature but lack of food. By reverting to the cold-bloodedness of their ancestral reptilians, the nestlings of the European swift can survive at least ten days of complete fasting—a very unusual ordeal for a young and growing bird.

Since very few birds have this capability of "false hibernation," those that do not migrate southward have some rough problems during the winter. The snow bunting, several kinds of grouse and partridges know when a bad arctic storm is coming and they will fly full speed into a soft bank of snow, insulating themselves against the wind chill and burying themselves without a telltale mark for predators. Sometimes, however, they will find themselves iced over in their refuge by freezing rain and die of starvation. Freezing rain is as dangerous to birds wintering in the north as it is for airplane pilots. During the night it will fasten the wings of chickadees and juncos to their backs. When they try to fly at dawn, they fall helplessly to the snow and most likely wind up in the stomachs of hawks. Long cold rain, even if it does not freeze, is actually more destructive to a bird than a prolonged cold spell, because the insulating value of the plumage deteriorates and one sees the pathetic spectacle of a dim-eyed bird vainly trying to ruffle up its bedraggled feathers. Wet clay soil often fatally embarrasses some birds who get their feet mud-caked just long enough to become prey for hawks and owls. The ruffling of feathers is, of course, a means which birds use to keep out the cold, the air ruffled in being a much better insulator than the feather surfaces themselves. Evolution uses the surface-to-volume factor in designing birds for cold climates, making them on the average larger (with less exposed surface for a given amount of body weight) than tropical races of the same species or genus. Small nectar-sipping birds, like the hummingbird and its Australian counterpart, the honey bird, and its African analogues, the sunbird and the honey guide (which is also provided with a clever bacterial intestine that is able to break down beeswax into usable food), would be unthinkable in the Arctic. In particularly severe winters in temperate climates, birds may change their appetites. Crows and magpies will pluck wool from the backs of sheep in snowy weather, probably to add lanolin (or sheep's-wool fat) to their diet. (The predilection of many perching birds for suet in the wintertime is well known.) During a winter famine the New Zealand parrot will go further than this; it will actually tear flesh from the backs of sheep. During the terrible European snowstorms of 1946–47 the crows and magpies were also desperate enough to peck through the hides of cattle and feed on their flesh. (When you are assaulted by flocks of birds, as were the people of Alfred Hitchcock's picture, please bear in mind that they are hungry and not possessed of some demonic crusading urge.) At times of famine in the arctic, the ivory gull will feed on the dung of polar bear, walrus and seal. Puffins and petrels eat large amounts of whale dung.

Some bird appetites appear to have formed as the result of thousands of years of intimate association with other animals. Bee-eaters can often be seen riding on the backs of ostriches and African bustards in order to catch the insects which these heavy birds disturb in treading the ground. The Egyptian plover will boldly dart into the mouth of its favorite crocodile to grasp small particles of food. A very recent trick of English titmice proves that smart little birds can take advantage of some of man's food-delivery practices. The titmice have learned how to open the caps of milk bottles, left on the front stoop, and drink the cream. (The sudden spread of this thieving technique over a wide urban area is proof that successful food habits in birds are not necessarily inherited through the long rain of generation after generation.) Pigeons, of course, have developed into a race of urban panhandlers, their stomachs having become adapted to a diet of stale bread crumbs and bagels. The pigeon is as much a commensal of lonely old ladies as is the Egyptian plover of the crocodiles, except that the lonely old lady does not get her teeth cleaned in the process. She is more likely to develop a mild case of psittacosis.

A special hazard exists for birds who subsist on the sap of trees, such as the sapsucker who has a tongue ending in thorny bristles. At times he will drink plant juice that has undergone fermentation and will find himself too drunk to fly right. Drunken flying (a growing hazard among private pilots in the human world) is not recommended for birds, because it usually winds up with the tippler in somebody else's stomach. Fruit-eating birds in the tropics often find themselves in a stuporous condition, either from alcohol (when the fruit is rotten) or from naturally occurring narcotic fruits.

One of the most instructive and common food habits of birds around us is that of the woodpecker. We do not often realize that he knows where to peck by a stethoscopic hearing. He locates the larvae of long-horned borers by the underbark clicking sound made by their jaws. (Try this sometime, if you can borrow a doctor's stethoscope on a quiet day.)

I have said that the wonderful, systematic migrations of birds is basically a food hunt. The tropics, where most migrating birds winter, is of course not only a yearly food mecca but there are many more species of birds who stay there all the time than there are who migrate northward in the spring. It is probable that the tropics also represent the kind of climate that existed world-wide in the Miocene and Pliocene epochs when the modern bird families were evolving. Nevertheless, as the northern spring packs the scene with succulent plant and insect food, the migratory birds decide that the competition is too heavy in their winter resort and fly back to favorite nesting spots in the Northern Hemisphere.

There is another kind of migration, mostly east-west in polarity, which undoubtedly also reflects food seeking but which is neither periodic or regular. It resembles in human history the invasion of the Huns and Mongols or more realistically the emigration of the Irish to America in 1846, or in general mammalian terms, the vast original incursion of rodents from Central Asia which, eventually covered the planet with rats and mice. These irregular bird-mass movements are called "irruptive." The sand grouse in the years 1863, 1888 and 1908 flew by the hundreds of millions from Asia Minor to Western Europe. In recent times (but before the days of hopeless air pollution) New York City was invaded by successive waves of purple finches and Boreal chickadees; Germany by uncountable flocks of Siberian nutcrackers. In east-west movements of this type it is the young birds who take the initiative, the older birds being held to their famine-locked habitats by ties of behavior—especially their settled place in the pecking order and in established territoriality. Sometimes a local population explosion will simulate an incursion, such as the tremendous multiplication of starlings and English sparrows in North America and of skylarks in New Zealand.

Before we leave the birds, we must consider one aspect of their anatomy which (beyond the gift of flight) gives them undoubted physical superiority to man. If we are to imagine ourselves constructing a tireless and winged man, we would first of all have to redesign the respiratory system. First, we must emphasize the blood-circulation plan of warm-blooded animals. Only birds and mammals have completely separate circulation paths for arterial and venous blood. In the four-chambered heart, the two right chambers pump used blood to the lungs; the left chambers circulate the aerated blood through the body. One of the reasons reptiles are cold-blooded is because their typical two- or three-chambered hearts can pump only mixed arterial and venous blood which cannot support a high enough

level of oxidation to maintain high body temperatures. The crocodilians have four-chambered hearts, but evolution played them a
dirty trick by placing a connection between the right and left aortae
so that the venous and arterial blood streams become mixed. In
birds the hemoglobin content is about the same as in mammals, but
the blood sugar, thus the energy content, is higher. The size of
the heart in birds, as proportion of body weight, reflects the evolutionary position. For example, the primitive pheasant has a much
smaller heart at the same body weight as that very advanced bird,
the raven.*

Man and other mammals breathe by means of an essentially
clumsy cul-de-sac respiratory system in which fresh air is mixed with
residual stale air remaining in the dead-end alveoli of the lungs.
The birds have improved on this by supplementing the lungs with
a system of sacs and connecting tubes that make possible a much
more thorough bathing of the lung cells with fresh air. In birds
most of the residual air remains in the air sacs (which fill much of
the body cavity and reach up into the neck), and the entire lung
is washed with "tidal" air on both inspiration and expiration. There
is no doubt that the air in these sacs is also used for cooling,
especially on long flights. In the wild duck the respiratory system
takes up 20 per cent of the body volume, consisting of 2 per cent
lungs and 18 per cent air sacs. The pigeon in flying uses one-
quarter of the air intake for breathing and three-quarters for cooling.
In male birds the testes, being internal, are cooled by the air-sac
method in order to encourage spermatogenesis; if these glands become too hot no live sperm will be produced.† The evaporation
of water in these air sacs takes the place of the sweating process
in mammals. As far as the breathing mechanism is concerned, ornithologists are by no means certain of exactly what path the air
takes through the labyrinth of air sacs and lungs. Air appears not
so much to be drawn *in* a bird's breathing apparatus as to be
drawn *through*. The ideal respiration system, which evolution has
unaccountably failed to provide in any animal, would be a lung

---

* So modern and intelligent is the raven that he has made himself at home
and a master bird in every continent, except inexplicably South America.
† The exposed scrotum in most mammals is also for cooling, yet the clumsiness
of this location in an erect biped, especially a pugnacious one, such as man,
is obvious. In certain human males, where imperfect descent of the testes
occurs at adolescence, the individual is usually sterile because of constant
exposure of the testes to body heat.

with a separate stale-air outlet. In birds the air-sac system approaches the ideal more closely than in any other vertebrate and this is responsible for their phenomenal feats of migratory flight. A man with such a system would be able to run a mile in less than three minutes, although he would probably also have to be outfitted with a bigger, more efficient liver.

Another trick that mammals have failed to learn from certain birds is to drink sea water. A bird's kidney can secrete urine with a high salt content no better than a mammal's, but marine birds in five different orders have developed nasal "salt glands," with tubules radiating out from a central canal. The experiments of Schmidt-Nielsen show that sea birds excrete fluids from these glands containing 5 per cent salt. In petrels the brine is squeezed through the tubular nostrils, but in other species it dribbles out of internal or external nostrils. A gull given one-tenth its weight in sea water excreted 90 per cent of the salt within three hours. Some sea birds are so adapted to drinking salt water that they will die if denied access to it. This trick of desalting involves special membrane pumps which are as hard to understand as the pumps which every nerve in your body uses to pump sodium or potassium ions against severe concentration gradients. If we understood exactly how these marine birds so casually separate salt from the ocean, we would be in command of much more important capabilities than that of desalting ocean water for our tremendous water needs; we would understand the extraordinary membrane chemistry of the living organism; we would perhaps be at the very portal of the understanding of all cellular life.

Since birds do not perspire, there is some problem of elimination which they solve in a curious way. Birds with a high metabolic rate discard some of their waste products in the form of feather pigments. Thus zooerythrin, a widely distributed carotenoid pigment, is responsible for the red of cardinals. Blue pigments are unknown in birds and may be seen to be an "illusion" (a structural hallucination, because of surface diffraction, much as the blue of the sky) by crushing a blue feather. The red and yellow pigments produce orange, and green is usually the result of a yellow sheath of keratin on top of the "structural blue." If you feed canaries red pepper, in successive molts they will change from yellow to intense orange—the bird's method of disposing of this alien pigment.

Birds need vitamin D, which they get from the uropygial or

preen gland, located in the skin, its flow being stimulated and some of it swallowed during the preening process. The oil from this gland is also used to waterproof the feathers. The man-of-war bird of Ascension Island, although a superb flier, is rarely seen out of sight of land, since the oil from its very small preen gland is inadequate to waterproof its feathers.

There are some things about bird behavior as affected by plant growth that we are just beginning to understand. The bird population is decreasing in country with big modern farms. A passerine bird would rather live in a suburb than in a thousand acres of Kansas wheatland, because there is too little *edge* in such fields, and most birds need small trees and other edge effects to breed and rear a family. A male bird cannot sing his territorial challenge when his territory is simply a monotonous row of cornstalks.

The Indian myna bird was introduced into Mexico and thrived by feeding on the seeds of the lantana plant, which it also helped to spread. Myna bird and lantana increased enormously, but the bird also included on its menu the army worm caterpiller, a sugar cane pest. In order to stop the spread of lantana the agromyzid fly was imported. The lantana almost died out and so did the myna bird, but the destruction of sugar plants by army worms went up out of sight. Other species of weed became even more pestiferous than the lantana. The lesson in never to fool with ecology until you have figured all the angles.*

The grouse in England were saved from extinction by a studious approach to ecological factors. Burning the heather partly away provided variety and created open sunning yards where chicks could dry themselves after rain and fog and, thus, the mortality from respiratory diseases (the most important ultimate cause of the grouse decline) was cut down. Wild birds are particularly susceptible to a biological principle known as the law of the minimum. Survival depends on that factor of the environment which in minimum amount controls the bird's well-being. Thus an otherwise well-fed and disease-free grouse will still weaken and die if the grit available to it falls below a certain minimum.

* A similar type of mistake was made in banana plantations in British Honduras. The pickers and shiploaders complained of spiders, so they were eliminated by drastic spraying. The next crop was entirely consumed by an insect pest (resistant to spray chemicals), and the banana company had to import spiders from the nearest Natural History Museum to get out of the ecological mess they had created.

FOOD FROM THE MOTHER'S BODY

The class of mammals is defined zoologically as vertebrates with hair and subcutaneous mammary glands, and the last part of the definition is the most important. There is nothing as revolutionary in the animal kingdom as the female providing food from her own body to her young, since out of this has grown the vast psychological gulf between animals controlled completely by instinct and animals who are taught. The educational process comes into the world with the teat.

We have seen that early mammals were small and generalized, rather like a small mongrel dog, skulking forlornly in a reptilian world. It is quite possible, according to the great zoologist George Gaylord Simpson, that mammals evolved more than once. The present monotremes, for example, including the duckbilled platypus of the Antipodes, either evolved separately (and therefore represent "living fossils") or diverged from the main mammalian stem at extremely remote times. It is a mammal all right, for its body is covered with hair and it has mammary glands. However, there are no nipples and the milk is merely exuded through innumerable tiny pores on the belly, and it lays eggs, rather than bearing viviparous young that have been nourished in the womb by a placenta. The marsupials are also quite primitive, the young being born at a much earlier stage of embryonic development than in placental mammals, and spending more time in the pouch than in the uterus. A litter of twenty newborn opossums hardly fills a teaspoon. The opossum is likely to be around for a long time, for in spite of its primitive nature it has shown admirable stubbornness and love of life. The skeleton of a present-day opossum is almost identical to those of 75 million years ago. Although the opossum probably spread over all the continents, something, about 30 million years ago, mysteriously exterminated all these little animals in North America. In the Pliocene, however, they waded across Central America from the Southern Hemisphere and have been with us ever since. Spending a lot of time in trees, they are careless but tough. Of ninety-five skeletons examined in Kansas, thirty-nine had broken bones that had healed.

Obviously it was not the marsupials that gave rise to the placental mammals but another, perhaps even more primitive trunk of the mammalian tree. In the fossil record this trunk can be distinguished from the contemporaneous small mammal-like reptiles by a larger brain case, a lower jaw composed of a single bone on each side instead of three or more, and, above all, by the teeth. The cheek teeth of mammals consist of complex molars and premolars, while those of reptiles form a row of mere conical pegs. We know nothing from the 150-million-year-old bones of the internal structure of the primitive mammals nor of the evolution from scales to hair. That this was not a total and complete transformation is shown by the scales on rodents' tails and on most of the body in one group of anteaters.

Although the placental mammals are regarded with peculiar interest since it is a placental mammal, man, who is the regarding animal, one cannot say that as a zoological class they are as successful as insects or nematodes or even as fishes. There are sixteen orders and some of them include only single groups of animals, such as pangolins, aardvarks, conies and sea cows, who are near extinction. Even in his own order (primates) man is witnessing the last days of the gorilla, the orangutan and the chimpanzee.

It is probably the order of insectivores which most nearly represent the original mammal that appeared in the Mesozoic. Insectivores are small, with many sharp teeth, an endowment that contrasts them definitely from the rodents which they otherwise somewhat resemble. The mole and the gopher, for example, are cursed in the same breath by the suburban lawn-proud citizen, although no two animals could be so different in their eating habits. In their ceaseless burrowing for underground-insect food, moles work day and night and, like most insectivores, are tremendous eaters, consuming up to two-thirds of their own weight every twenty-four hours. The gopher, on the other hand, is a rodent that lives on vegetation. Instead of a long series of pointed teeth, he has a pair of chisel teeth in the front of each jaw for cutting off roots and stems and a row of flat-topped teeth for grinding pulpy material. The shrew is another insectivore with an absolutely ravenous appetite. Like the hummingbird he is so small and therefore loses heat so fast that his life is a constant, frantic scramble for food. A mammal any smaller than a shrew would be unable to eat fast enough to avoid starvation. In fact, without food, a shrew will starve in two or three hours. Although primarily an insect eater (and luckily, since this is the only living prey plentiful enough to satisfy him) he will unhesitatingly attack a mouse twice his size. The water shrew is probably the most ferocious animal on earth. It can kill a fish sixty times its size by biting out its eyes and will fasten its terrible little teeth on a frog and eat him alive. Eskimos have a thing about the shrew. If disturbed, Eskimos thought, the shrew would dart at the intruder, burrow into him and kill him by entering the heart. E. W. Nelson tells of an Eskimo hunter who, meeting such a shrew, stood like a stone for several hours until it disappeared. On reaching home, his friends all congratulated him on a very narrow escape. Another familiar insectivore is the hedgehog which, although equally protected by bristles, is not even a remote relative of the porcupine which is a rodent.

In the order of Chiropteriformes, the bats are the only mammals with actual flight and admiring attention should be paid to the highly developed sonar system possessed by many species. These and most other bats eat insects, but they do not compete with birds because they work at night. The bats that fly out of the Carlsbad Caverns in New Mexico every evening have been estimated to number as many as nine million and in a single night they consume several tons of insects. The bat is a success. There are seventeen families and almost 2000 species, varying from the two-inch-long pipistrel to the great flying fox of the East Indies with a wingspread of over four feet. The latter are fruit eaters. The bloodsucking vampire bats of South America have been cursed by cattle raisers because, although their sharp teeth inflict almost painless razorlike cuts, they often carry the rabies virus, the symptoms being paralysis rather than the "mad dog" type. Since 1956 it has been discovered that even the insect-eating bats can carry the rabies virus; hence bats are not regarded with such blandness as before.

In the past, the rabbits, hares and pikas were placed in the same order as the rodents. Most zoologists now place them in a

separate order of lagomorphs (*lagos*, hare). The fossil record shows
that the lagomorphs and rodents were separate from remote
Cenozoic times. The cottontail rabbit, as a typical vegetarian
lagomorph, represents a supreme triumph of reproductive capability
and valiant will to survive in the face of a surrounding host of
fierce predators, the most deadly of which is the man or boy with
a gun. This rabbit is practically a staple food product for the
coyote. The weasel, the fox, the mink, the eagle, the big owls,
even the dog and cat are after him. He is not very hard to catch.
His scurrying hops are strikingly different from the long rapid bounds
of the jack rabbit and the varying hare. Luckily for him, he thrives
on many types of vegetation. When autumn frosts mow down the
succulent plants, he will change his diet to twigs, barks, buds and
evergreen needles. All lagomorphs chew with a sideward motion of
the jaw. When the animal's left molars are grinding a leaf, the right
molars cannot meet because the lower tooth row is inside the upper
row. Strictly speaking, the word "rabbit" should be reserved for the
cottontail. The ears and hind legs of the rabbit are much shorter
than those of the hare and the digestive tracts have important differences. At birth, rabbits are hairless and blind while hares are
well furred and their eyes are open.

Lagomorphs have found their natural way to all parts of the
world except Madagascar, Australia and New Zealand. The European rabbit was deliberately transported by man from England to
Australia and New Zealand in 1860, where it has no natural enemies.
It multiplied with such fearsome rapidity that the rabbits ate most
of the grass and herbs over thousands of acres, the land being
lost for grazing and put in serious danger of erosion by rain. The
first use of a selected virus for killing off an animal species was
tried in the 1950s in Australia. The virus was that of myxomatosis,
which had been discovered among the Brazilian rabbits, where it is
not fatal, but experiments had shown it to be 90 per cent lethal
to the European rabbit. Carried mainly by mosquitoes, this proved
effective until immunity developed, not over a period of centuries,
as had evidently happened in Brazil, but in a few years. By 1960,
Australian rabbits could shrug off the myxomatosis virus as no worse
than a mild cold. The rabbit eradicators had to fall back on fluor-
acetate poisoning and mass shooting.*

---

* It would seem sensible to introduce a rabbit-specializing predator such as
the coyote, but Australian ranchers have heard such horror stories from the

The varying hare changes from brown to white with the seasons. Like the arctic hare, its long toes and soles covered with coarse hair, which grows longer in the winter, have also given it the name snowshoe hare. The European hare is a huge creature (twelve to thirteen pounds) native to Europe, but raised for food also in this country. Wild hares are habitual sun bathers. Arctic hares will follow the spring sun from one side of a bush to the other, since they need vitamin D after long months of darkness. Unfortunately, in this basking mood they are easy prey for the arctic lynx who spends most of his life trying to capture them, since this particular variety of cat will eat nothing else. When the hare has disappeared in a trough of the population cycle, the arctic lynx will die rather than revert to the fat mice that pullulate in the fields about him.

The rodent order is the most successful of all mammals in number of species—about 3000, divided roughly into three groups or suborders. The myomorphs (*myos*, mouse) are the mice, rats and their relations. The hystricomorphs (*hystrix*, porcupine) include, besides the porcupine, the chinchillas and the capybara of South America, the largest of all rodents, about the size of a small pig. The sciuromorphs (*sciurus*, squirrel) includes squirrels, gophers, beavers and the like. It is difficult to put one's finger on the reason rodents are so successful. Most of them are small and the larger exceptions, such as the beaver, have been able to reduce their size to escape extinction. Adaptability among the rodents has been swift and sure (witness the rats and mice). Not a single family has been known to become extinct since the origin of this great order in Eocene times. It is important to realize that the evolution of the rodents probably forced the early primates (the ancestors of monkey and man) to abandon their habitat on the grasslands as a sort of Paleocene squirrel-like creature and take to the trees. The victory of the rodents was so massive and final that many primates, specialized for only a ground life, became extinct. It is probable that except for the all-conquering invasion of the rodents, the primate line might have abandoned the trees much earlier than it did in the case of man. Perhaps we gain at least a clue to the unsinkability of the rodent order by examining some

---

United States on chicken stealing and lamb killing that they evidently feel this cure would be worse than the disease.

instances. Let us first compare two familiar laboratory rodents, the guinea pig and the rat.

The guinea pig is a domestic form of a species of rodent called the cavy and is a native of the Andes. It was domesticated by the Indians of Peru, Ecuador and Columbia long before the arrival of the Spaniards and had about the same honored place on the native menu as Cornish game hen has with us. Before the promotion of this gentle grass-eating animal to its present position as a pet and a living machine for biological research experiment, it was also eaten by gourmets in Western Europe (and may still be).

A fine example of the effect of the evolutionary past on eating and drinking habits can be gained by keeping a guinea pig and a rat hungry and thirsty for some time. When both are offered water and food, the rat will drink before it eats but the guinea pig, reflecting its ancestry in the dry mountain plateaus, will eat first and then drink.

The rat is a favorite for food research, because nobody cares whether you starve him or not. He has a bad popular image. It has been found that the food intake of a rat (and perhaps of all mammals) is controlled by a blood factor. The proof is that when the blood of a hungry rat is mixed with that of well-fed rats, the deprived rat's food intake is dropped to 50 per cent below normal. It is when the blood factor falls below a critical level, not when a hypothetical "hunger factor" rises above the threshold value, that rats become hungry.

A rat is omnivorous but likes to kill and eat. It will average eating 25 per cent of its own weight every day. The so-called house rat that follows men around the planet is divided into *Rattus norvegicus* (brown rat) and R. *rattus* (the much smaller black rat). Both species apparently originated in Central Asia. Rats outnumber human beings. By about the year 1910, rats in the United States and Canada began to exceed the human population. It is not generally realized, however, that this population explosion was not a result of congregation in the ghettos in the big cities, where the rat frequency has actually decreased by about 50 per cent, owing to extermination campaigns, principally motivated by the fear of rats as carriers of the fleas that spread bubonic plague. It is on the farms that the bulk of the rat population lives and the barn-infesting animals will proportion their number to the amount of food available, including chickens, which rats will kill faster than does a fox. If living conditions are to the rat's liking, the female will breed throughout the year, bearing up to twelve young per litter. Theoretically a pair of sexy rats would give birth to over 350 million descendants within three years. However, disease destroys tremendous numbers when the population reaches a peak density. When the food supply runs low, rats have no hesitancy about turning cannibal. (Except for man, the rodent order is unique in this respect.) The rat is better than a cat in controlling house mice, but the average homeowner would think twice before making this trade off. In spite of their ferocity, experiments with laboratory rats have shown that they are judgmatical eaters—they can learn to distinguish foods that contain vitamins from those that do not, presumably because they feel better after eating the enriched food (but this could be an oversimplified explanation; they may have food chemireceptor senses simply more sophisticated than ours). They have no mechanism that regulates the intake of protein. Lorenz has proposed that an omnivorous animal, such as a rat or a human being, samples small amounts of novel foods and then forms a sort of nervous engram of its reaction to each. This view is supported by the fact that rats eat only small amount of foods that are new to them. Men, unfortunately, are even more conservative; hence the hairiest problem in world-wide prevention of starvation is not to find more nourishing food but to persuade starving natives to eat the kind of food that we can send them.

The name mouse derives significantly from the Sanskrit *musha*, meaning thief. Its ancestors lived in Central Asia and were small, scaly-tailed rodents living on dry grasslands and even deserts. As the primitive peoples of this heartland migrated east, west and south, the mice somehow decided to go along, stealing from the scanty traveling supplies of wheat and barley, bumming rides in the baggage and establishing new colonies everywhere the people stopped. There is only one species (*Mus domesticus*) but four subspecies are recognized, three of which produced "commensals"—fitted to live and eat with man. The house mice of the United States and Canada descended from the wild Wagner race, which originated in Russian Turkestan and came as stowaways with the Spaniards. They have been here only four centuries or less and have really not had time to work out distinctive ways of life. When conditions are favorable and most resemble those under which their ancient ancestors lived in Asia, our house mice can still hear the call of the wild very

clearly. This is why suburbanites often say that during the warm
weather, the mice that have been thumbing noses at them within
their kitchens all winter and have even chewed the paste and glue
out of their bookbindings, have "gone back to the fields." They find
a warm welcome there from owls, cats and snakes.

The meadow mice and other American voles have been here
ages longer. They are extremely busy little mammals, mostly busy
being eaten by hosts of predators, but their appetite is matched only
by their fecundity. They sleep amazingly little for mammals, at the
most two or three hours out of every twenty-four, and eat their own
weight in food. The Indians took advantage of the field mouse's
food-storage habits and every fall would systematically rob their
tiny burrows of edible roots and tubers.

The pocket mouse is a busy and miserly little creature who
never overeats. It stints and saves for a rainy day. Each cheek
pocket holds up to a half teaspoonful or up to twenty mesquite
beans. The smallest species in gathering mustard seeds has been
observed to carry away and store three thousand seeds in an hour.
Unlike the meadow mouse, it will not bite. It does not hibernate
but stays indoors during cold and wet weather, gloating over its
ample rations. Seed-eating rodents such as these often increase in
population where pastures are overgrazed, with the consequent re-
placement of grass by weeds. Thus the pocket mice may be living
it up while the cattle starve. In spite of his thrifty and sober life,
the death rate of these mice is enormous, due to predators. While
his life expectancy in a state of nature is about four months,
he can be kept alive in a zoo for six years. Most species of
pocket mice do not drink water but instead maintain their water
balance by manufacturing it internally by oxidizing starch. This use
of "water of metabolism" is a trick used by many desert rodents
and also by the camel. In addition, various desert mice in Australia,
Africa, Asia and North America, although unrelated in genetic
lines, have all developed the birdlike habit of concentrating their
urine and reducing the output of water in the feces.

The wood rat is another 100 per cent vegetarian and a modest
eater. During hot desert weather he likes to eat cactus. Wood
rats do not compete with cattle for grass. They have long been
known to be good to eat, tasting something like quail. For centuries the Indians of the Southwest have depended mainly on wood
rats for meat, and they are still prized also by working-class Mexicans,

generally being found on sale in country markets. The Mexicans consider this flesh better than rabbit or chicken, and wood-rat soup is the Sonoran equivalent of our chicken soup for the sick, the puny or the finicky. The muskrat is a water rodent who builds elaborate broodside dens and dines heartily on fresh-water clams and mussels. Since his fur is salable he has been remorselessly trapped, but he shows incredible stoicism in chewing through his own skin, flesh, tendons and bones to escape. Sometimes a muskrat is seen who has lost three legs by self-amputation but is still able to make a living. This indomitability may be the secret to the rude success of the rodent order. Note, for example, how hard it is to kill a woodchuck. His vitality is so great that, unless he is killed instantly by a slug, he will manage to scramble so far down his tunnel that the hunter cannot recover the body. The woodchuck (also called ground hog) eats vegetation three times a day and naps the rest of the time. He walks to a point about three feet inside the doorway of his burrow and listens. Frequently he gives a low whistle, often followed by a forlorn call that dies slowly away. (This is why the French call him "siffleur.") The kangaroo rat has the instincts of a grocer, who is his own best customer. Almost fourteen bushels of seeds and dried grasses, cut in short lengths, have been found in one burrow. The food is stored methodically, each kind of seed by itself. He does not hibernate and, unlike some desert rodents, he cannot go to sleep during the summer drought; therefore he tries to keep food always on hand. His thirst is very slight, being partly quenched by green leaves and stems or by sipping dew when available, although some metabolic water is converted from his body starch. Being very proud and fussy, two of these grocers are seldom seen in the same burrow, except at mating time. They are native Americans as are the pocket mice. One of the most pestiferous of rodents is the rice rat, which consumes vast amounts of rice in the southeastern United States. They even dig up the seed.

The suborder of squirrels, although generally thought well of by writers of children's books, contains some notable rodent pests. Because of their fondness for grains and alfalfa, the Columbian ground squirrels can be more grief to a farmer than a plague of locusts. Their deep burrows often channel rain water into underground streams that erode the soil and cause landslides, while their tunnels in the banks of irrigation ditches may result in washouts. The striped ground squirrel (sometimes called the "federation squirrel") on the other hand is a hearty meat eater. He pounces on grasshoppers and can even catch deer mice and meadow mice. So fond of flesh is he that he will even eat the crushed bodies of his own family on the highway. Birds hate him, because he kills fledglings and steals eggs, crowning the insult by giving a quavering whistle that is like a birdcall. Ground squirrels in the north go into complete winter hibernation. Their blood temperature falls far below normal and they scarcely breathe.

Of the tree-living rodents, the red squirrel eats more than nuts, because people who have shot this tiny animal in the hopes of a princely stew are often disappointed by a bitter taste due to resins that the squirrel has absorbed from feeding on pine twigs. He will eat fungi and his system is immune to the powerful poisons of the toadstool. Only certain individual red squirrels have developed an appetite for birds, just as only certain perverted tigers are deliberate man-killers. The red squirrel does not hibernate, but winter is a time of leisure in which he can luxuriate on the ample food stores he has collected. The gray squirrel and the red squirrel do not get along well but the stories of systematic biting off of testicles are probably apocryphal. The western gray squirrel in the Sierra Nevada mountains has learned a specific food-hunting trick that has made him exceedingly unpopular among California woodpeckers. He robs their caches of acorns in preference to collecting his own. The eastern gray squirrel used to overrun the country when the first colonists came to America, and Pennsylvania in 1799 offered three pence a scalp. Some 640,000 gray squirrels were killed as a result. The tassel-eared squirrel once lived in one big western family but this was dispersed about a million years ago when the Grand Canyon was formed. One of the strangest unsolved problems of animal psychology is embodied in Kennicott's ground squirrel, found mainly in the Yellowstone National Park. This squirrel is a mild vegetarian but he has one incredible gift of valor. This is the only small animal that can stand up to the ferocious weasel, and not only face him down but chase him into his den and beat him in wrestling matches. This is almost as if a cottontail rabbit had suddenly developed a habit of chasing dogs. It is an instance of the plastic potential for outrageous behavior that seems to cling to the order of rodents.

Of all rodents, however, probably the most complex is the beaver. The giant beaver that lived in North America thousands of years ago was larger than a black bear and obviously was too big for competency as a working rodent, for he became extinct along with the mammoth and the dire wolf, yet his smaller relatives thrived until man nearly extinguished him for his coat. In Europe only a few stragglers hung on in tiny colonies, but they built nothing. (As in the case of many animals, a minimum population seems to be necessary for colonial animals, such as beavers, to exert their instinctive natures.) For centuries beaver dams were unknown in Western Europe. Then the French government extended protection in the Rhône valley, and the beavers went back to work, constructing dams and lodges exactly the same as those built by their cousins in Canada or Colorado. A beaver eats more than the bark of poplar trees, which early naturalists insisted was his sole diet. He also likes cottonwood, aspen, maple, willow, beech, cherry and even at times dines on conifers and aquatic plants. In the north the thick ice would cut the beaver off from his food supply if it were left piled on the bank of the stream. Hence he has to tow the logs he has cut to the bottom of his dammed pond, ram them fast in the mud or pile stones on them. The average beaver requires the equivalent of an aspen tree between one and three inches thick at the butt end every day to eat. As they cut away the trees around their pond, they will construct canals to nearby groves and bring in new food and building material by water transport, and if this is hydrologically impossible, for reasons of terrain, they will abandon the colony and migrate, since they will not under any circumstances walk on the ground more than about 500 feet from the lodge. The beaver has valves in the nose and ears that close automatically when under water. A pair of small eyes in tightly fitting lids see only dimly in air but better under water. His lips are so loose because he can draw them together tightly behind his protruding teeth. In this way a submerged beaver can cut and chew wood without getting water in his mouth. Extra-large lungs and liver allow him to carry enough air as well as oxygenated and fuel-rich blood to stay under water for fifteen minutes at a time.

In spite of his industry, his caution and his strong sense of family ties, the beaver does not have an exceptional life expectancy—about ten years in the wild, compared with some twenty years in captivity. This is excluding the earlier trapping peril which caused him during the latter part of the nineteenth century to become virtually extinct in the western United States. At one time (when all politicians wore beaverskin hats) the beaver pelt became the basis of values of trade in the northern frontiers. It took one pelt to buy a pound of tobacco and four pounds of shot, and twelve fine ones to acquire a long rifle. The Astor millions were founded on such barter. Now, under restrictions, the beavers are numerous enough to be a liability in some places. When the Idaho Fish and Game Department received thousands of complaints that beavers were flooding fields and roads, it removed 3000 beavers to sparsely settled mountainous regions, and many game commissions have followed this lead. The beaver's damming activities in the mountains are an asset, since they make reservoirs that prevent erosion and the carrying of damaging silt on to irrigation projects, and also provide water storage during droughts for grazing livestock as well as wild life.

Let us look at one more rodent—the porcupine. This creature was a native of South America but emigrated about a million years ago to this continent. Porcupines, being all but invulnerable, have thrived in a modest ecological niche, but they are not a favorite of forest managers, since, living mostly on bark, their girdling kills limbs and whole trees, especially seedlings. They also eat coniferous foliage and are especially fond of mistletoe. Although they are not known to eat meat, they have a craving for bones, on account of the mineral content. This is also the reason for their seemingly perverse habit of chewing up the handles of axes or other hand tools left around; it is the residual salt from the human perspiration that they are after. Tables and chairs on which salt has been spilled will be gnawed and sometimes devoured. (The embarrassing question of how a male and female porcupine manage to achieve a satisfactory love life was dealt with in *The Sexes*.*)

In the order of carnivores we have a whole zoo of animals to consider and shall content ourselves with describing only a few. There are two major groups, the fissipeds (*fissi*, divided) and the pinnipeds (*pinna*, pointed). Fissipeds include seven quite distinct families: dog, raccoon, bear, mink, civet, hyena and cat. The pinnipeds include the sea lions, seals and walruses.

* Published in 1970 by Doubleday & Co.

In the dog family, except for our favorite pets, the most important groups are wolves, foxes and coyotes. Like other wild dogs, foxes cache much of the bodies of animals they have killed, and this wild habit shows up in the instinct for a dog to bury his bone in your backyard. Husky dog foxes, or at least the males, sometimes prey on young deer fawns, on lambs and on grown turkeys. The lemming is the most important item in the diet of the arctic fox. When the lemmings die off, as they do in cycles, the arctic foxes starve. However, members of the dog family do not starve easily. Even your house pet, if he is in good health, can go at least a week without food or water, without serious harm. Most dogs in "developed" countries are grossly overfed and share the disabilities of their affluent and food-conscious masters and mistresses—overweight, liver trouble and atherosclerosis. Wolves, coyotes and domestic dogs all belong to the genus *Canis* (Latin for dog) and sometimes can mate. When a coyote mates with a dog, the puppy is even more nervous and untamable than the wild parent. Because of their fundamental difference in temperament, wolves and coyotes seldom, if ever, interbreed. Wolves regard coyotes as poachers and kill them whenever possible, and in this respect Texans are in agreement with the wolves. The poor coyote is really an excellent and successful wild dog, a scavenger who helps us keep our streams free of dead animals and holds the jack rabbit population in the southwest United States at a tolerable level. (We shall discuss later the dangerously irrational campaign originated in Texas, to eradicate this native American animal.) The first white men to see the coyote, so similar in appearance to the jackal of the Old World, were the Spanish explorers who modified the Nahuatl name, *coyotl*, to identify it. Since some Americans deliberately go out of their way to mispronounce Mexican-derived words, the pronunciation has become "ky-yōt" in every state except California.* The coyote, as a bold, ingenious and valiant animal, has spread itself as far north as Alaska and as far east as New York State. He has his troubles in northern winters and may starve in the presence of deer because of his lack of ability to get around in deep, soft snow. The coyotes flounder

* This unlovely practice is also noticeable in the Spanish-derived word *rodeo* which, again except in California, is invariably mispronounced ró-dee-oh, to rhyme with vo-dodee-oh. Compare this barbarism with the correct, mellifluous ro-dáy-oh.

about in the drifts and cannot catch anything. Since a winter of soft snow is good for the big game, there is little carrion to resort to. The coyote does not sleep through the winters, since after two or three days he gets so hungry that he leaves the winter den (or an open bed under a tree or bush) and strikes out hopefully, through the snow, looking for rabbits or rodents. The coyote is not only one of nature's garbage collectors, and, never on strike, he serves like the cougar to winnow the easily overmultiplying deer, antelope and other hoofed mammals who, without him, would overeat their ranges, become fat and lazy and have cirrhosis of the liver.

Wolves are clever and tireless hunters and their pack method of bringing down big game is similar in some respect to the way lionesses hunt co-operatively. A wolf can canter along for hour after hour without fatigue. He can kill the largest mammals, even musk oxen and bison, if desperate, but he is often forced to be satisfied with smaller prey. He never eats fruits and vegetables, as coyotes often do, but may nibble a little grass occasionally. (You have seen your dog do this.) The male wolf is a faithful husband and a good father.

In spite of the charming theory of Lorenz about the bifurcated origin of domestic dogs from jackals and wolves, it seems most probable, from all the evidence, that this animal was first domesticated in northern Europe about 6000 years ago, its wild ancestor being the northern European wolf. Thousands of volumes have been devoted to this subject, but it is sufficient to say that the dog spread to all continents, including Australia, where it escaped to the wild and, probably because of lack of competition with other placental mammals, became a separate and reasonably successful species—the Dingo.

Except for the polar bear, the eating habits of most members of the bear family can be characterized as mixed carnivore-scavenger, herbivorous and insectivorous. Although the recent misfortunes of certain people have served to paint the grizzly at least as a ravening monster, I know of no authenticated case of any bear making a meal out of a man, woman or child. The human body makes a good punching bag and smells sufficiently of food to cuff around and chew up a bit, but it turns out to be disappointing provender. Man is an antagonist but not good to eat.

The ordinary American black bear (*Enarctos Americanus* and

relatives) is actually quite variable, and an embarrassed black mother may give birth to a blond, a redhead and a brunette in the same litter. A "blue bear" may occur in southeastern Alaska and an albino in British Columbia. This color instability caused the original describer of the genus to call it the "short-clawed American bear," which is accurate because the grizzlies have much longer toenails.

Such bears are not natural predators of other mammals. Even when both bears and deer are abundant, practically all the supposed "kills" turn out to be carrion, for indeed the blue bear likes his flesh rank, even foul and will roll in it, to show his pleasure, much as your dog will roll merrily in horse turds. The bear also likes crickets, grasshoppers, ants and bees and will overturn and mash a beehive, cleaning out the honeycomb and eating the bees, to whose sting he is impervious. Although brown bears and grizzlies are good fishermen, the black bear is strangely clumsy at this pursuit. Occasionally a black bear will develop a perverse appetite. One animal in Idaho was seen to dine continuously on the udders of nursing ewes. Although the sheep were not killed by this cruel attack, they died later of infection. Sometimes the bear would eat the heart and liver but not the rest of the meat. The grizzly's everyday menu is about the same as that of the black bear—only more so. He is perhaps more herbivorous, digging up roots and in the summer he crops huge quantities of grass, grazing like a cow.

All bears take the easy way to store food for the winter—they simply gorge themselves until they are fat. People in the bear country claim that one can tell when a very severe winter is coming, because the bears will get fatter than usual. The adult female is almost invariably pregnant by the time of the first snow and she is quite fussy about choosing the den which is to be not only her bed but her place of accouchement (truly a twilight-sleep affair, usually in January). In regions where the winds come from the north she selects a bedroom with a southern exposure; thus the winds pile snow around the dwelling and insulate her in her sleepy parturition. The male bear turns in just anywhere. Even the soundest sleeping bear does not truly hibernate, in the sense that ground squirrels do. Its temperature remains normal and it breathes four or five times a minute, which is about the breathing rate of a person in a deep sleep.

Polar bears feed almost entirely on seals. The marine food chain in the arctic depends initially on the "krill" or copepods, which thrive in the vicinity of icebergs and upon which fishes feed; seals eat the fish and polar bears the seals. As would be expected of such specialized predators, the bears play some mean tricks, one of which might be called the "blowhole caper." If a blowhole is not too far from the edge of the ice pan, the polar bear takes a deep breath and swims under the ice. Once under the hole, it makes a tiny scratching sound, imitating a fish. The charmed seal dives into the hole right into the hungry embrace of two mighty forearms. A young walrus is a delicacy to the bear but the mother is watchful and she is too big to be dominated. Polar bears stranded on northern islands in the summer will graze on grass like grizzlies. If a whale or walrus becomes stranded and helpless, polar bears will gather for miles around. Except for the liver, the meat of polar bears is wholesome and much appreciated by Eskimos. The liver, although delicious, causes nausea, dizziness, splitting headache and sometimes peeling of the skin. This is because it contains a high concentration of vitamin A.

We have time to consider only a few more of the endless natural zoo of the fissiped carnivores and shall limit our eating story to animals found in North America. Consider the raccoon, *Lotor*, which means "the washer." It will always wash its food when near water. Even a frog or crayfish (its favorite diet) just caught from the water will be sloshed about until the raccoon feels the time for a bite has arrived. Zoologists are not sure what this is all about—certainly it is not because the animal is a compulsive hygienist—rather, he apparently gets some pleasure in his very sensitive hands by the dunking process. The journeys for food begin after dusk and the whole family may participate, eating probably more vegetables in the long run than meat. When food is scarce in the northern winters, several families may bunk together but, as in the case of bears, they do not truly hibernate. The raccoon is a fierce fighter, when cornered, and will beat off or cripple two or three hounds. It has been known to lure a dog into water, climb on its head and drown it. The success and perhaps the enchantments of an all-night coon hunt for groups of men and dogs lie mostly in the whiskey that is drunk, but also in the fact that some inexperienced coon will go to the trees, where, amidst the baying and yelping of the dogs below, his eyes will reflect a flashlight and he can be shot down.*

The badger is a splendid animal, methodical, preoccupied and formidable. He makes a living by digging faster than moles, marmots, ground squirrels and pocket gophers—going after them and gobbling them up. The badger does not hibernate in the winter, but since his favorite prey are usually hidden in their hibernaculums, he just gets drowsy and nature cuts his appetite. A batch of sleepy skunks which often den together gives him several weeks supply of food. The entrance to their den may require only a little quick and expert enlarging to enable him to enter and meticulously eat every one of them. In northern Ohio the badger is considered very evil indeed, since he has been accused of robbing graves. Since this felony appears to be a geographical oddness and perhaps based on insufficient data, one should hold judgment in abeyance. The demand for badger fur has encouraged attempts to grow them in captivity, but they do not stand it very well. With their voracious appetites they eat up all the profits. A standard sport in Oklahoma in territorial days used to be to match two bulldogs and a badger, but the badger usually won.

The wolverine (*Gulo sp.*), sometimes called the skunk bear, is the largest (about three feet long, including tail) of the weasel tribe and his nature assuredly is an example of the tribal ferocity. How many bulldogs it would take to match him is impossible to guess. *Gulo* means gullet, and he is precisely a clawed, fanged, wildly insatiable, clever-brained eating and fighting machine. His digestive system disposes of food so efficiently that he can consume immense quantities of anything he can catch. The only animal not immediately attacked by a wolverine is man, and this shows that his ferocity is tempered by shrewdness. If he finds and takes a notion to follow a trap line, he will ultimately ruin the trapper. He will remove every bit of bait, every trapped animal and will often hide the traps or destroy them, but is almost invariably too smart to get himself caught. Three large coyotes have been seen to leave their meal of a dead horse when a single wolverine advanced, with hair and tail standing up. Even black bears abandon their carrion

* Such coon hunts are becoming rare on the east coast where Archie Carr thinks the country menfolk now prefer to watch the late, late show on television at night, and as a result the raccoon has tremendously proliferated and has almost exterminated certain kinds of sea turtles by devouring their eggs.

and become interested suddenly in the scenery over the next hill when *Gulo* appears. Two mountain lions prudently retired from a deer they had just killed when a wolverine in California stalked toward them. The Eskimos prize wolverine fur far out of proportion to its market value. Because the guard hairs will not accumulate frost, the pelt is a favorite trimming for parka hoods and cuffs. Aside from this, the best-dressed Eskimo is the one with the most yards of wolverine skin, apparently because the hide of the animal of such unexampled ferocity should spread an aura of valor. From an ecological point of view, the wolverine is almost exactly matched in Africa by the hyena; both are bone-crushing, implacably active scavengers.

Looking at the cat family, in the cougar (also called mountain lion, panther, puma and *Felis concolor*) we see the tendency of carnivorous felines to be one-prey animals. Just as the arctic lynx depends almost entirely on the snowshoe rabbit, the cougar makes a living from killing deer and has been consequently regarded as a villain, with a bounty on his head. Luckily this shortsighted policy is coming to an end, as the scientifically minded wildlife commissions realize that he is needed, not only to prevent the deer population from exploding to the point where it starves itself to death but as one of nature's winnowers, since the cougar quickly weeds out the subnormal deer (those for instance with hoof deformities or prenatal injuries), thus keeping the species normal in size and body proportions. The cougar can and will, if necessary, knock over a sheep, hog, goat or colt or even a full-grown steer or horse, but deer is the staple diet. The cougar is such an efficient killer that it may make a fresh kill every night, leaving uneaten portions for the bears and coyotes. As Lorenz has so perceptively emphasized, the "quick kill" on the part of the felines is a matter of self-preservation. Such a predator cannot afford too much thrashing around and the chance of being injured by sharp hoofs, for a disabling injury or infection will put him out of business. (In killing cattle and buffalo, the Indian tiger tries to grab the prey forward and by pressing its head to the ground, using the paw as a lever, to make the victim topple over itself, breaking its own neck and thus killing itself in the first few seconds of the first round of confrontation.)

The course of hunger satiation in a keen hunter, such as a cat, may be followed by watching what happens when you give a cat one live mouse after another. First, the cat stops eating but kills a few mice, leaving them untouched. Next the killing bite disappears but the cat continues to stalk and catch the mice, merely playing with them. Later still, the cat simply stalks the mice and chooses those farthest away from her. The hunting instinct cannot be suppressed, only diluted and turned into a comedy by a full stomach.

In the mink family there is a hierarchy of predation. The mink itself is a crafty killer and, although not as fast as a weasel, kills many small mammals and can chase down and catch fish. It has a special fondness for muskrat flesh and will pursue these large rodents into their burrows and kill them. Sometimes a few minks will clean out a whole muskrat colony. Like the weasel, a mink will break into orgies of senseless slaughter, leaving the dead bodies for scavengers. A mink is not only mean, he smells terrible because of his peculiar rotten musk glands. There are some predators other than man that get to him, including the lynx, bobcat and the great horned and snowy owls. The marten is a larger, tree-minded weasel and the worst enemy of the red squirrel. Unlike the mink and weasel, it does not kill more than it needs and what it does not eat immediately it buries. The famous sable is only a larger marten that lives in the Siberian pine forests. The fisher, a superior member of the mink family, with the face of a weasel and the tail of a fox, does not fish, although in emergencies it will eat a dead fish. It snatches meals from the treetops, being the fastest tree traveler of any mammal known. It will run down and kill the marten, as the marten runs down the tree squirrel. It can even outrun the snowshoe hare on the ground. Since it has few enemies, it is curious that this magnificent animal has not proliferated to a greater extent. In California its only important predator is the golden eagle, a bird on its way to extinction.

The skunk goes through periods of proliferation which are not well understood but are under active study, since being at home around people its tendency to contract rabies is a matter for some worry. As any owner of a demusked pet skunk can testify, this affectionate little animal is a much better mouser than a cat. During the spring the wild skunk depends on meadow mice for three quarters of its living. Through the winter (in which it becomes drowsy but does not hibernate) it feeds also on white-footed and jumping mice, pocket gophers, ground squirrel, shrews, moles, chipmunks and cottontails. The skunk is often denounced for destroying ground-nesting birds, eggs and domestic poultry. It destroys bees but cannot climb, so fencing the hives is sufficient protection. This by no means completes the menu for this extraordinary eater. A live skunk is probably worth more to agriculture than to the fur trade, since it devours whole hordes of cutworms, potato beetles, white grubs, May beetle grubs, army worms, tobacco worms and other larvae. Because it was so good at destroying the hop grub, the New York legislature, at the insistence of the hop growers, put skunks on the protected list.

Among the pinniped carnivores, the seals and sea lions are, of course, most oppressed and most admired (except by professional fishermen). Seals have strange stomachs. Since their teeth are not fitted for chewing, they must bolt their fish food whole and alive. Seals have been found with stones as big as hen's eggs in their stomachs. These are possibly swallowed for "roughage" or for grinding food, as birds eat gravel. The two families are the eared seals (the sea lion and the fur seal) and the earless or "true" seals. The fur seal, along with the sea otter, was nearly wiped out in the senseless massacres in the northern breeding islands, which we shall discuss later. The Steller's sea lion, common on the California coast, is larger than the fur seal of Disney fame and does not have as many wives, contenting himself with a mere ten to fifteen. He is not of a jealous nature and does not fast as long in the breeding season. Most of the trick seals we see in the circus are female sea lions. The fur seals and sea lions are not the natural fishing competitors that the fishing industry would have us believe, since their main diet is herring; they eat very little salmon and no halibut. Unfortunately this is not true of the earless seals. The ringed seal, also called the fjord seal, is a common native of the arctic, not being a migrator like the fur seal. His standard summer food, like that of his close relative the harbor seal, is cod and, before the runs start, he feeds heavily on salmon. The walrus is a mighty eater. He uses his great tusks not only for fighting but for digging clams. The space between the tusks limits the size of his food, but bristly pads on each side of the muzzle are very good forks and knives. When satisfied, a walrus' stomach contains enough clams to fill a washtub. The Eskimos considered as a supreme delicacy the half-digested clams from the walrus' stomach. A lone walrus may turn savage and take to eating seals.

The order of cetaceans includes both the toothed whales, such as the sperm whales (like Moby Dick) and the porpoises, and as a distinct suborder the baleen whales, which instead of teeth have enormous brushlike sieves (baleens or whalebones) hanging around the edge of the upper jaw. The whole order possesses high intelligence, surprisingly developed communications systems and sonar capabilities. The larger toothed whales often eat giant squid, an amazing accomplishment that proves, I suppose, that a mammal is intrinsically superior to even the smartest mollusk known, but precisely how they make the kill is not known. The scars made by large squid suckers are often found on their skin. Porpoises eat mostly fishes. The toothed killer whales eat their smaller relatives, the porpoises, and anything else they can catch. Whalebone whales, like the tremendous blue whale (the largest animal that has ever lived, ten times as big as the biggest dinosaur) live on a diet of plankton, the minute mixed plant and animal life swarming in parts of the ocean, which he captures in the mouth with his whale-bone sieves.

There is a blood problem in vertebrates, such as the cetaceans, who decided to return to the sea, much like the problem faced by the first bony fishes back in the dim Paleozoic. The blood of marine mammals is more concentrated than that of land mammals but not enough to hold water against the higher osmotic concentration of the sea. In part the problem is made less tough by the fact that whales and porpoises are air breathing and so do not have gills constantly exposed to salt water. Also, marine mammals can secrete urine which is more concentrated than sea water. Another blessing is that porpoises and some of the smaller whales live largely on bony fishes, which have solved the osmotic problem by excreting salt, hence if these cetaceans are careful not to swallow too much sea water when they eat, a diet of teleosts will not add much salt to their systems. The problem is toughest with large baleen whales, which live on marine invertebrates (plankton species) whose blood and body fluids are more concentrated than that of a mammal. It has been calculated that if the kidneys could excrete some-what more salt and urea and reabsorb more water than land mam-mals, all would be well. Apparently it is all well, since they have been getting by for millions of years, but we do not know quite how. Another thing we do not know is how the cetaceans got back into the sea. The earliest sirenians (the order including sea cows) show similarities to the ancestors of elephants, but cetaceans have been very distinct from all other forms of mammals as far back as the fossil record takes us.

An ordinary-sized toothed whale will eat for breakfast a ton of sardines topped off with other smallfishes or crustaceans. The baleen whale has an enormous tongue and his method of eating shows why. When it has swum with its mouth open, engulfing billions of plankton organisms, the tongue forces the water back *out* the side strainers and the whale then swallows the food that is left on the whalebone. The whale could not afford to swallow the water, or the cells of his body would swell up and burst. The whale's air ducts are not connected with the mouth or throat as in other mammals. A set of valves automatically closes the breathing portal (or blowhole) when the whale is submerged. A whale does not spout water when he comes to the surface. It is his water-laden breath of exhalation expanding into the cooler air and condensing the water in it. Rather than a water spout, it is entirely analogous to the condensation trails left behind high-flying airplanes or to the vaporous exhalations we ourselves give off when skiing. The problem of how a whale manages to sound to crushing depths and then surface again without getting the bends turns out to be a simple one. If we could hold our breath as long as a sounding whale, we could not get the bends either. The bends in divers are due to a high pressure of nitrogen being absorbed into the blood; then upon decompressing, when coming to the surface, an explosive evolution of nitrogen injures our vascular system. But note the entirely different processes that a sounding whale and a deep-sea diver use. The whale, with a surprisingly small lung, carries down with him only the precise amount of nitrogen that he has breathed in before sounding. On the other hand, the diver is being supplied continuously with high-pressure air, hence the amount of nitrogen absorbed per unit of body weight is larger than the whale has to cope with by a tremendous factor. A tougher question, and one not solved entirely to anyone's satisfaction, is how the whale at the depths to which he descends manages to keep his body intact in view of water pressures so high they would flatten out an empty steel pipe, sealed at both ends.

Before leaving the sea mammals, we should mention again the order of sirenians: the manatee and the dugong, or sea cow, all large, gentle vegetarians with pectoral but no pelvic limbs. A disappearing type, they can still sometimes be seen in coastal waters and in rivers. The pectoral position of the breasts and the mother's endearing habit of holding the young to them with her flippers is the source of old sailors' tales of mermaids. The largest sirenian is the Steller's sea cow seen in the Bering strait, but occasionally in Florida the Atlantic manatee can be seen drifting placidly up to a wave of river grass. They seem to be sitting upright, heads above the water. Like all well-mannered and harmless mammals who are saying good-by forever to the planet (like the impassive gorilla, forever chewing his bamboo sprouts and minding his own ruined business), they seem to radiate the calm of impending extinction.

The order of artiodactyls (*artios*, even+*dactylos*, finger) includes the larger herbivorous mammals with an even number of toes. One suborder includes pigs, peccaries, and the hippopotamus, another the sheep, camels, cattle, deer, giraffes, antelopes, etc. The latter are indeed successful animals because their eating needs can be so simply furnished by the soil. Because many of these animals chew the cud, they are sometimes referred to as ruminants (*ruminare*, to chew the cud).

The somewhat elfin and intellectually popular writer Donald Barthelme, in one of his satirical reports for the *New Yorker*, describes a project in which some mysterious Middle Eastern savants and weirdos have decided to solve the hopeless Malthusian dilemma of too many people and not enough food by implanting ruminant digestive systems in human beings, so that the starving poor of India, for example, could be put out to pasture. Although this idea does not go quite as far as the projection of the noted Cal Tech biologist James Bonner in which the problem of overpopulation in backward countries is solved by the simple expedient of making such excess humans into food for the "developed" countries (as the Morlocks feed on the Eloi in H. G. Wells' future planet of *The Time Machine*), it is nevertheless a basically constructive notion, although I am sure Mr. Barthelme did not view his contribution in this light. Let us see how a ruminant's stomach system works.

In all artidactyls the stomach consists of four chambers (except in pigs and hippopotamuses), the first being the rumen, a pouch that acts like a warehouse for raw material, much in the nature of a bird's crop. This holds raw but undigested food until it can be regurgitated and chewed at leisure. In the herbivores (vegetarians), the canine teeth have disappeared or nearly so, and the molars have become grinders with flat, corrugated tops. The actual process of regurgitation takes place from the reticulum or honeycomb, where the cud is saturated with saliva. After chewing, the food is swallowed a second time, it slips along a groove on one side of the reticulum, through the folding corridors of the psalterium and into the abomasum, which is the digestive center of a ruminant's stomach. A complicated mess of ciliate protozoa swarm in the stomach and the large intestine of ruminants and play a crucial role in the digestion of cellulose—thus cows appear to be as dependent on their little guests in the guts as are cockroaches and termites.

Now, aside from the breaking down of cellulose, the bacterial flora in a ruminant's stomach has the exceedingly important capability of making the twenty essential amino acids from other amino acids and even from simpler nitrogenous compounds, such as urea and ammonia. Besides, the ruminant digests and swallows the bacteria. The stomach of people (and of poultry and swine) do not have this capability, hence it is a much less exacting job to feed a cow than a pig or a chicken, aside from the matter of cellulose digestion. A still further chemical complication in the ruminant's stomach has been added by the discovery that the rumen is not solely a warehouse for raw grass or hay. In forming the cuds the unsaturated fats from plant tissue have been broken down into glycerine and free fatty acids and the fatty acids have been hydrogenated. It is this process that has made it a modern medical axiom to cut down on animal fats in order to reduce the dangers of human atherosclerosis. If it were possible, without otherwise injuring the ruminants who provide us with steaks, to eliminate the fat breakdown and hydrogenation steps in the rumen, we would presumably reduce greatly the incidence of heart disease in our species.

Aside from this, however, the versatility of the ruminant stomach recommends itself to us. In the biological engineering of men who can survive an inevitable planetary food shortage, we should closely examine the possibilities of changing man's stomach apparatus to true omnivorousness, so that not only could he eat and digest grass and hay for carbohydrates but would be able, as the cow does, to transform the plant amino acids into the amino acids that man's blood and liver will accept as true body-building blocks and to eat furthermore the bacteria that do the transforming. It does not seem necessary to include the storing pouch in this new kind of stomach, for we are not biologically in need of a raw food storehouse (which is for animals that feed and gulp, because they are under the constant surveillance of predators) and also because we do not want to rely on hydrogenated fats. The main problem is to induce either in our stomachs or intestines or both the growth of a benign, specialized protozoan population which is able, without going wild and hurting us, to carry out the jobs of cellulose digestion and amino acid synthesis from the planet's almost limitless supply of hay and leaves of trees. By consuming plant tissues thus directly, we detour around the intrinsically inefficient method of first growing an edible animal out of (to us) inedible plant tissues. There does not appear to be any theroretically impossible barrier in such a biological development, since we already have in our bowels a swarming population of bacteria, mostly of the hardy *Escherichia coli* type, which have certain digestive functions, but not the function we need most to build a world of hay burners. We would have to spend most of our time eating.

At the end of the Cenozoic era, forests were giving way to grasslands as the climate became drier. Succulent leaves and buds and fungi were harder to come by and many animals were faced with the critical choice of either learning to eat grass or to eat other animals that ate grass. Grass is full of silica and not easy to eat, requiring special dental equipment (although it can be processed to remove silica for the more generalized teeth of men). In coming out of the trees, the ancestors of man decided to eat grass-eating animals. It would be one of evolution's pleasant ironies if we now found ourselves forced to reverse this choice on the part of our Australopithecine forebears and to make grass a steady diet rather than a Nebuchadnezzar frenzy.

Reluctantly retreating from this speculatory diversion, let us consider some of the arteriodactyls. However, we should remark in passing that the normal animal balance between sodium chloride and potassium chloride is not supplied by a purely vegetable diet. The reason may primarily be that plants do not have nerves, and in all animal nerves a membrane process involving both sodium and potassium ions is involved. Vegetable food contains plenty of potassium but little sodium. The deficiency has to be made up by eating salt (hence the importance of salt licks for cattle, the vegetarian porcupine's hunger for perspiration-stained wood and even your dog's habit of licking your flesh, especially on a hot day).

In the old days of North America, when the walking was good between Asia and Alaska, the elk helped along with the Indians to colonize this country. The Shawnee called them "Wapiti," which some naturalists prefer today, since the term "elk" was what the English colonists who settled Virginia named them and which is still the common term for the European moose. The elk and deer are first cousins, and we should say something about the food value of their antlers. When they shed every year, these castoffs are scarcely to be regarded as organic litter. They are immediately devoured by porcupines, rabbits, mice and other small creatures because of their high calcium content. Pregnant rodents especially gnaw on them. The antelope's horn sheaths, being less durable, are even eaten after shedding by the antelope himself. The antelope incidentally is the only native American of all our hoofed animals, and is not even a second cousin of the African or Asiatic antelope. Bones of his early American ancestors have been found which date back about one and a half million years. Our modern deer, moose and elk are all immigrants. The caribou alone show an extremely interesting and almost incredible ruminant characteristic. In summer when the lemmings are going through one of their immense population explosions, caribous have been seen, while grazing, to swallow the lemmings whole. It is possible that this is an act of exasperation rather than of hunger since the caribou's digestive system is no more designed to handle a live rodent than is a cow's for swallowing a kitten. The reindeer is merely the domesticated barren-ground caribou of the Old World and was introduced into Alaska from Lapland. The 1280 animals imported between 1891–1902, chiefly to the Seward Peninsula, have increased to over a million. Since they have been in captivity for generations, the reindeer are much more tractable than the wild caribou, which are killed by native Alaskans on sight, since they will hang around a reindeer corral and "toll away" the domesticated animals and mate with them, the hybrid offspring proving to be (as in the case of the hybrid between domestic dog and coyote) an untamable creature.

(We shall later treat with the survival problems of elk, antelope, deer, caribou and buffalo.)

The bighorn or wild sheep of North America do not bear wool

like domestic sheep but have heavy coats, more like that of a deer. The mountain goat is not a true goat; it is an antelope closely related to the European chamois.

It should not be forgotten that the hippopotamus is an artiodactyl and makes a living mostly by grazing enormously at night. In the transitional period of balmy weather throughout the planet which prevailed between the Pliocene and Pleistocene, the hippo flourished as far north as France. On the other hand the rhinoceros is a perissodactyl (*perissos,* off+*dactylon,* fingers) with an odd number of toes and belongs to the same order as the horse-ass-zebra group and the tapirs. The whole order is herbivorous, and the rhino does not get any nourishment by charging intrepid African safaris nor does he devour the flesh of people he has trampled on.

In the case of horses which walk on one elongated and thickened toe on each foot—the hoof is the toenail—there are vestigial "hand" bones on either side of the main "fingers," the bones horsemen call splint bones. In the recent fossil ancestors of horses these are much larger and each is tipped with a small hoof, while in the remote ancestral fossils, there are four working toes on each front foot and three on each hind foot. The evolution of the horse is carefully documented and shows that natural evolution favored that strain with the most elongated bones in the "hands" and feet and fewer toes, and with heavy, corrugated, grinding molar teeth; in short, those better adapted for running on the prairie and eating grass. The genus *Equus,* which includes as separate species the contemporary horse, the ass and the zebra, first appeared in the late Pliocene. The charred bones of extinct horses are found in the fireplaces of Stone Age men in California, but long before Europeans arrived on this continent, the native horses had become extinct. This is a mysterious fact of animal history, but it probably had something to do with the fact that horses are not very bright and had become too big and too vulnerable. Like the American mastodon, the mammoth, the saber-toothed tiger, the giant ground sloth, the giant beaver, the American horse could not survive all the way through the extraordinary climatic tensions of the Pleistocene. The horse would probably be extinct today if he had not been domesticated. The zebra, a cannier fiercer species, with a climatically equable habitat, obviously is a more successful animal.

For the present we must skip over the order of elephants (Proboscidiformes) in spite of the fact that they and their ancestors have been objects of awe and excitement since before history, as shown by the drawings of the cave men all the way to the writing of the eloquent contemporary Frenchman Romain Gary who regards them as the only hope and spiritual solace of a degenerating human race. There are two mysterious orders, however, that we must mention before passing on to the food-eating habits of the primates. The conies, belonging to the order of Hydracoidiformes are queer little mammals, who look like guinea pigs. "Cony" is the biblical term used for the Syrian and African *hydrax*, who lives among rocks and is a vegetarian. It is actually a hoofed mammal. Its teeth resemble the artiodactyl dentition, but its reproductive system and blood proteins show the closest relationship to the elephants. Although a subdued little creature, it has been a sort of continuous crossword puzzle to zoologists and a veritable monster of strange, seemingly incompatible genes, and yet it perseveres in its unassuming ecological niche.

There are some inconsequential orders, once lumped together as edentates, including the Xenarthiformes (armadillos, tree sloths and South American anteaters), Pholidotiformes (the scaly anteater or pangolis) and Tubulidentatiformes (the aardvark or South African anteater), all being highly specialized, mainly insectivorous and lacking teeth.

We shall return later to the armadillo, because of the remarkable capability of this animal of producing identical quadruplets (a habit that is very suggestive for the future of higher man). The armadillo's armor consists of a bony case, partly solid, bucklerlike plates and partly movable crossbands. These animals eat roots, insects, worms, reptiles and spiders and are mostly nocturnal. Armadillos have been found as far north as Oklahoma, although they do not hibernate and suffer a great deal from the cold. They are among the most sociable of animals and forage together. As noted previously, gregariousness is a characteristic of animals who can find their food almost anywhere. Their flesh is regarded as delicious, especially when barbecued with hot chili sauce. It tastes like pork and in fact is often called "poverty pig" in East Texas.

15

THE VEGETARIAN MONKEY AND HIS CARNIVOROUS DESCENDANTS

The primate order of mammals which includes man and the various apes, monkeys, lemurs and tarsoids is actually hard to distinguish from the primitive insectivores from which it evolved. Some animal, similar to the present-day shrew but larger, took refuge from the rodents with whom he was competing unsuccessfully and learned to live in the trees, to eat foliage and fruit and insects and birds' eggs that he could find there. Probably the living animals that most resemble this pre-monkey primate are the lemurs and tarsoids. The distinction between these small, dwindling primates and the insectivores and other mammals would only be appreciated by a philosophical dentist. The other placental mammals have six incisors, while primates have only four. True lemurs are found only on Madagascar and nearby islands but their close relatives, the loris and the bush baby are found from the East Indies across southern Asia and into Africa. They are all shy nocturnal animals, still living on the ancestral diet. Some species have the indescribable primate "look" about them, while others look like bushy-tailed squirrels or cats. *Tarsius* is the only living member of the Tarsoid suborder. It is found only in the East Indies and resembles a lemur but has a better-developed brain, enormous owl-like eyes and, like an owl, can look only in different directions by turning its neck.

There is a lamentable scarcity in fossils between the lemurlike stage of primate evolution and the monkey. Animals that live in trees do not come down for any reason, even to get water. They get all the water they need in the fruit and leaves. They die in the trees, and when the bodies fall to earth they molder with the humus and their bones seldom become fossilized. (Bones on the highly populated floor of a forest are up for grabs for any mineral-hungry rodent.)The most ancient monkeylike fossils so far discovered were found in the earlier Oligocene strata in Egypt—*Parapithecus*, which may have constituted the base population from which both Old and New World monkeys diverged, but there is a good deal of difficult detective work still to be done. The suborder of anthropoids, for example, in addition to apes and man includes two major groups, the platyrrhine (flat-nosed) monkeys of South America and the catarrhine (downward-nosed) anthropoids (monkeys, apes and man) of the Old World. The catarrhines are the only monkeys with prehensile tails (sharing this gift with several unrelated South American animals—the opossum, for example). Did the South American monkey evolve independently, regardless of the vague primitive fossils of Parapithecus? There are some logical reasons to believe they did. For example, the migration route between America and Asia via the Bering Strait ceased to be available for creatures adapted to a continuously warm, well-wooded habitat, while fossil evidence shows that American anthropoids evolved *after* these forbidding conditions had come into existence. The crossing of the boreal straits, while possible much later to a clothes-wearing, weapon-carrying Stone Age man, was inconceivable to a monkey who had never come out of the tropical trees. If parallel evolution for platyrrhines and catarrhines is accepted, it is one of the greatest front-page stories in all biology, since it disproves the pessimistic notion that evolution to man is a matter of miraculous contingencies, million-to-one shots followed by random geographic radiations. To some extent it offers philosophic support, not only for Coon's theory of the development of human races from different types of primitive man but for the starry-eyed assumption of the science fiction writers that life of our kind must exist elsewhere in the universe. If a lemurlike insectivore in South America can develop into so complicated a social animal as a howling monkey (*Alonatta*) or other advanced anthropoids of the Cebidae family, such as *Cebus*, the organ-grinders' monkey and *Atales*, the spider monkey, there is no reason why a million or more years might not have seen the larger anthropoids and a manlike animal evolve independently in South America. This is not to argue for an independent evolution of the South American Indians or the Incas, but to point out that the way had been paved. All that was lacking apparently was some climatic or nutritional incentive or perhaps the South American monkey's invention of a prehensile tail proved an ultimate disadvantage, since it took the pressure off of improvement of hand-mindedness.

Eloquent popularizers of the new findings concerning man's African descent through the twenty-million-year-old monkey-ape, *Proconsul,* and the Australopithecines, who came out of the trees with blood in their eyes and killing weapons in their hands, have made it unnecessary for anyone once again to repeat this dramatic scenario, yet there are certain points worth re-emphasizing, since they are basic to the question of what we do next, having reached, so to speak, an evolutionary dead end.

In order to earn a living, the tree-living monkeys had to have certain special equipment which included stereoscopic and color-perceiving eyes. This is true whether you climb and jump, like the monkeys, or brachiate (swing from limb to limb) like the gibbons; depth perception and a clear contrast between green leaves, blue sky and colored fruit are indispensable in your arboreal business. And, of course, for all this climbing or brachiation you need good hands (although prehensile feet and tail are also useful, perhaps *too* useful if you want eventually to evolve into a biped and rule the world). Thus man's most remote arboreal ancestors had the kind of eyes and the kind of hands we have and, to a great extent, the kind of digestive and nervous systems. And yet to come down out of the trees, to become a predator and to compete with other carnivores, a great change had to be made. In man's ancestors, the Australopithecines, the change occurred in a mere blink of geologic time. The master biological novelties adopted by these Hominidae included the enlargement of the brain, the redesign of the legs and buttocks to allow for bipedal walking and running and, perhaps, not the least, the development of right-handedness. One-handedness or unidextrality is a feature introduced for weaponmaking or fine manipulation. All tribes and nations of men, no matter how primitive, contain from 85 to 95 per cent of right-handed people, and all cultures frown—sometimes with great illogic—on left-handedness. In even the most advanced apes, such as the gorilla or chimpanzee, ambidextrousness is, on the contrary, universal. That *Australopithecus africanus* went around armed with rocks and antelope bones presumably in his right hand and killed, among other animals, his fellow primate, the baboon, who had also descended from the trees, seems to be generally accepted today, in spite of the puritanical shock of scandal that first greeted this fossil interpretation by Raymond Dart shortly after the Second World War. This early mastery of tooled predation, especially the use of the pebble tool, seems to have given *Australopithecus* the equivalent in weaponry of the fierce canine teeth that he had lost. *Australopithecus robustus*, another species who was around about the same time became a vegetarian with square munching molars and, although he had a sagittal crest on the top of his head, like a gorilla, to anchor the powerful grinding jaws, he also had lost the ape's fighting canine teeth. Apparently he was a born loser, since it was only his carnivorous relative A. *africanus* that survived.

The lightning-quick evolution of the latter seems to be another instance of neoteny, which we have mentioned in regard to the development of invertebrate phyla and classes (e.g., the rise of the insects from larval millipedes). In many ways, man seems to be a "fetalized ape." In the embryos of all mammals the brain is much larger in proportion to the size of the body than it is in the adult. Simply having a large brain at maturity may therefore be regarded as a neotenous trait. The lack of hair completely covering the body is a fetal trait in the apes but an adult trait in man. Since man's descent from the trees presumably occurred during the Pliocene, a period of drought so harsh that there was seldom enough water in Africa to fossilize bones, it was not necessary for an animal to be concerned with hair at that time, a lack which man regretted later during the Pleistocene with its ice ages. Although we are the only relatively hairless primates, we have more hair than certain other mammals which developed at approximately the same time, such as the elephant and the rhinoceros. If the theory of the neotenous evolution of man is correct, there does not seem any point in dreaming up elaborate adaptive reasons for his loss of hair, such as the author of *The Naked Ape* has done.

The age at which the bony sutures fuse in a man is much later than fusions of the same bones in the apes and monkeys. The anatomical structure of the brain of a newly born chimpanzee more closely resembles the structure of the human brain than does the brain of an adult chimpanzee. In tooth development man is greatly retarded compared with the monkeys and apes, and this is true both for the milk teeth and the permanent teeth. All in all, it is fairly clear that man is a modified ape that becomes sexually mature without becoming fully adult anatomically. His plastic Peter Pan nature was at the bottom of his capacity for learning and for rapid progress. Being more primitive and unspecialized than a gorilla, he was able to learn to rule the planet, while the gorilla ate his placid way to extinction. And yet even the anthropoids probably owed their relative braininess to neoteny. Inquisitiveness is a strong drive among all young mammals but declines as they get older. The anthropoid way is to continue the habit of curiosity into adult life. If a neotenous animal is late in maturing sexually, is dependent upon learning rather than upon inborn reflexes for its behavior, it is likely to profit from a long life. *Homo sapiens* fits this picture.

In his neoteny, the Australopithecine had to do the following major things, and in a hurry: the brain had to treble in size, and this had to be done, not in the womb, but rapidly after birth. Childhood had to be lengthened to allow this brain, divested of most of its instinctive responses, to receive, store and learn to use information that it received from others, mainly its mother. The family bonds had to survive seasonal mating and become permanent "for the sake of the child." (How many anguished times has this phrase been used in the modern crisis of family bonds?)

As Loren Eiseley has so charmingly pointed out, the ultimate in neotenous man was a black African vaguely related to the modern Kalabari Bushman. His brain was bigger than modern man's and his face was childlike, reminding us of the Eloi of H. G. Wells and of the kind of sweet-faced, giant-brained type that anthropologists are predicting in the Man of the Future. Yet obviously he came before the world was ready for him and his genes have long been scattered among degenerate dwarfs and are irrecoverable.

When *Australopithecus* became *Homo erectus*, a scatter of manlike creatures throughout the world took place, hence we have fossils of Java man, Peking man, Heidelberg man and the like. In the Chinese caves there is evidence that early man was cannibalistic and continued the practice with a good deal of mystic or symbolic skull treatment. By the time of the Neanderthals in Europe, man had unquestionably learned to talk, since there is evidence of burial rituals, and silent rituals are unthinkable. Cro-Magnon man was the successor in Europe after 100,000 years of Neanderthals and his brain size was normally greater than that of modern man. In view of his magnificent works of art, cave painting and bone

carving, his tall, straight body, his large, gracious cranium, it is
evident that not only had a super race arrived on the scene, but
that it is ourselves whom we flatter when we identify him as *Homo
sapiens*. He was a many-splendored creature (even sober anthropologists have reconstituted his face, curiously enough clean shaven, (as
a kind of thoughtful Charlton Heston) but he still had not yet
learned (as a Paleolithic man) to grind tools but rather used a
chipping process for making stone axes, spear points, knives, lamps,
etc. He also made full use of reindeer bones and antlers. From
the bones around their fireplaces and deep in their caves, it is
certain that Paleolithic men also ate horses, waterfowl, fishes, clams
and in some places other men.* Several skulls from Australia show
that *Homo sapiens* reached that continent during the lowering of
the sea level which resulted from the expansion of the ice caps
in the Northern Hemisphere. There are no earlier fossil remains
of any species of hominoid found east of "Wallace's line" (which
marks an oceanic trough separating the Antipodes from the southeastern Asia archipelago). A large number of Upper Paleolithic
skulls from different parts of the world resemble those of many
living Australian blacks, except that the fossil skulls are larger. The
earliest Paleolithic human fossil in Australia dates back somewhat
over 30,000 years, where the remains are found in association with
the bones of the giant marsupial lion, the giant kangaroo, the giant
wombat and the Tasmanian tiger. The kangaroo at that time was
ten feet tall and the wombat as large as an elephant. Gigantism
in such mammals can be tentatively regarded as a climatic response
to the ice age, embodying once again the law of surface-to-volume
ratio—the larger the volume, the less the loss of heat per unit of
vascular tissue. Evidently Paleolithic man had developed some heat-
conservation tricks too, which have been inherited in the present-
day native-Australian savage. The young physiologist H. T. Hammel
had always wondered how these aborigines managed to keep warm
at night, so he used himself as a control among them. The skin
temperature on Hammel's feet after he took his shoes off rose

* Such cannibalistic habits must be regarded for the most part as ritualistic
and perhaps even religious. In a modern head-hunting tribe, the pattern of
behavior associated with the practice has become so profoundly imbedded in
the community that the sometimes successful attempts of missionaries to eradicate
it have caused the whole social structure to collapse. The tribe existed thenceforth
in a kind of subhuman stupor.

and fell more than once during the night but was never less than 86 degrees Fahrenheit. The Australian had no shoes to take off and his foot's skin temperature fell steadily from 73 to 45 degrees. The capillaries close to the surface of the skin contracted and blood almost ceased to run through them. When he awoke in the morning and began to exercise, the capillaries recovered their normal size and he was as spry as usual. On the other hand, the physiologist continued to lose the body heat which his circulation system brought to the surface in a feeble attempt to keep his skin warm. He awoke, a weakened animal, in dire need of a hot breakfast.

Most anthropologists agree that the American continents were populated by bands of Paleolithic hunting peoples who wandered from Siberia into Alaska. There is no evidence that anyone lived in either North or South America until after the invention of clothing, hunting gear and habitations suitable for survival in the arctic. The distribution of native languages suggests that the last group to arrive had penetrated no farther south than Arizona before the Europeans arrived. Archeological data show that the later Indian populations in the southeastern United States were taller than the earlier arrivals, whereas in California the converse seems to be true.

There is a curious but logical reason for believing that the Paleolithic or earlier emigrants from Africa to Europe and to the Northern Hemisphere in general were, like all African early men, black in pigmentation but that they lost melanin pigment in the skin for reasons of nutrition. Farnsworth Loomis has based this deduction on the theory that the skin pigmentation in a hairless animal such as man regulates the biosynthesis of vitamin D. Unlike the water-soluble vitamins, too much vitamin D causes trouble and probably even death. It is not normally ingested in terrestrial foodstuffs and resembles a hormone in that it is synthesized by the skin in a reaction catalyzed by ultraviolet light and then is distributed to the body. Rickets in adults is common among these women of India who follow the custom of purdah, in that they stay indoors out of the sun. In the nineteenth century there was a very high incidence of rickets in London and Glasgow because in these latitudes the midday sun is less than 35 degrees from the horizon for five to six months of the year (thus shielding out most of the ultraviolet) whereas in Jamaica, for example, where the sun's midday altitude is never less than 50 degrees, rickets is virtually unknown. Too much vitamin D results in excess calcium and phosphorus in the blood, the multiple calcification of soft body tissues and renal disease secondary to kidney stones. Evolution did not provide an *internal* control of vitamin D, hence it was natural for it to seek outside control in the skin: a regulator technique which would maximize ultraviolet catalysis in the northern latitudes and minimize it in the southern ones. The simplest answer was ultraviolet screening pigmentation in the tropics and reversible loss of pigmentation in the north. (In northern summers the sun-tanning phenomenon provides temporary defense against D-vitaminosis.) The keratinization (or yellowing) of Mongoloid skin provides a sort of compromise solution. The famous pink-and-white cheeks of Northern European children and especially of young Scottish and English people (too young to have acquired the blush of whiskey) is due to the fact that the skin of the face is uniquely transparent, and the color is simply the high visibility of blood circulating in the subepidermal region. An exception seems to be the Eskimo, but his diet of fish oil contains several times the minimum dose of vitamin D, which is also probably true of any coastal people of Europe and Asia that live mainly on fish.

It seems superficially paradoxical that black skin absorbs only 25 per cent of total incident light and white skin 64 per cent. One might think that the heat-absorbing black skin would therefore be found in cold climates. Since the opposite is true, it is obvious that ultraviolet is more important than total light, including infrared, and this is shown by the fact that black men can outwork native light-skinned peoples of the Caribbean.

16

THE AGRICULTURAL REVOLUTION

We should recall once more that the digestive systems of the termite and of the ruminant mammal are unique in the variety of single-celled flora and fauna that assist not only digestion but are themselves partly digested and that these single-celled helpers do not need protein food. They can obtain from ammonia all the nitrogen they require to prepare any protein in the book, and hence when the cow (for example) digests them, her liver can get any amino acid it has ordered. Since we cannot feed raw ammonia to a cow without killing her we give her instead, as supplemental food booster, the simplest of nitrogen-containing organic compounds such as urea or biuret. Such compounds are rapidly hydrolyzed by bacterial enzymes to yield ammonia which then serves the bacteria as a building block for protein synthesis. We get faster growing cattle and sheep this way, because there are more bacteria to digest.

It should not be overlooked that this mode of making a living was not entirely neglected by the primates. The langur, an Old World monkey, has recently been found to have a ruminant-like device in the form of a diverticular or pouchy stomach appendage which permits bacterial digestion of cellulose and allows the langur to live comfortably on leaves, which are not enough food for other monkeys. The langur is not a very intelligent monkey (just as a cow is not gifted with a high I.Q.), and in its case the genes which were responsible for a diverticular stomach in evolution's streamlining probably canceled out the genes which would have favored a more exploratory diet and a more inquiring brain. Once again, in the future of man, however, we cannot overlook the possibility of biological sculpture in which "diverticular genes" would be reactivated so that men could eat simple abundant vegetation, like grass or hay. As mentioned, since grass is full of silica, we might also have to devise new kinds of teeth.

At the present stage of human evolution, by far the largest part of the human race, unable to eat grass, is essentially at the dietary level of where the archaic squash-beans-maize people of ancient America would have been, had their numbers been multiplied overnight by a factor of about a million.

How did we get into this bind? It was, of course, the agricultural revolution in which man turned from a hunter or a food collector to a farmer. This was not a sudden happening like the Industrial Revolution but occurred over periods of thousands of years. (The domestication of a trivial weed to a special plant with corn on the cob, entirely dependent upon man for its reproduction, took the work of scores of generations.) It was the ability to grow vegetable food which not only made it possible for very large populations to subsist, but in a very real sense changed the nature of most human nutrition for the worse. Paradoxically the diet of the modern middle-class American is closer to that of prehistoric man than is that of the Asiatic or South American peasant. While North Americans average over 100 grams per day of protein (mostly meat, well balanced in amino acids), the average southern Asian averages only 50 grams (mostly vegetable protein and poorly balanced in amino acids).

In order to make grains and vegetables a workable food, cooking had to be invented. A raw potato, for example, is indigestible since the body's enzymes are unable to break down all the raw starch. Cooking was indeed a wonderful discovery for various reasons. It helps preserve animal flesh. More important, it kills the parasites that chronically inflict all carnivores who eat raw flesh or fish. (People who make a habit of eating uncooked fish or "steak Tartare" are inviting into their bodies whole populations of undesirable aliens.)

In cultures which lack refrigeration devices, food preservation becomes a horribly complex problem. While the Indians of the Pacific Northwest developed sun-drying to a high technology, medieval Europe resorted to spices, either to preserve (as in the case of cloves) or to mask the odor and taste of decay. A pound of ginger was worth a sheep and a sack of pepper was worth a man's life. It is hard for us in a refrigerated culture to imagine the terrific incentives to discover sea routes to the East—the land of spices.

At the level of cultures in which people accumulate in large cities, the food inevitably tends mostly to become cereal grains, because farming, without itself becoming truly industrialized, cannot produce a sufficient excess of plant food to give to animals to provide cheap meat or milk. The conversion of plant food to animal protein is an intrinsically wasteful process—except where good pastureland is available. Cattle and sheep with their peculiar stomachs do not compete with us for food but the productivity of grassland, even assuming its availability at all, varies enormously. In the open ranges of low rainfall of the Rocky Mountain states it takes twenty hectares to support one cow, which may produce one calf every two years. Yet on the productive lowland pastures of New Zealand and northern Europe, steers can be reared and fattened with a land allowance of only one-fifth of a hectare.

When we are talking of simply keeping people alive after a fashion, the yield of food calories is greater by 50 per cent when good land is used to grow potatoes or grains than to produce milk, the most economical form of animal food. Intensive milk production and wheat growing produce about equal amounts of protein, but the biological value of the milk protein is greater in the ratio of 71/41, and milk contains more vitamins, calcium and phosphorus. Nevertheless it should be recognized that, with the single exception of vitamin B_{12}, a wholly vegetable diet *can* be nutritionally adequate. (B_{12} deficiency caused stunted children in the British sect of "Vegans," who refused even to add synthetic vitamins.) The Western demand for animal products, especially for well-marbled steaks containing tissue fat, may be simply a tradition arising from our method of cooking, since the American is no better nourished because he consumes 100 kilograms of meat per year, compared with 70 kilograms in the United Kingdom or 27 kilograms in Greece. Even when an Oriental becomes wealthy he does not go in for fancy meats as we do. Food as a fuel depends on how fast the body expends energy and the body tends to be parsimonious, which is why we walk or ride rather than scuttle around all the time like cockroaches. If the potential energy from a steak dinner were released all at once, the body temperature would increase by 70 degrees Fahrenheit, and we would of course die. Laborers, athletes and the famous diving women of South Korea, who spend their working lives recovering edible seaweed from eighty feet of cold water, need over 3500 kilocalories per day, but the average male Westerner can get by comfortably on 2900.

That a straight vegetarian diet is sufficient to increase populations is shown by the fact the country Irish, before the 1845–46 famine, existed and multiplied vastly almost entirely on potatoes (the portion right next to the skin is high in protein) and is also proved by the reality that our present population-explosion problem is peculiarly intensified among peoples who eat mostly rice, corn or wheat. Of the total world population of some 3.5 billion, 71 per cent is in the underdeveloped countries, which produce only 42 per cent of the world's food and earn only 21 per cent of the world's income. The immediate problem is not famine. Famines occur due to biological accidents, such as the Irish potato blight, or because of wars, such as the Biafran catastrophe, the Thirty Years War and the effects of World War II, especially in western Russia. Without food philanthropy on the part of countries with grain surpluses, it is possible to conceive of famine—in India, for example, during the years 1965 and 1966 when the monsoons failed. But famine is not the real problem.

The real problem is the inability of people to perform on unbalanced diets: to behave like human beings. There is a lot of stretchability in this concept since it covers everything from mental retardation in children and "laziness" in adults to an incapacity to understand why they would be better off with fewer children and with modern agricultural machines instead of bent sticks.

In the underdeveloped countries there is not only the lack of enough protein (the average East Indian getting only 50 grams per day while 70 grams is deemed a minimum for good health) but a lack of essential amino acids, since wheat is low in lysine and methionine, corn is low in tryptophan and lysine, while even soya meal is deficient in methionine. Bananas, sweet potatoes, tapioca and some other root vegetables, staples of the diet in many places, simply do not contain enough protein of any kind. Taro, a potatolike vegetable, is the staff of life in thousands of Polynesian Islands, but it is supplemented with fruit, fish and coconuts. Some food deficiencies are self-inflicted out of pride or ignorance. Thus the polishing of rice takes out the native thiamine. Cooking with sodium bicarbonate, often added to vegetables to improve the color, accelerates the loss of ascorbic acid (vitamin C). Using large amounts of cooking water leaches out essential minerals and water-soluble vitamins; that is, unless you drink the water or use it as "stock." A comparison of the health of white and Negro sharecroppers in the southern United States showed that the blacks were in better shape because they used the "potlikker" to soak their corn bread in or even drank this rich brew, while the whites regarded "potlikker" as beneath their dignity and gave it to the pigs. The Chinese method of cooking vegetables in soybean oil is a life-saver because it not only preserves their food values but it adds vitamin E and linoleic acid, an essential food element, although nobody knows why.

The hidden effects of protein deficiency show up in lack of resistance to disease. Measles and chickenpox, which we regard merely as childhood nuisances, are often fatal in the underdeveloped countries. But there is worse than that. Recent research, both on laboratory animals and on man, has confirmed the terrible fact that lack of proteins and of protein or amino acid balance re-sults in lack of intelligence. In rats such deficiencies are inherited, so that the grandson of a protein-starved rat, even if he and his parents were well fed, could be a rat moron. Poor nutrition of the pregnant woman is now believed to be the single most important cause of subtle birth defects, from lower intelligence to speech and hearing deficiencies. While attention has been focused upon such gross protein-starvation diseases as kwashiorkor and marasmus, it is now obvious that the potential of a human being, the quality of his life, can depend on the food his mother gets while he is still in her womb, the richness of her milk after his birth and the kind of foods he is weaned on. Human beings on unbalanced diets are in a self-perpetuating trap. They lack the intelligence or the energy to do something about the quality of their food, which in turn has been responsible for their lack of intelligence or energy. One typical example is Lebanon. Because it is not realized there that weaned children need proteins, the man of the house gets all the fish or meat while his wife and children fill up on thin soup and mashed vegetables. But for the most part there is simply not enough protein for anybody. Critics who object to substituting soya flour for milk powder do not seem to have got it through their heads that there is not now and for the foreseeable future will not be enough milk to go around.

In the United States we have 1650 pounds of grain per person per year. We eat only 150 pounds of it and feed the rest to animals which we eat. Compare this with India. There on the average each person has 340 pounds of grain and he eats 295 pounds of it. In a land of subsistence farming one cannot afford to give grain to a pig or a chicken. Part of this immense gap between industrialized and subsistence farming lies in technology: the use of better seeds, mechanized equipment, fertilizer, insecticides, water management, soil protection—all the paraphernalia of modern Western-world agriculture. When, for example, immense sums are spent in semiarid countries for impounding and distributing water, one has to hope for the same skill in applying the water as in collecting it. No one tolerates "subsistence engineering," but the average South Asiatic or South American simply does not know how to use the water. In another sense they are also unprepared. People that for generations have known only subsistence farming as a way of life, if and when they are persuaded to take advantage of modern technology, *must enter the market*. Mass distribution and mass storage of crops turn up as new problems for them. In order to double-crop or triple-crop, the soil can no longer be prepared at the leisurely pace of a bullock or a water buffalo. This means the farmer must acquire capital or credit to buy modern equipment. Very quickly the dynamics of a free society begin to separate the energetic and future well-to-do from the lethargic and the perpetually poor. From a condition in which *everybody* is poor and works for himself, the scene changes to one in which some become prosperous landowners and the others become tenants or farmhands. But there is now a surplus of food in the land. There is even enough to raise animals, to milk cows, to fatten chickens. Theoretically at least the people of the cities as well as the farms can have enough protein to bring the quality of their lives up to the promise of the twentieth century.

17

PROGRESS?

According to a recent report from the President's National Advisory Commission on Food and Fibers, the world's food production will have to be increased from 2½ to 3 times in the next thirty years to feed a population expected to double in that time. A good deal of hard work has been done by many brilliant people in trying to cope with this titanic problem.

Leaving aside for the moment the matter of balanced proteins, the way in which plants prepare themselves to be food for animals has been re-examined. Most modern food plants were not designed by evolution to use the full energy of sunlight, perhaps because the amount of water and ground nutrients, such as fixed nitrogen, phosphate, potash, etc., were growth-limiting, rather than the sun's energy. Nearly all plants therefore show the phenomenon known as "light saturation." When you plot a curve of the rate of photosynthesis versus the radiation intensity you reach a plateau around an intensity of 0.5 calories per square centimeter per minute. Significantly plants such as maize, where genes have been tampered with extensively by man, show at least a partial independence of the saturation effect. There thus appears real promise, over the long pull, in the ability of plant geneticists to develop crops with a better response to bright light. In conjunction with fertilizers this could amount to a great increase in leaf surface per unit of soil, and might directly multiply the value, for example, of leaf crops such as alfalfa.

Another novel approach, especially in Israel, is to use salt water to irrigate crops. This appears feasible for certain food plants if the sand contains no appreciable amount of clay.

In cereal grains spectacular advances in plant breeding have given whopping increases in yield, growing rate and hardiness. The "Mexican wheats," products of some two decades of work sponsored by the Rockefeller Foundation, are proving adaptable throughout Asia. The new varieties are all short-stemmed so they can absorb large quantities of fertilizer without "lodging" (growing top-heavy and falling down). New rice varieties have come from the International Rice Research Institute in the Philippines and from the Indian Aduthurai Experimental Station at Madras, India. The Philippine rice (IR-8) ripens in 125 days compared with 150 to 180 days for conventional varieties and is insensitive to the length of the day; thus it can be planted any month of the year when enough water and heat are available. India's own hybrid rice (ATD-27) is a cross between a local variety and a Japanese strain, matures in 105 days and requires only a minimum of fertilizer. Double cropping was successfully risked in 1967 with four times the former yields. Importantly the taste is acceptable to the rice eaters of India. The Rockefeller and Ford foundations have supported work on improving corn, sorghum, and millet designed specifically for India. All such developments have been called euphorically by Mr. Gaud of the Agency for International Development (AID) the "green revolution."

It is important to observe, however, that so far the "green revolution" by itself has not solved the problems of protein deficiency and protein balance. Most of the new high-yielding varieties of grain generally have in fact lower protein content. In the direction of grain better designed to nourish human beings the most exciting discovery, as one might expect, is in that biologically sculpturable plant, hybrid corn. The introduction of the "opaque-2" gene in hybrids (so-called from the opacity of the uncooked kernels) increases the lysine and tryptophan content with a consequent 75 per cent upgrading of the nutritive value of the protein fraction of the corn. And there is more protein per kernel. Food nutritionists have found that opaque-2, ground up and used to make tortillas, has the same nutritional value as skim milk. There are a lot of problems to be licked before this miracle maize can be established abroad. For example, resistance to local diseases must be bred into the corn. Because the hybrids require specially grown seed each year, developing countries will have to grow the seed on their own or commit to importing each year. Furthermore the hybrid must be grown in fields isolated from normal corn, since wind pollination would result in another hybrid lower in lysine and tryptophan. Although opaque-2 is expected to sell in this country at a premium over standard No. 2 yellow corn, it would still be less expensive than soya meal and would be used almost entirely as feed for simple-stomach livestock, particularly hogs and poultry. In South America or India or Africa one would expect opaque-2 to go to the simple-stomach creature, man.

The meal from oil-bearing seeds such as soya, cottonseed, peanuts, sunflower, etc. is a large reservoir of protein, for the most part largely unexploited in the underdeveloped countries but highly researched (especially soya) in the United States. It is chiefly from soya meal that protein isolates have been prepared commercially which when spun like synthetic fiber have been structured and flavored to look and taste like bacon, chicken, veal or what will you have? They have attracted a special market among vegetarians and diet-conscious people, and in the consummate chemical skills demonstrated in such delicacies there is unquestioned promise of tailor-making high-protein foods on a much larger scale for filling the protein vacuum of the poor countries. The problem is can the poor countries afford such tailored food? At the present time protein from oil seeds is the swiftest economic solution for protein starvation (although not for amino acid imbalance), since the extracted oil pays part of the cost. There are, however, problems of toxicity.

Obtaining fully balanced (if usually smelly) proteins from the sea is another approach that has not only been researched but nearly talked to death. It has been difficult to get the approval of the Food and Drug Administration for Fish Protein Concentrate (in which all the tissues of cheap, plentiful fish, such as hake, are processed) for human consumption, although as a supplement for poultry and hog feed, fish meal has long been used. In 1968 over 68 million tons of fish were caught in the world, over 30 per cent of this going into fish meal for use either as animal food or fertilizer. The trouble is with what are known as the "organoleptic" qualities (flavor and odor). Even when completely deodorized, Fish Protein Concentrate (FPC) can hardly be introduced in bread or pastes for human consumption in concentrations over about 3 per cent, since "flavor reversal" takes place (that is, the FPC starts tasting like fish again). Because of this organoleptic memory, fish even when digested and incor-

porated in a chicken begin to assert their identity. Thus more
than about 5 per cent of fish meal in a chicken's diet makes it
taste fishy. This is too bad since poultry is a very thrifty way to
convert one protein to another. One gram of fish protein produces
almost one gram of chicken protein.

18

ARE THERE ENOUGH FISH IN THE SEA?

It has been airily assumed by ocean enthusiasts that all the catchable marine fish, either eaten directly or ground into fish meal for poultry or for poorly fed people, would provide enough protein to eliminate the basic nitrogen hunger of the world of, say, 1990. These persons believe that all one needs is more efficient harvesting of an inexhaustible fish population. They ask, why didn't the Irish eat fish when the potato blight struck the land? That is an easy specific question to answer: until the very modern development of giant floating, refrigerated fish factories, such as are now in common use by the Russians, marine fishing was the most dangerous of all occupations, more hazardous by far than coal mining. It was and is especially perilous on the Atlantic coast of Ireland. During the famine nearly as many fishermen perished off Galway as died in that coastal county of hunger or typhus.

As for fish saving the world from kwashiorkor and mental retardation, one needs a rather realistic look at the ocean as a place to live and as a garden of human food.

The beginning of the food chain consists of tiny phytoplankton —single-celled plants that need sunlight and can thus exist only in that upper layer of the seas which is permeable to light. Although the sun is prodigal, of every million photons (packets of light energy) that reach the earth's surface, only some ninety act in the production of basic plant food. About fifty of these eighty photons countribute to the growth of land plants (mainly tropical jungles and inedible bushes) while about forty photons are absorbed by phytoplankton. This mass of marine vegetation, amounting to billions of tons per year is a great source of oxygen and in fact these oceanic plants made the earth habitable in the first place for all oxygen-breathing animals. However, an extraordinarily large proportion of these plants are too small to match up in the sea-food chain for commercial fisheries. Some of them are so small they are called nanoplankton (*nanus*, dwarf) and, unless they occur in colonies, they are hard for any larger vegetarian creature to chase down. It is only when they occur as larger cells that they can be captured and eaten by the single-celled zoo-plankton and by the minuscule shrimplike organisms that constitute what fishermen call krill—the food for the baleen whales and other large marine creatures.

Now there is a discouraging thing about this size discrepancy and diffusivity of marine plant life. The large plankton and the colonial plankton, which may occur in the form of long sticky ropes or sphered cities of creatures which the clupeoid fishes (sardines, anchovies, pilchards, menhaden, etc.) may munch upon, are not very abundant in the oceans. They thrive chiefly in upswelling areas located along the west coasts of continents at subtropical latitudes where there are prevailing offshore winds and strong eastern boundary currents, such that the surface waters are diverted and replaced by nutrient-rich deeper and cooler waters. Such areas are biologically the richest parts of the ocean. They exist off Peru, off California, off northwestern and southwestern Africa, Somalia and the Arabian coast and off Antarctica. The area of all of them together, producing about one half of the world's fish supply, is about the same as that of the state of California. Moreover, not all these upswellings are productive the year around. The richness of the Arabian Sea area is related to the monsoon winds and the antarctic fishery is limited by lack of sunlight during half the year. Nearer the coasts and especially off the deltas of great rivers are fishes that have been caught for millennia, but the open sea (nearly three quarters of the earth's surface) is practically a biological desert.*

---

* All the great rivers of the world, except the Congo, have built up deltas or sedimentary wedges that extend into deep water. The shallow parts of these wedges are swarming with marine life. It is a mystery as to what inhabits the fan of the Congo. That vast river, because of the invasion of a submarine canyon into its mouth, has built no wedge but rather is depositing an enormous alluvial fan in the two-mile depths of the Angola basin. What resides in this mysterious deep-sea city may be unique and even terrible. It represents a challenge of the highest magnitude for oceanographers, but two miles is a long way down.

Senator Hiram Fong of Hawaii has tried to get Congress to teach the Hawaiians how to catch skipjack tuna. As it is now, they rely on bait fishing and spend nearly half of their time in fishing for bait rather than the skipjack. In the meantime the Japanese, the Australians and the ubiquitous Russians gobble up all the remaining skipjack in the western Pacific with heavy purse seines. Tuna schools are sighted by the Australians by airplane (these fish like regions of quickly varying temperature) and could also be located by earth-satellite surveillance. The sad truth is, however, that all the fish of the tuna family are so overharvested that they may be extinct before the end of the decade. This is already nearly true of the yellowtail tuna of the eastern Pacific.

The United States is amateurish compared with the Japanese, Russian and Norweigan fishing fleets, which, having succeeded in depopulating the antarctic of the blue whale, now are concentrating on harvesting the 100 million tons a year of krill that all baleen whales feed on. This direct attack upon a lower link in the marine food chain may be successful, if you like krill, but it is expensive, since the fuel expended in catching it, the power needed for extracting it from the tiny mineral shells, would seem to be prohibitive. In the long run it would be more economical to allow baleen whales to make it into flesh and oil. These sea monsters, if prudently harvested rather than indiscriminately murdered, would provide a better food source. But nations as collective fishermen are the most arrogant and selfish and shortsighted of all collective minds.*

The first major international conference to examine the state of marine fish stock on a global basis was held by the United Nations Scientific Conference on Conservation and Utilization of Resources in 1949 at Lake Success, New York. The conclusion was that the only overfished stocks were a few high-priced species in the North Atlantic and the North Pacific, particularly plaice, halibut and salmon. The learned ichthyologists produced a map showing thirty other species that they considered under fished. By 1968 half of those fish were seriously overharvested, including nearly all tuna, herring, haddock (nearly extinct), ocean perch and in the southeastern Pacific, anchovy. The Peruvian government in April

* We shall later describe how the otherwise sophisticated and charming Danes are causing the certain extinction of that magnificent fish, the Atlantic salmon.

1970 announced the nationalization of its anchovy-based fish-meal industry (its largest business) when the yield went into a tailspin in 1969. Peru up to now has yearly exported 1.6 million tons of fish meal or 66 per cent of the world's supply. The North American poultry feed and chicken producers are the major buyers of fish meal. They need about 800,000 tons a year, but American fisheries yield only about 180,000 tons, mostly from hake.

Water pollution, especially by spilled petroleum, has all but wiped out caviar-grade sturgeon which used to flourish in the Volga River and the Caspian Sea. (We shall discuss marine pollution in greater detail in Part 3 of this book.)

What it boils down to, according to careful observers such as John B. Ryther of the Woods Hole Oceanographic Institution, is that the most optimistic estimate for the latter years of this century predicts a total world fish harvest of 100 million tons, or less than twice what it is today. If overfishing, especially of small fish in the intermediate links of the food chain or of sexually immature fish is continued, it may be much less than this—even less than now. Obviously the oceans are not the answer for the tremendous protein deficiency facing the human population of the planet.

Earnest efforts to improve on these depressing statistics have been undertaken. One approach is to breed genetically superior fish. For example, Lawrence Donaldson of the University of Washington has succeeded in crossbreeding salmon and trout (which are of the same family) and over a period of thirty years of experimenting has achieved a giant rainbow trout that weighs up to three pounds as a yearling and over seventeen pounds when three years old. He is trying to crossbreed these giants with steelhead so that he will get fish that migrate to sea and return to their birthplace to spawn and can be persuaded not to die, as normal Pacific salmon do, in the process. This is a form of "mariculture," but the trouble with the idea is political; most likely on release to the Pacific Ocean such hopeful monsters would wind up in the nets of the Japanese. Our own fishing industry is too stupid and archaic to compete. The New England fishermen in particular are torpid beyond belief. The crews of trawlers get the receipts for 60 per cent of the catch while the boatowner gets only 40 per cent. This holdover from the days of the eighteenth century simply insures that fishing-fleet operators will refuse to sink money for new equipment. When New England fishermen of the old tradition were told that they could use modern methods to catch tuna off Cape Cod, the only response was the paleolithic "*duh*." Oceanographers invited a West Coast tuna team to come east, and for five days work in the summer of 1962, each man in the crew made $6000.

American imports of fish and fish meal have grown from 20 per cent of the total U.S. consumption in 1950 to over 80 per cent in 1970. Fishermen other than Americans take twice the amount of fish from waters near the North American coastline than do Americans. Our own chief contribution to the cause is to shoot sea lions, to poison sea-catching birds with oil spills and to provide untreated sewage that certain trash fish thrive upon but which are likely to season their protein with disease organisms. Delaware makes a smelly example. Menhaden have vanished from its coastal waters along with the croaker, once a Delaware specialty. In 1958 Delaware's oyster industry was virtually wiped out by the appearance of a pollution-bred parasite called "MSX." The oyster, unlike the menhaden and the croaker, could not give notice and simply move away from an undesirable neighborhood. One of the peculiarities of the oyster, however, is its ability to pump itself clean. Thus in a process of desperation, oysters can be placed on trays and immersed in large tanks filled with constantly flowing sea water which has been sterilized with ultraviolet light. After holding in this "hospital" for about forty-eight hours they can be transferred back to a natural unpolluted habitat (if any remains). Like all hospitals, this is a dismally expensive procedure.

Aquaculture (analogous to agriculture) of certain fishes, mollusks and crustaceans is an ancient art, but there are modern circumstances that give it a certain economic perkiness.

Although the first treatise on fish culture was written by Fan Li in 455 B.C., the Chinese have obtained genetic control only over the carp and some species of trout. They have grown the common carp in conjunction with other species of the minnow family (to which carp belong) to make use of all depths of a body of water. The carp is a bottom feeder, the grass carp and the silver carp feed on plants while the bighead carp dines on surface plankton. The history of the carp in North America on the other hand has been a sadly stupid one. When kept genetically pure the carp is a magnificent food fish. But after being brought to the United States from Europe in 1877, carp were allowed to escape and breed indiscriminately in lakes and rivers, reverting to an excessively bony and scaly trash fish. There is a fascinating possibility in renovating the carp not only for food or fish meal but as saviors of senile lakes and for the utilization of bodies of water exposed to "thermal pollution" from electric power plants, especially of the nuclear type. Instead of mindlessly screaming about the hot-water effluents from such plants and of the eutrophication of lakes by algae growing on detergent phosphates and excess fertilizers, the genuine conservationist would seek biological answers. The carp not only thrives in an eutrophying lake, browsing on the algae as a cow eats grass, but is singularly unbothered by warm water and in such water will consume sewage. The drawback (as in Japan) is the tendency of the native to prefer uncooked or undercooked fish, which are therefore a source of disease. Automatically they can be sterilized in the process of making fish meal or simply by careful cooking.

It is a foolish mistake to assume that "thermal pollution" is a disaster. It can be used by those that are clever enough to combine hydraulic engineering with advanced aquaculture. One progressive grower of Long Island shellfish uses about 57,000 quarts per minute of cooling water discharged by the Long Island Lighting Company. The water has been taken from deep sections of the bay and is full of nutrients. Its warmth actually promoted in the presumably "thermally polluted" lagoon the year-round production of hard clams and oysters. At the nuclear power plant at Hunterston, Scotland, the warm sea-water effluent is fed into large cement troughs for the raising of sole and plaice. Both species grow to marketable size in six to eight months compared with three to four years under natural conditions.

Instead of enforcing impossible laws on the nuclear plants at Turkey Point on Biscayne Bay (apparently because President Nixon happens to have a winter palace there), efforts by the University of Miami to *use* thermal pollution for the increased production of shrimp and pompano should be accelerated. They already look promising. Superficially it might seem unrealistic to expect aquaculture to alleviate the world protein deficiency but, as John E. Burdach of the University of Michigan points out, luxury foods stop being luxurious when they are mass produced, as evidenced by the chicken industry in the United States and in Western Europe.

It has recently been discovered that tricks such as "hypophyzation" (treatment of aquacultures with pituitary hormones) can be used to make some fishes spawn more often and to relieve the breeding restraints of certain other species. This has influenced aquaculture all over the world, from catfish growers in the southern United States to sturgeon breeders in the Ukraine and to the fishing co-operatives of mainland China where it makes carp produce eggs three times a year and facilitates the propagation of the carp's cuprinid pondmates whose eggs, unlike the big ones of the common carp, were hard to collect in rivers before the process of hypophyzation was developed. It may also prove important in brackish-water culture for milkfish and gray mullet. Aquaculture is especially promising for lands, such as those facing on the Indian Ocean, where refrigeration will probably remain costly for many decades and where it thus becomes important to harvest fish food near to its market.

A very different kind of aquaculture could be practiced which would have the advantage of cleaning up lakes and streams suffocated with aquatic plants such as water hyacinth, water fern, water lettuce, water milfoil, cattails, water lily, spatterdook, rushes, arrowhead, alligator weed and so on. At the same time we could rescue from oblivion a harvestable vegetarian mammal, the manatee, which thrives precisely on such plants. This adventure would be much more productive and less expensive than simply trying mechanically to harvest the bulky plant growth and less dangerous than trying to kill it with herbicides. It is analogous to a program which I shall describe later of reintroducing the camel to the brushlands of the southwestern United States and northern Mexico. Such ventures, if bolder, are more promising than trying, for example, to harvest algae as direct human food.

This cultivation of marine algae has been thoroughly investigated, especially that of the genus *Chlorella*. Since this is a plant, it does not yield a fully balanced protein, the efficiency ratio being 2.17 on a scale in which fish meal is 3.0 and soya flour is 2.04. (The numbers represent the weight gain of a laboratory mammal per weight of protein consumed.) There is not much interest in algae of this sort any more because of high processing cost, the existence of marked "light saturation," unpleasant flavor and severe gastrointestinal disturbances over long periods of trial feeding. However, we are in the realm of the single-celled creatures and in the blue-green algae used for food for centuries by the natives around Lake Chad in northern Africa, we begin to get a full quota of amino acids, while in the yeasts and bacteria grown on the normal paraffins (including methane) from petroleum we have arrived back at the secret of the cow's stomach. These single-celled creatures produce all the elements of life, just as their ancestors did at the beginning of evolution.

It is not within the purview of this discussion to explain in detail the ramifications of both the microbiology and chemical engineering involved in the accelerating technology of "Single Cell Protein" (SCP). From a global standpoint it is sufficient to say that with the use of only a small percentage of the world's petroleum production, the planet's protein requirements could easily be met with the killed bacteria that* can be urged to grow on mineral oil or natural gas. Actually much the same kind of organism can be grown on molasses or even on the effluent sewage from paper factories, and yeast production from these sources has been successfully practiced for some time. A typical converter contains also the ammonium salts, magnesium and potassium salts, phosphate, sulfate, chloride and trace minerals that any living organism has to have.

If bacteria must oxidize so combustible a material as paraffinic hydrocarbon to obtain their energy, there is going to be a lot of heat evolved and indeed this is one of the principal engineering problems in growing SCP. Refrigeration must be provided to carry off the surplus heat or the bacteria will stop growing. Most organisms which make good food, when killed, like to grow at moderate temperatures where heat transfer is unfortunately costly. However, if plant geneticists can transform such a paltry weed as the original maize into such a magnificent food plant as "opaque-2" corn, it is obvious that microbiologists, with the constant turnover of generations, cannot only rear mutant bacteria that can stand higher temperatures ("thermophilic" organisms) but can rear bacteria as specialized food products with a minimum of nucleic acids, a minimum of tough cell-wall amino sugars and a maximum of those essential amino acids that are hardest to come by in agriculture.

There are questions that must be answered before SCP of this type can be regarded safely as human food rather than animal fodder. For example, what proportion of viable (unkilled) organisms can be tolerated in human food? Are the indications of excessive stomach gas from yeasts serious? If normal paraffins from "gas oil" or kerosene are used to feed the bacteria, to what extent does the oil have to be chemically or physically treated to remove traces of aromatic compounds possibly carcinogenic in nature? These and a dozen other questions must await the laborious work of animal-feeding experiments before we dare use human beings in mass-feeding trials.

More immediately on the horizon is the enrichment of common protein-impoverished foods in the developing countries with amino acids and other supplements. We are so used to flour enrichment with vitamins in this country that we do not realize the novelty of this mode of operating in places where malnutrition has been the habit of centuries. The Indian government itself, with some outside help, has developed "modern bread," in which the flour is fortified with vitamins, minerals and lysine. Both lysine and methionine are being added to noodles for Tunisia and to spaghetti and other starchy Italian cereal foods. All the essential amino acids can be synthesized and it is a matter of cost as to whether one adds protein concentrates or pure amino acids. Lysine and methionine are probably at least economically possible now, while threonine and tryptophan may be in the future.

A large number of protein porridges or powder or soft drinks have been introduced, using concentrates, isolates or amino acids in various countries. To name only a few: Incaparina, Vitasoy, Saridele, Saci, Pro-Nutro, Nutresco, Arlac, CSM, Balchar, Frescovita, Fortifex, Superamine. Many have had governmental or foundation support. As commercial enterprises, most of these have had rather checkered careers for reasons we must now review.

19

TO EACH HIS OWN

As previously pointed out, if we examine the food habits of various wild animals we are struck with the fact that *omnivorousness* is a rare gift. Take away the coconut and the robber crab becomes extinct. He will eat only coconuts. The arctic lynx will eat only the arctic hare, and when the hare finds nothing to eat the lynx starves with it. The arctic fox on the other hand will eat only the lemming. He will die rather than eat an arctic hare and often does when the lemmings go through one of their cyclical troughs of population.

After the agricultural revolution some of this kind of food prejudice descended upon many human populations. During and after World War II some of the East Indians refused to eat Western wheat and rioted and died rather than accept it. The rice-eating Bengali proved in 1944 that they would rather starve than use wheat flour. Riots broke out in Kerala in 1966 when people felt that the government was forcing them to eat wheat. Some immense populations thrived and insisted upon certain flavors. The soya bean is often called the "cow of China" and the organoleptic complex or aura of the soya is pleasing to the Chinese. It is not surprising, therefore, that of all the protein soft drinks Vitasoy, developed by a Hong Kong merchant of Chinese extraction, is by far the greatest commercial success of all health potions. Yet it is not pleasing to an American palate, being compared in *Time* magazine to library paste. Efforts are therefore being made to Americanize Vitasoy and presumably to make it taste more like Coca-Cola or like a "choc-malt." This seems to be a vast mistake and typical of the exactly wrong approach to the food problems of that part of the world that most needs better food and which outnumbers our part of the world by a ratio that grows greater every year. If they like the library pastiness of a soya soft drink, why take away its library pastiness? Try instead to find *more* things that taste like library paste.

In some cases the food fondnesses and prejudices are not mental or traditional but are based upon an acquired physical handicap. It has only recently been realized that otherwise healthy Orientals have more than an "allergy" to milk; they actually cannot digest it. This is attributed to a genetically developed deficiency in lactase (the enzyme that digests milk sugar). It is believed now that there are two kinds of intestinal lactase, an "infantile" enzyme which is naturally required for all nursing babies and a second or "adult" lactase which is absent in people who become intolerant to milk when they grow up. The important point is that the adult lactase appears to be lacking not only among many Orientals, but milk intolerance is also common among native Africans. Indeed it now seems probable that most of the world's adult population (in the underdeveloped countries) cannot digest milk. This is a finding of unexampled significance. It sets a limit not only on the kind of philanthropic food shipments we make but on the way in which the native protein-food planning is set up. There is no use in the raising of cows or female elands or nanny goats if the grownup gets only a bellyache from the milk of these animals.

It is possible that as we do more research on what various peoples eat and what they like to eat and, most importantly, on what they *refuse* to eat, we shall find more than religious taboos and popular superstitions behind what we now deem to be food eccentricities. As cooks we may learn things we did not know before. Take, as an example, the preparation of soya foods. Foods based on *fermented* soya, or soya partly freed from indigestible fractions by various age-old traditional methods have always been eaten with relish in southeastern Asia. These methods would repay sophisticated research for they may prove preferable to processes mainly dependent on heating, now used in the West. There is the advantage that it is known that the native processes yield a food that the southeastern Asians like.

Farmers of all countries are natural conservatives and in the poor countries this conservatism is deepened by the fact that the farmer has never gone to an agricultural college or even heard of one, and he is proud. In one country the farmers would not buy an improved variety of seed. They would not even use it when it was given away. But when poorly fenced demonstration plots were set up, enough seeds got stolen at the end of the year to open the way for general improvement. This in fact was the technique that Parmentier used in the seventeenth century to introduce potatoes into France. It is obvious that the "hard sell" is not the way to do things in the greater part of the world.

An instructive example of sales resistance was the early lack of success in India in persuading the peasant farmers to change over from their traditional wheat to a rust-free variety with higher yields. The traditional wheat had a "beard" on each grain which the farmers claimed discouraged birds from eating it. There was no scientific evidence of this discouragement: in fact the birds, being possessed of sharper eyes and better sense than the peasants, were actually attracted rather than repelled by the beards. Nevertheless scientists at the Atomic Energy Research Station went to work and irradiated the rustless wheat until eventually a bearded version appeared which the peasants were willing to accept.

The peculiarities of many cultures must be realized and tolerantly accepted if one is to do business there. One must not, for example, overlook the *machismo* (roughly, "maleism") slant of many Latin Americans. Sexuality and food are commonly in association, although Del Castro's theory that high-protein consumers have low fertility is no longer in favor. As mentioned before, the great green marine turtle of the Caribbean is in danger of extinction not so much because people like turtle soup but in large part because the eggs of this splendid reptile are dug up and treasured as aphrodisiacal food by Mexicans and Colombians.

The complex subcontinent of India has at least sixteen distinct cultural groups, each with its own food habits. There is no use simply to dump unlimited cargoes of wheat on such a diverse population or even enriched flour. It is one of the only established and certifiable facts of food science that the nutritional value of a food that is not eaten is precisely zero.

20

SOME HAZARDS

In the midst of the "green revolution," in which new varieties of wheat, rice, maize, sorghum, etc. are being grown for the first time in the countries that most need them, we must remember the lesson of the Irish potato blight. The potato was "exogenous" (foreign) to Ireland and some two centuries later it was destroyed almost overnight by a fungus disease. We cannot overlook the possibility that exogenous strains of wheat, rice and maize may suddenly succumb to blight or disease or to some particular insects.

The protein loss to insects, fungi, rodents, birds, even to monkeys is astronomical. The preventable loss of protein during grain storage alone is greater than the current world production of oil-seed proteins. The dirt floors of grain-storage warehouses in many countries are a continuous maze of rat burrows, ideal for a rat population explosion. One pair of bandicoot rodents and their offspring are capable of producing a ravening regiment of 900 within a year. Losses of one-third of the grain per year stored in such circumstances are not uncommon.

There is a far from trivial danger of getting cancer of the liver from eating peanut meal contaminated with aflatoxin, a fungus poison produced by the mold *Aspergillus flavus*. Liver cancer is peculiarly prevalent in tropical countries. This danger can be overcome by sophisticated fumigation methods in the field or by chemical treatment of the peanut flour or protein isolate. Clean, hulled peanuts can also be solvent extracted to produce high-grade protein-rich flour for humans but, although India produces 30 per cent of all the world's peanuts, cheap food-grade solvents are not readily available there nor the know-how for preparing them.

Cottonseed meal contains gossypol, a yellow polyphenolic pigment which is toxic to simple-stomached ("monogastric") animals, including man. The gossypol is concentrated into many small dark spots in the cottonseed, which have been called "pigment glands." This dangerous contaminant could probably be eliminated by the introduction of a gene for "glandlessness," such as is found in a wild variety of cotton in Southern California or in a new radiation-induced Egyptian mutant strain, "Bactim-100." Plants develop these poisons to combat insects, but insecticides must be used to obtain good yields of even present cotton crops, so the elimination of the "glands" would be no genetic handicap.

Even raw soya meal contains a so-called "antitryptic" factor which inhibits the human digestive enzyme trypsin and which must be destroyed in processing.

It is true, of course, that many classical foods are dangerous at times, including the puffer fish (which kills about one hundred people in Japan every year) and oysters, mussels and clams that have consumed certain microsopic diflagellates and may cause "paralytic" shellfish poisoning. Poisonous mushrooms kill more people every year than snakebite. However, when a *new* kind of food is introduced into a country the natural prejudices multiply many fold any possible hazards involved in improper processing, contamination or spoilage. This cannot only entail illness but liability. Projects entered into in improving a nation's diet with new balanced or enriched foods must be accompanied by truly professional know-how and the setting up of effective biochemical inspection systems. In the future case, for example, of Single Cell Protein foods the nutrient bacteria or yeasts must be kept free of pathogenic strains and even of bacteriophage viruses. The problem of the digestion or elimination of tough cell walls and of nucleic acids must be solved with certainty. There are dozens of other purely technical difficulties in planning an invigorating new menu for a malnourished population.

Yet these technical problems can be solved. More difficult are the cultural problems. As has been intimated previously, a kind of "sociological salesmanship" is required. Most of the new high-protein foods or beverages, whose names have been mentioned, inevitably get first to the stomachs of people who probably do not need them—the people of more-than-average income who read the newspapers, are susceptible to advertising in the press or by radio and TV and who are less set in their ways. This is probably inevitable.

In fact, a new food that is promoted as "for the poor" may find itself with no market at all, since even the poor in their pride will refuse to buy it or will refuse to accept it even if it is for free. In order to see that new foods pass their first test (that is, that they are eaten by the undernourished), a very sophisticated sort of sales campaign must be undertaken. How can one be sure, for example, that a special high-protein baby food, taken home by an ignorant peasant woman, will actually ever get to the baby? Experience shows, in fact, that it seldom does. If other food is scarce and if the sample tastes good, the mother herself or her husband and older children are more likely to get it than the baby.

Two things are obvious: (1) the direct selling of new food to the undernourished must be undertaken by agents who are not interested merely in delivering the food to a country or to a warehouse but by agents who *are willing to make certain that it gets into the mouths of people who need it most*; (2) the selling of food to underdeveloped countries must go hand in hand with the *education* of the undernourished. Simplified fast education methods along the lines of the "talking typewriter" and the "talking paper" must be applied so that illiterates can be taught how to eat and how to farm. Nutrition schools for children as well as for adults are needed, which could be combined with trial feeding, to explore taste preferences. The combination of education and better food is a powerful, perhaps irresistible one and, as we have seen, intelligence and good food are themselves inseparable companions.

21

MALNUTRITION IN THE UNITED STATES

We have been writing in a rather snooty way of protein starvation in the underdeveloped countries, not until now admitting that a large segment of our own population eats poorly. This segment is by no means confined to the ghetto or to tenant farmers in the South. Infants in the middle and upper classes are definitely more poorly nourished than they were twenty years ago, since they get less milk and more canned baby food, often oversalted to please the taste of the mother rather than the child.

Among the poor, protein starvation is very deceptive, since especially the women in the family turn out very often to be plump, even pig-fat, but this is because they stuff themselves with starchy foods such as spaghetti and bread. Their protein starvation shows itself in stupidity and apathy. But the general nutritional malaise in the United States is more directly due to lack of vitamins and minerals. The Food and Drug Administration has not helped. In posing as the family physician it has propagandized what is known in the trade as the "crepe label" doctrine: that supplementary minerals and vitamins are not necessary, in fact may be harmful, if Americans eat "commonly available" food. (It makes an exception of extra iron for pregnant women.)

What is "commonly available" food? For an old widow, living alone, it may be tea and toast. For an old man living alone it may be whisky and soda crackers. The old lady is greatly helped by the social visits of welfare people since she is then seized by sufficient incentive to prepare a decent meal that both she and her guest may enjoy. This is a well-known phenomenon among welfare workers.

The FDA is pursuing a collision course with modern nutritional science. It has tagged some vitamins (E, K, pantothenic acid, folic acid) and some minerals (copper, magnesium, manganese, zinc, sodium and potassium) as "not essential to human nutrition." This would limit the "essential" factors to eight vitamins (A, B, B_2, B_6, B_{12}, niacin, C and D) and the four minerals (calcium, phosphorus, iron and iodine), but, as mentioned, the "crepe-label" doctrine claims these are contained in "normal foods." The exceedingly important biotin is not included in either category.

Recent research has shown the significant relationship between vitamin E (tocopherol) and fatty acids in the tissues. It is especially important as an antioxidant in the body when people choose to eat unsaturated fats in order to avoid atherosclerosis and other circulatory diseases (a common dietary trend). Wheat-germ oil, a rich source of vitamin E, prevents the destruction of red blood cells. It has also been shown that people with arthritis need less cortisone if they take vitamin E. It prevents anemia in premature babies. It is also an effective remedy for digitalis poisoning—a not inconsiderable advantage considering the number of people who take digitalis—containing drugs for various heart irregularities.

Vitamin B_6 (pyrodoxine) has been found in more than normal quantities to prevent pregnant women from developing dental cavities. Lack of B_6 can induce mental torpor. Animals with B_6 deficiency don't learn so fast or remember so well. There is evidence that deficiency in one vitamin is often related to deficiencies in others. Thus a shortage of B_6 can bring about a shortage of B_{12}.

It is now believed that a high percentage of people in the United States are starving for B_6. The vitamin plays a profound role in the metabolism of all fatty acids, saturated or unsaturated. In the total absence of B_6 the body cannot properly use proteins or fats, cannot manufacture red blood cells and the nervous system becomes a disaster area. Studies of children by David Coursin of St. Joseph's Hospital, Lancaster, Pennsylvania, show that B_6 deficiency during the first weeks of life affects normal brain development with symptoms including hyperirritability, weird behavior and convulsive seizures. The electric brain-wave patterns are fantastically wrong and biochemical tests reveal excessive urinary excretion of amino acids. The cure is dramatic. Giving the child 100 milligrams of vitamin B_6 corrects all symptoms within a few minutes.

A recent survey of typical schoolchildren of all ethnic groups, ten to thirteen years old, in New York City showed that blood levels of thiamine, biotin and ascorbic acid were markedly below the minimal requirement levels for the total population. This kind of analysis is now being used as a test for so-called "subclinical malnutrition" (i.e., the children are the walking wounded and the mentally retarded but not sick enough to go to the hospital, which in any case would not be able to accommodate them).

Among those people poor enough to be on welfare, the situation is an incredible mess. People who run the Headstart Program see children who most of the time are too quiet, too listless, who may fall asleep in class but also may burst unpredictably into tantrums and become as irritable as baby scorpions. The middle-class-adolescent diet of fatty hamburgers, candy, high-sugar drinks, pizzas and fried chicken* may well be responsible for subclinical malnutrition. This evidences itself in vulnerability to drugs, social irritability in the form of tremendous emisson of decibels (transistors playing rock music at full blast), in shouting obscene language, in throwing rocks through college windows and so on. It is a statistical fact that the American adolescents of the 1960s and 1970s were and are dangerously undernourished and their social anarchism may well be simply a mania of semistarvation. Many nutritionists predict that the present younger generation, subsisting on highly atherosclerotic diets, may be the shortest lived generation in modern history. There are clinical signs of this deterioration in post-mortem analysis of adolescent victims of automobile accidents.

Down in the ghettos, where free food is passed out, the people regularly refuse flour, rolled oats, dry milk and corn syrup. They don't know what to do with it. For lack of refrigeration the food stations are unable to give out cheese, which is acceptable. Frequently the flour is refused because the women don't know how to bake. The only thing universally accepted is bread. Only 10 per cent of the available vitamin concentrates are taken home by these wretched and ignorant folk.

---

* There is a curious thing about chicken. The flesh of the mass-produced, hygienically impeccable chicken is remarkably insipid compared to that of the old-fashioned barnyard fowl. Food scientists of the University of Wisconsin believe that intestinal bacteria present in the barnyard chicken, but absent in the germ-free chicken factories, impart flavor just as intestinal microbes often manufacture vitamins for the host animal. They have not, however, been able to identify the microorganism. One result of this phenomenon is that chicken is largely consumed in this country plastered with sludge from hot, flavored grease.

When poor mothers come from the country to the big city they commonly make the grave mistake of imitating the "with-it" people of higher income and abandon breast feeding too early. The substitute formulas are so expensive that the child not only gives up his only perfect source of nourishment but gets insufficient protein because the mother cannot feed him enough substitute. Babies critically malnourished during this period never recover normal brain power. Furthermore, even if subsequently well fed, the female infant when she grows old enough to become a mother will produce a mentally retarded child.

The protein starvation in such places as rural South Carolina approaches downright famine. As did the Irish babies in 1846, some infants were reported by Dr. Donald E. Gatch as having lost the hair on their heads but grown it on their faces so they looked like monkeys. Dr. Gatch treated many children for kwashiorkor (a Ghanian word meaning "disease that takes the child after it leaves the mother's breast"), for marasmus and for rickets. Many had loss of memory and the so-called Wernicke syndrome of "confabulation" (filling in a memory gap by unconscious lies that the patient accepts as true). Gatch attributed this to lack of thiamine. Pellagra was far from rare and most of the undernourished children were wormy. Three out of every four children in Beaufort County had either roundworms or whipworms or both.

A perversity common among poor black women, especially when pregnant, is eating clay or laundry starch (laundry starch in the cities is actually less expensive than clay which costs twenty-five cents a pound, and the taste is similar). Clay and starch eaters have more anemia, apparently because of the blocking of iron absorption in the blood, and the women more frequently give birth to dead babies. In Georgia most clay eaters favor white kaolin used in the manufacture of paper, ceramics and so on. Many women in the rural areas have secret spots where they dig up clay and may send it to friends or relatives in the cities. (A somewhat similar "geophagia" has been noted in hungry sparrows. They will peck down a house, brick by brick, apparently because the soil from which the bricks were made contains some mineral for which the birds developed a craving).

The diet of the well-to-do American adult is heavily dependent on the animal of the genus *Bos*—beef cattle. Aside from the fact that choice beefsteaks are quite unhealthful because of high saturated-fat content, the selection of this animal as a nearly universal source of food was an unfortunate one. *Bos* showed up in prehistoric Europe and Asia as a great crescent-horned beast and was killed or paraded around mainly for religious reasons. It would have been economically better in North America to have domesticated the bison, since bison (and other large grazing animals such as the eland in Africa) are much more efficient converters of grass into protein food than *Bos*. The caribou and the antelope would have been better too.

Consider the only hunting society currently familiar to us— the Eskimos. They probably represent our own North American paleolithic ancestors who killed off the native camel, the mammoth and other formidable prehistoric mammals. As described by Richard K. Nelson, who lived with the Barrow Eskimos, most of the hunting is for seals, but that meat is used only for dog food, since the natives *eat only caribou*. The polar bear is one of the only animals that will stalk man. The Eskimos believe that polar bears are left-handed since the bear kills the seal with a left-handed blow. Thus when a hunter is charged by a polar bear, he waits until it is very close, darts to its right side and then shoots it in the neck when its head is up.

Walrus hunting is a dangerous and exhilarating business. The herds are located sleeping in the ice pans very far from shore. In the spring, when the ice is open and the fogs are heavy, the walruses are located by their bellowing—a very deep hollow rhythmic belching or growling that lasts fifteen to twenty seconds. During a hunt the Eskimos speak only in low tones because they believe walruses understand human speech. The walruses are not afraid of man and when part of the herd is killed the rest will often attack the hunters. The wounded have to be killed at once. Their bellowing might bring others to rescue them.

After a walrus hunt the Eskimos drink tea. Then they spend eight hours or so butchering the slaughtered while the rest of the herd goes lurching about nervously, watching the men. If such a group does not leave soon, the Eskimos become uneasy and begin speaking to them. They repeat "tarzaaktugut" (we are finished) and tell them to go home. The mood is now melancholy, but the excitement of a walrus hunt is tremendous.

Eskimos taken out of this environment, washed and given

the usual food of poor North Americans, quickly develop body degenerations, the first sign of trouble being teeth cavities.

It is evident that, although the late-twentieth-century American has no occasion to see even the cattle slaughtered and knows meat only as paper-wrapped chunks in his freezer, the industry based on *Bos* needs improvement. It is still not too late to change or at least to simplify our meat economy.

The vast unused shrublands of the Southwest and of Mexico could be a natural pasture for camels. Cattle will not touch such shrubs as creosote bush. In one part of Cochise County, Arizona, a representative desert community produced 12,000 pounds of dry vegetable matter per acre per year, which is twice the annual grass production in most short-grass prairie ranges in the western cattle belt. But it is mainly in the form of creosote bush.

We know from the examination of Pleistocene animal droppings (fossil feces or "caprolites") that there were some animals that consumed creosote bush, yucca and the like. (These plants had developed resins and spines to prevent themselves from being eaten out of existence, but some of the Pleistocene animals were not repelled.) By the end of the Pleistocene (within the last 100,000 years) an Asian horde of caribou, mountain goat, mountain sheep, musk oxen, moose and even *Bos* itself (as a kind of yak) had immigrated into the new world by way of the Bering land bridge. The Asian camel is an animal whose lineage has a far longer history on this continent than the bison, a genus that arrived only in the middle of the Pleistocene many millions of years after the American origin of camels. When reintroduced in a rather tentative way by the U. S. Army over a hundred years ago, the camel showed an understandable affinity for the Southwest, preferring to browse on mesquite and creosote bushes and greasewood. He was back home again after an exile of tens of thousands of years.

Much of the western range industry came about simply through substitution of grazing animals such as cattle and sheep for other, actually more efficient, grazers such as bison and antelope. But the *browsing* habitat goes unused and prevails over about one million square miles on either side of the United States-Mexico border. Theoretically this could support from fifteen to twenty million camels consuming the available energy now going to waste.

Jesús Uribe Ruiz, president of the Mexican Academy of Agricultural Sciences, is a great believer in the camel as a meat source. He has dined off camel and believes Mexican peasants alone could raise fourteen million camels for food. It is sheer foolishness to insist that the livestock chosen in a rather romantic way over 6000 years ago is the only appropriate one for all of modern man's varied ecosystems.

WESTERN VEGETARIANISM

It was pointed out earlier that in inventing agriculture and the plough (tillage increased the growth of vegetation by a factor of 2500), man entered a lower order of nutrition. It must be remembered that, as we have seen, even cereal crops do not provide a potent enough balance of proteins. Moreover, another evolutionary point must be underlined. Even domesticated plants are not far enough away from their wild ancestors to be safe. Plants over millions of years have fought a profound battle against animals—principally against insects but partly against vertebrates. They fight it yet. Although many insects and some higher animals have been long enough on earth to develop tolerances for plant poisons, this is not true of man who is a Johnny-come-lately in the biological history of the planet. For example, if any real human being imitated Popeye the Sailorman in his consumption of spinach he would quickly die of oxalic acid poisoning.

Vegetarianism (a word that dates back to 1842) is only possible at all because we usually cook plant food or because we are such large animals that the poisons designed by evolution to kill insects are not enough to kill us outright.

Over five million people in the United States are vegetarians (about the same as the number of alcoholics). Perhaps the most famous one, certainly the richest, was John Kellogg, founder of the Battle Creek Sanitarium, inventor of about eighty cereal foods, including corn flakes. Dr. Kellogg combined boisterous showmanship with a knack for money. His big punch line was "How can you eat anything that has *eyes?*" Kellogg kept a morose chimpanzee for use in lectures. He would toss a juicy beefsteak to the chimp who would examine it with wrinkled nose and slam the meat right back to the beaming doctor. It is not exactly clear what this was supposed to prove except that one of the chief distinctions between monkey and man is that man is (or started out being) carnivorous while apes are not. Mrs. Annie Besant, the nineteenth-century theosophist and all-around sibyl, wrote *Vegetarianism in the Light of Theosophy*. She describes how she felt a profound depression of the spirit coming into Chicago because she was receiving astral messages of reproach from the spirits of thousands of beasts murdered in the Chicago stock yards. Sylvester Graham, a revered preacher of the early nineteenth century, denounced meat as a stimulus of sexual vigor, a statement which probably did not have exactly the effect on his audience that he intended.

Some vegetarians of severe Puritanism do not accept milk, butter, cheese, eggs and honey, since their motto is "You may as well eat the Devil as drink his broth." Some eat only "aspiring" vegetables, i.e., those that grow in the light of the sun, hence refuse tubers or roots. Vegetarians are reticent on the subject of Christ, since he performed the miracle of the seven loaves and the little fishes, which fed 4000 men (not counting women and children) with seven baskets of fish left over.

The raw-vegetable cultists are endangering their lives and those of their children. This point will be made clearer in Part 3 of this book, when we consider the interminable chemical warfare that all life wages against competing life.

We have seen that the sociology or ethnology of food purveying is at least as important as the technology of food production.

This is for the short pull. In the long run, with the continued population increase, we will *have* to go to more massive and revolutionary methods such as Single Cell Protein from petroleum. Since in this kind of process we are, so to speak, burning fuel to make food, its practicality depends on how much fossil fuel we have left in the earth. However much we have now, the answer is by some future time "not enough." If tremendously accelerated, the single cell protein processes might get us away from catastrophic protein famine in protein-poor regions of the earth but clearly it would constitute a reprieve, not a full pardon. It might be an early twenty-first-century solution but not, let us say, a twenty-third-century remedy.

It is evident that, in order to avoid *eventual* famine on a planet pullulating with human animals, we must somehow change drastically the nature or the habits of these animals. Furthermore, in the standard methods of avoiding famine, which are simply to produce more of the same food we eat (traditionally or experimentally) now, there is a grave risk of eliminating ourselves not by famine but by poisons. This will be the theme of the last part of this book. But first, before contemplating how man as a species may come to an end, it is useful to examine a few instances of the decline and fall of whole orders of creatures.

PART II

The Rise and Fall of Conquerors

Aside from the sudden effects that the supremacy of a master animal, such as man, can cause with his widespread pollution, deliberate and sometimes insensate exploitation of other forms of life, all types of animals appear to undergo a sort of Spenglerian cycle of proliferation and decay. Eons before man, or before mammals, the planet had seen stupendous catastrophes in both animal and plant phyla. Roughly 2500 families of animals with an average longevity of seventy-five million years have left a fossil record. Of these, about one-third are still living. A majority dropped out of sight without any descendants. There are nearly as many theories about such extinction cycles as there are paleontologists, and we shall mention some of them as we go along. To start with, however, it is surely not science fictioneering to point out once more (as did Robert Ardrey) the extraordinary concatenation of almost universal extinction of various animal types with the galactic clockwork. Every time the Sun and its planets have completed approximately a single 250-million-year swirl around the galactic wheel, something ominous seems to happen. At the close of the Cambrian era 450 million years ago nearly two-thirds of the existing families of trilobites and thousands of other species had disappeared. By the end of the Permian (coincidental with an unparalleled ice age) nearly half of all the known families of animals throughout the world vanished. And in the Pleistocene ice-age period, from which we are just emerging, many of the large herbivores and carnivores, which had been virtually world-wide throughout a great range in climate, became extinct within a few hundred years. Some attempts have been made to correlate mass extinction of animals with the nearby explosions of supernovae, pouring torrents of cosmic rays on the earth. Mass disappearances of certain fauna have occurred about once every sixty million years since Cambrian time, and rough estimates show the probability of a neighboring star explosion showering us with a dose of at least fifty roentgens of cosmic radiation every fifty million years. However, the radiation from supernovae explosions cannot account for the extinction of small marine organisms, protected by a layer of water. Man has always been prone to blame things on the constellations and the stars, and it may be that if an immortal astrologist had lived on earth since life began he could have written the horoscopes of all the great phyla and classes of animals. However, we do not know enough about astronomy as yet to build a theory on only three data points of the galactic clock and pure speculation as to supernovae occurrence. Let us look instead at the trilobite, which left the planet for good some 200 million years ago but which still holds the record for durability.

1

TOTAL EXTINCTION IN THE ANCIENT SEAS

Although a marine animal, the trilobite looked rather like a magnified wood louse and was conceivably ancestral to both the jawed and the chelated arthropods. Fossil remains of its innumerable races and sixty families nearly choke out all other animal remains in certain lower Cambrian deposits. Its body had the typical annelid-derived segments and its back was marked by two lengthwise furrows dividing it into three lobes (hence the name tri-lobite). The middle lobe or head had five segments, with "free cheeks" bearing its compound eyes. The body segments numbered as few as four and as many as forty-four, and these were freely movable, along with a tail shield, also segmented, so that it could curl up into a ball, head to tail, like many wood lice today. Although it seems to have been closer to a crustacean than to an insect, it had no shell or carapace. In size the members of this once immensely luxuriating subphylum ranged from one-quarter of an inch to twenty-seven inches in length. These creatures lived, some on sandy or muddy bottoms, some on coral reefs, some perhaps in the deep sea, but in numbers they ruled the planet through at least one whole revolution of the galaxy.

It seems unreasonable that they should have lasted as long as they did. The stomach was absurdly located in the middle of the head, so that the larger the stomach, the smaller the brain. Furthermore, an animal without a strong carapace, living in the shorelands or in shallows, would seem to be as helpless a prey as a soft-shelled crab. Yet so vast an impression of life stability had this fossil made on the minds of paleontologists that during the epochal scientific voyage of the *Challenger*, Sir Charles Thomson hoped to the end to see dredged from the deeps some lone living species of *Trilobita*. It never appeared. The last of the trilobites died in the Permian—over 200 million years ago.

One has to look here for causes that may never be discovered. Probably the trilobite lived on marine algae, but, if so, he eventually competed with a horde of different creatures that tapped this same food source. When animals make their living in the same way, it takes only a slight edge to result in the eventual disappearance of the disadvantaged animal. The slighter the edge, the longer the process of extinction. Slender variations in the rate of birth rate to death rate may shift the balance. For example, in the case of birds, from 80 to 90 per cent of the eggs fail to develop in the wild into breeding adults. However, in the case of mackerel eggs the percentage is 99.996 per cent, hence a mackerel must spawn an astronomical number of eggs for the species to continue. One would think that even small increases of radioactivity would have some crucial effect on the survival of delicately balanced animal species either by damaging the sperm or the fertilization process, but, if so, this has not yet been demonstrated in the waters off the Bikini atoll, where crabs scuttle around with ridiculously high amounts of radioactive strontium and, so far, neither parents nor offspring seem embarrassed by the baneful load they carry.

It seems more logical to discover the cause of the trilobite's extinction in the thinning out of his food, whatever it was. The Permian period was not only a time of terrible glaciation but of tectonic terror. The Appalachian Mountains range was thrust up, carrying with it Paleozoic sediments which had been pressed into fossil-bearing rock strata thousands of feet thick. The climate was dry and cold. The lush carboniferous forests of the two preceding periods dried up and the tree ferns all but disappeared. Although plant life in the sea is not so likely to wither away under the incursions of ice, it may be that the particular food that the trilobite depended upon grew scarce and competition for it more strenuous. Not being a brainy creature, he could not adjust and was swept into oblivion.

2

THE PERMIAN CATASTROPHE

One other great group of animals that disappeared at this time was the fusulinids—complex protozoans that ranged from microscopic sizes to three inches in length. They had populated the seas for only some eighty million years, and it was a great pity that they had to go, since the scientific availability of a three-inch long single-celled animal might have revolutionized some of our stodgiest biological preconceptions.* It seems probable that these animals also were starved out because of lack of sufficient algae food. By the close of the Permian, 75 per cent of the families of amphibians and over 80 per cent of the reptile families had vanished (but the dinosaurs had not even appeared on the scene). The Permian decimation took among its toll the fifteen-feet-long salamanders who had made the Pennsylvanian epoch the Age of Amphibians. The Devonian armored fishes had gone for good and so also had the trees of the "coal measures." It was not until late in the Triassic period, some fifteen to twenty million years later that life recovered its equilibrium, and perhaps we can attribute the comeback of animal life to the concurrent efflorescence of land and marine plant life. Each of the three successive principal land floras, the ferns and mosses, the gymnosperms and the angiosperms were ushered in by short episodes of rapid evolution followed by a long period of stability. Once a major group of plants became established, it continued for millions of years. Indeed many groups of major plants (including the redwood) are theoretically immortal. But a land plant cannot run away south from a glacier, as an

* One of them is that an animal in order to have a nervous system has to have separate neuron cells; hence, by definition, no protozoan has a nervous system.

animal can, hence the glaciation of the Permian, which extended even to Australia and South America, caused more havoc in the plant than in the animal kingdom.

Some animals lost their glory but managed to cling to the planet in a more modest way. Thus the sea scorpion, or eurypterid, which was a remote Silurian relative of the trilobite and grew to a terrible nine-foot monster, had a habit of sacking up in the shores of Silurian limestone, thus probably ancestoring the little air-breathing scorpion, which may therefore qualify as one of our oldest living fossils. The genus *Limulus* or so-called horseshoe crab was also probably a close relative of the extinct sea scorpion. It is very much still with us, having undergone virtually no evolutionary change in some 175 million years. A famous mollusk, the pearly nautilus, shared the rule of the seas with the trilobites just after the Cambrian epoch. The uncoiled shell of some of its species grew to a length of thirty feet. The decline of the order began actually before the Permian. From an original of over 3000 species, it has shrunk to four species of the genus *Nautilus* living in the South Pacific, but nonetheless it still lives. However, the ammonites, who belonged like the nautilus to the cephalopod class, had a curiously checkered and ultimately tragic history. After the Permian disaster, they survived and flourished, reaching a kingly peak in the Triassic with twenty-five families of widely distributed species, their shells getting to be as large as six feet in diameter. All but one family suddenly disappeared at the end of this epoch but that one thrived mightily, giving rise to scores of families in the Jurassic and Cretaceous and in fact probably becoming during this period the dominant forms of marine invertebrate life. Then they all died out at once. There are no survivors today. This is a whodunit of spectacular proportions, but so complicated and impalpable are the sinews of interwoven marine life that we shall probably never know the answer, and if we were intellectually so princely as to guess it right, we should also be able to date the probable death of our own species.

Not all kinds of marine animals felt the impact of the Permian cataclysm. For some species, like the brachiopods or "lamp shells," which had flourished at the beginning of the Cambrian and throughout the whole immensity of Paleozoic time, this period was not different from any other. From age to age some species of this peculiar phylum (the members of which do not have an anus) became extinct but others appeared. They rocked along, rolling with the punches, so to speak, of geologic adversity. You have probably seen *Lingula* on the beach and mistaken him for a bivalve, but when you opened his shell, instead of the muscular foot and fleshy belly of a clam, to your surprise you found the interior seemingly almost empty except for what looked like some watch springs that somebody had used a hammer on. When you did this, you were looking at incomparably the oldest creature on earth. He has survived virtually unchanged for at least half a billion years.

In the phylum of echinoderms, the more primitive group of Pelmatozoa (*pelmatos*, foot+*zoa*, animals) once covered the sea bottoms with their waving, muscular fronds. Although they looked like sea weeds, they were animals much more complicated than the jellyfish and fed on tiny particles of dead or dying microorganisms falling in a ceaseless rain from the upper levels of the ocean. One can see that if this rain of food turned sparse, because of change in climate of the upper ocean, the pelmatozoans would find things tough, and they did. Of the numerous groups whose fossils can be traced back to the Cambrian, only one class, the sea lilies or crinoids, live today, usually growing in deep cold water. At widely separated spots on the ocean floor, where conditions are just right, there are evidently forests of crinoids up to three feet high, for occasionally a dredge will bring up thousands of stalked crinoids from a single haul.

3

EXTINCTION BY BEING MUNCHED ON

We see today a remarkable example of echinoderms of a different sort destroying a majestic colony of coral (Australia's Great Barrier Reef), and it is possible that our great-grandchildren will have witnessed the nearly complete extinction of the reef-building Coral class of coelenterate animals. Since it is possible that man may be partly implicated in this fantastic marine disaster, it appears worth explaining how reef-forming corals go about their business. Algae play a crucial role in reef formation.The entire reef is made solid by the skeletons of calcareous algae and, more important, the reef-building corals give tenancy in their tissues to symbiotic algae, the so-called zooxanthellae. Since the latter absorb carbon dioxide for photosynthesis, they build up tissues which are broken down by the coral animal in its metabolism. Furthermore, chemical equilibrium in the neighborhood is shifted from soluble calcium bicarbonate toward insoluble calcium carbonate, thus forming the base of the limestone reef. Corals which do not have symbiotic algae do not build reefs. One must always remember that the living coral lives on top of his limy mineral graveyard.

What has happened lately is that giant starfish (the so-called Crown of Thorns species) have taken to feeding on the living coral of the Great Barrier Reef, which extends for 1200 miles along the northeast coast of Australia. Robert Endean of the University of Queensland has reported that in some places 80 per cent of the coral has been destroyed and tourists are now noticing that the reef is losing its beauty. The starfish are proliferating immensely on this pasture and each echinoderm kills about twenty-four square inches of coral per day. Several months ago the operators of one Barrier Reef resort began paying skin divers ten cents for each starfish killed and some 50,000 were dispatched before the realization dawned that this was like trying to stop an epidemic of malaria by shooting each *Anopheles* mosquito with a popgun; the rate of the giant starfish population explosion had gone overwhelmingly beyond the capacity of any control by individual killings.

What caused this *Crown of Thorns* species suddenly to decide to wipe out the coral colonies? One rather tenuous theory is that the fault is that of the tourists themselves who eagerly buy up the shells of the giant mollusk known as the Triton, who flourishes in this area. As has been mentioned, starfish have few predators, because a mouthful of starfish is something like fish-flavored cement, but although the starfish's favorite food consists of mollusks such as clams and mussels, the triton mollusk (which looks like an eighteen-inch-long snail) can dispose of a starfish every day. However, even if every tourist also bought a triton shell every day, this, like the skin diver expedient, would seem mathematically pusillanimous from an ecological standpoint. With the swarming of starfish, so should the tritons swarm. Nevertheless, so delicately strung are the networks of marine population controls, it may just be possible that man has again put his foot in it and the reef-building corals are bearing the brunt of the disequilibrium.

It should be emphasized that this explosion by now is not confined to the Great Barrier Reef. Coral is being destroyed off Borneo, New Guinea, the Fiji Islands, Truk, Palau, Yap, Poto, Saipan, Wake and Johnston Islands, Midway and Guam. Richard Chesher of the University of Guam has made a careful study of the problem, since, as he points out, on most of the islands of Oceania the natives get their protein from fisheries enclosed by coral reefs and when the reefs are destroyed the fish leave the fisheries for good.

The fearful, still unexplained aspect of this menace is its suddenness. *Acanthaster planci* (the Crown of Thorns starfish) was regarded as a rarity until about 1963 and before 1967 was hardly known in Guam. Chesher does not believe the triton is an effective control, since in experimentally arranged encounters between the two animals, he has noted that the triton manages to bite only pieces of the starfish. Even if the predator bites the starfish in half, the living half regenerates itself within two months. His theory is that blasting and dredging operations have made fresh surfaces of reef available for the larvae of the starfish, which in larval form is commonly controlled by filter feeders such as the coral itself. This theory in turn is disputed by J. L. Fisher of Tulane who points out that both Guam and Truk, now experiencing the starfish invasion at its worst, were both heavily bombed during World War II. During his stay on Truk in 1949–50 he saw no starfish invasion and on the contrary was impressed by the rapidity with which new coral began to grow again on the bombed areas. He believes the starfish predators, whatever they are, have been killed off by pesticides, such as DDT.

The last thought seems most persuasive, especially in conjunction with Noel Workman's contention that the chief predators of starfish larvae are sardines and particularly another small fish called the "hardyhead." Although he emphasizes that these fish were driven from parts of the Great Barrier Reef six years ago by pile-driving operations for a new jetty, it is even more likely that the appetites for starfish larvae throughout the Pacific and Indian oceans have in some way been affected by DDT or perhaps some other poison, thus allowing this wicked, voracious creature to survive through its life cycle in an unnatural degree of complacency. Indeed it is possible that the Crown of Thorns may be one of the only creatures on earth that thrives on pollution by DDT or something else, perhaps petroleum residues, while all its important predators are weakened or killed by these earth poisons. This problem, a sort of living reprise of marine dramas of extinction that have been played over and over again in the life history of the planet, would seem to deserve the most exhaustive scientific scrutiny.

4

THE DECLINE OF THE GREAT REPTILES

Obviously man cannot himself be blamed for the most dramatic extinction of all, the disappearance of the mesosaurs, the dinosaurs and the ichthysaurs during the Cretaceous epoch. The 150 million years of reptile domination, which had been delayed by the Permian disaster, saw a classical example of one of those evolutionary explosions known as *adaptive radiation*, in which, like the nematodes of today, the animal-type spreads across the planet by becoming specialized for thousands of different ways of making a living in thousands of different environments. Biped carnivores like *Tyrannosaurus* preyed on leaf-eating dinosaurs like *Triceratops*, which had three massive horns. In the lush swamps guzzled the eighty-foot *Brontosaurus*. In the sea, marine reptiles competed successfully with sharks and in the air were flying pterodactyls, snatching fish in their clawed wings and devouring them in the water before their ponderous take-offs.

How to explain how this giant clan all vanished some seventy million years ago? It is easy to blame it on the climate which changed for the cooler at this end of the Mesozoic. Being cold-blooded, they could no longer shake off the torpor of the cold nights and probably therefore could not remember from one day to the next what the score was. This does not seem a very compelling explanation, since even though the cooling and drying of the temperate regions may account for the failing of the great reptiles there, many of them still could have flourished in the tropical regions of Central and South America, Africa and South Asia, or in the ocean. But when they failed, they failed all over. Furthermore, in compensating for their cold-bloodedness, some great land reptiles had developed a most ingenious morning exercise.

Dimetrodon, for example, had a set of long spines articulated to its vertebrae, enabling them to be raised and lowered. The spines contained blood vessels and were connected by a membrane through which blood flowed. By raising the spines, *Dimetrodon* could expose the membrane to the rays of the rising sun, thus warming his whole blood system and snapping him out of the usual reptile morning-after stupor in time to get around before his neighbors and perhaps breakfast upon them. But he too went down with all the rest.

A second possibility, which I find quite cogent, is that it was actually man's own ancestors, the primitive mammals, who caused the downfall of the dinosaurs and their kin by eating their eggs. When we think of the fact (which we shall presently discuss in more detail) that the impending extinction of marine turtles is mainly to be charged to the eating of their eggs by man and other mammals (especially the raccoon), the large-scale depredation of the eggs of the turtle's own ancestors hardly seem farfetched. Even the ancient marine reptiles, like the present turtles, had to lay their eggs on the land, as did the pterodactyls. Morever, a dinosaur did not lay eggs as bountifully as does a chicken. Who was around, save other reptiles, to steal these great eggs? Who was a thief in the night, when all reptiles became clotted in their viscous blood? A mammal, of course, whose warm blood made him a natural nocturnal prowler. Actually it may have been the availability of the clutches of giant concentrated food packages that gave the runty little Cretaceous mammal his start in life. I find this theory comfortingly realistic and moreover it makes man, through his skulking ancestors, responsible for the fall of a majestic dynasty—a fitting prelude to the latter history of this most destructive of all animals that ever lived on earth.

Some zoologists do not buy this but suggest instead that some colossal epidemic of a viral, bacterial or even protozoan disease wiped out the great reptiles. This is a safe theory, since it is impossible either to prove or disprove, but, unlike the egg-eating hypothesis, modern wild animal groups do not show any likelihood of this kind of vulnerability. For example, the tsetse fly, which transmits the trypanosome of African sleeping sickness, has made it impossible to raise domestic cattle in large areas of Africa, but the native relatives of cattle, like the various antelopes and gazelles, have developed enough immunity to flourish and even to serve as reservoirs of the disease. One could hardly imagine a creature as adaptable as a reptile not having also attained, through 150 million years, immunity, somewhere, to unseen enemies that only his blood can fight.

Another, and perhaps the most popular, theory is the somewhat too subtle one of "overspecialization." There is no validity to the old concept of "racial senescence," but obviously through evolution animals can be caught in a trap of specialization. When an animal has developed such narrow talents that it can no longer start out in a fresh direction of development when environmental conditions change in such a way as to render these talents useless, this animal is doomed. One of the common specializations, which has affected mammals as well as reptiles, is size. Here possibly we deal with sexual selection. Because the female prefers the larger male, the species goes into a fatal spiral, in which only the largest males can win females, but eventually the animal type becomes too ponderous and needs too much food to become an efficient machine of survival. Gorillas today, in which the sexes differ greatly in size, have eaten themselves toward the brink of oblivion. Among the carnivores, male lions now depend almost entirely on their more agile mates to make the kills, while they merely stand about and roar for their supper.

Perhaps the scenario for the extinction of the gorilla has already been written in the history of the great ape *Gigantopithicus* who flourished at least five million and perhaps nine million years ago in the savannas and forest fringes of Asia. This was the largest primate that ever lived (nine feet tall, weighing over 600 pounds) but he was a born loser. Most of what we know about him is deduced by E. L. Simons and Peter Ettel of Yale from recently discovered fossil fragments in China and India. His teeth structure shows that he was a hard-core vegetarian (not a fruit eater) and, in spite of his enormous stature, he seems to have been a prey rather than a predator, probably attacked by gangs of *dholes*, the ancient wild dogs of Asia. *Gigantopithicus* had to eat so much that he failed to take the right track toward hominid habits of hunting and using the brain. Instead of becoming a spear maker, his specialized feeding habits (the ingestion of small tough morsels —grass seeds, stems, rhizomes) led him to total extinction from which we rescue his memory only because a few teeth and jawbones are the leftover contents of ancient porcupine burrows.

Luckily for most mammalian animals, the tendency toward

gigantism was reversible in part. The enormous beaver of the Miocene obviously had sized himself out of a reliable supply of trees for food and lodging, but smaller relatives still survive, as specialized as they otherwise are in their habits and behavior.

5

DISASTERS OF THE RECENT ICE AGE

Norman Newell, one of the most thoughtful students of natural animal extinction cycles, has insisted that climate (even glaciation) has little or nothing to do with the matter. At the time of the maximum extent of the recent continental glaciers some 11,000 years ago, the ice-free land of the Northern Hemisphere supported a rich and varied assortment of large mammals, as does Africa today. Nine thousand years ago the horse, elephant and camel families roamed all the continents except Australia and Antarctica. As a matter of fact the maximum rate of extinction of these large northern beasts took place precisely when the climate had become milder and the glaciers were shrinking. Many of the large herbivores and carnivores had become virtually world-wide through a great range in climate, only to become extinct within a few hundred years.

Newell's theory is that throughout geologic time the evolutionary development or the extinction of animals has depended on the fluctuation of sea level. During much of the Paleozoic and Mesozoic time (540 million years) the land surfaces were much lower than they are today. Any appreciable rise in sea level would result in the flooding of large areas, while a drop in sea level caused large areas to emerge. These changes had explosive biological repercussions. Evolution speeds up, diversification is greatest during times of major flooding, because this produces such a large number of habitats—and ways of making a living. Extinction and the rigors of natural selection are most intense during periods of major withdrawals of the sea. During the past 600 million years there have been at least thirty major and hundreds of minor oscillations of sea level, and Newell seeks, with a certain degree of success, to correlate them with the ebb and flow of animal and plant species. Although his hypothesis has a good deal of explanatory power, it obviously cannot be the whole story which probably is many-faceted and fraught with the whims of sheer biological luck as well as concatenations of various circumstances.

The above paragraph, although pleasant with ambiguity, might be subject to the classical although ungrammatical riposte "Who are you kidding?" Every recent finding, especially those of Paul S. Martin and John S. Guilday of Yale, Olaf F. Prager of Kent State University and many others, point irresistibly to the fact that *prehistoric man himself extinguished the marvelous, great Pleistocene animals*. In every well-documented case, human beings were clearly present in those areas in which extinction occurred. It was gang murder and it proved gang murder to the point of extinction. Perhaps it is prudent to sum this viewpoint up in the cautiously worded professorial indictment by Arthur J. Jelinek, from which one finds it difficult to find persuasive defense attorneys for our savage Paleolithic ancestors*: "*Homo sapiens* remains [during the Pleistocene] as a new element in the environment, with a formidable potential for disruption, whether directly as an extremely efficient and rapidly expanding predator group, against whom no evolved [animal] defense systems were available, or indirectly as the source of profound changes in ecology already under the process of adjustment as a result of considerable climatic stress."

* But at the same time one feels an unreasonable pride of species. Few as they were in the fearsome changeableness of the Pleistocene, these stouthearted men were able to feed their families by attacking giant beasts who would have scared the hell out of even an Ernest Hemingway equipped with powerful primary and stand-by big-game rifles.

6

MAN AS AN ANIMAL ERASER

In fact, the worst piece of luck that the non-primate animal world suffered was the evolution of man. In his short history on earth, man has been directly responsible for the disappearance of more than 400 species of animals.

Although the heaviest toll in number of creatures have been associated with such close-to-hand horror stories as the annihilation of the passenger pigeon, it should be pointed out that the sorriest statistics in *species* destroyed came from the West Indies and the islands of the Pacific and Indian oceans where seventy species of birds, for instance, have become extinct in the past few hundred years. At the present time, in spite of massive national and international wildlife conservation gestures and noises, each year as regularly as the clock of doom, one species of bird and one species of mammal become extinct—a rate of disappearance far higher than in the times of greatest geologic crisis before man arrived on the scene. Every curator of a zoo anywhere in the world can tell you that there are at least seventy-eight species which probably will disappear from the planet before the year 2000. These include the grizzly bear (whose fate was probably sealed by some sensational bad behavior in 1967), the black-footed ferret (who must feed on the rapidly disappearing prairie dog), the ivory-billed woodpecker, the Ne-Ne goose (the state bird of Hawaii), Kirtland's Warbler, the maned wolf, the Spanish lynx, the Indian lion and the Javan tiger (of which only ten are believed alive).

Directly because of man, the world has lost 110 kinds of mammals since the birth of Christ and another 1000 can be viewed with solicitude. Since 1689 (when the last dodo expired), 162 species or subspecies of birds have been exterminated.

Among the first species of mammals wiped out were the Cape lion, the Barbary lion, the Eastern cougar, seventeen species of bear, five species of wolves and foxes. Among ungulates ruthlessly exterminated were the European wild horse, the aurochs, the Eastern wapiti, the Oregon bison, the Badlands bighorn, the Algerian wild ass, the Syrian wild ass and the rufous gazelle.

Although the rise of Christianity may have been good for the human soul, it was hard on other animals. Especially in its Western form, Christianity is the most anthropocentric religion the world has ever known. As Lynn White, UCLA historian, has pointed out, by destroying pagan animism Christianity made it possible ruthlessly to exploit nature in a mood of indifference to the feelings of natural organisms. Despite Darwin, we are *not* at heart part of the natural process. We believe ourselves superior to nature. The concept of the "sacred grove" (a profoundly ecologic notion quite foreign to the mind of the typical western rancher or politician) is regarded as heathenish and contemptible. For nearly two thousand years, Christian missionaries have both figuratively and literally been chopping down sacred groves and killing their inhabitants, and certain politicians have epitomized this philosophy when they said, "When you've seen one redwood tree, you've seen them all."

The emergence of "anti-conservation" is evident in the widespread practice of the Baconian creed (most powerfully since about 1850) that scientific knowledge means technologic power over nature. Its acceptance as the normal, the *moral* pattern may mark the most significant event in human development since the invention of agriculture.

The greatest radical (the perfect anti-Baconian) in Christian history was St. Francis of Assisi. He was so clearly heretical that a general of the Franciscan Order, St. Bonaventura, attempted to suppress the early accounts of Franciscanism. St. Francis tried to depose man from his monarchy over creation and to set up a democracy of all God's creatures.

A typical example, recorded by White, concerns a time in which the land around Gubbio in the Apennines was being ravaged by a wolf. St. Francis, according to legend, talked to the wolf and persuaded him of the error of his ways. The wolf repented, died in the odor of sanctity and was buried in consecrated ground.*

---

* Curiously enough Martin Luther, an unlikely ecologist, soothed his children by answering them that their beloved dogs, when death came, would find a

Needless to say, the Franciscan doctrine of the animal soul was speedily stamped out. The present wasteland of the world's environment is a product of the dynamic technology which was starting to thrive in the Western medieval world against which St. Francis was rebelling. It is obvious that we shall continue to have a worsening ecologic crisis until we reject the Christian axiom that nature has no reason for existence, except to serve Man. I heartily second Lynn White's nomination of the good friar of Assisi as a patron saint for ecologists. The prayers of modern Catholics should begin with the plea, "*Help us, Dear St. Francis!*"

In contrast with the ravening exploitation of Western man, the subcontinent of India as early as the third century B.C., under the Emperor Asoka, took a positive stand on wildlife conservation. India until recently had not exterminated a single mammal, although the white tiger is now in jeopardy.

We must examine in more detail the human drives that have been responsible for and continue to underly some of these erasures of splendid irreplaceable animals from the universe. The least guilty motive is simply carelessness, above all in the introduction of domesticated or parasitic animals to lands that had never seen them. Thus the flightless Dodo was quickly wiped out by pigs, dogs, cats and rats when man moved in to live on the Mascarene Islands of the Indian Ocean.

In 1918 a shipwreck left rats on Lord Howe Island off Australia, until that time considered a unique bird paradise. Since then the rats have exterminated five species of native birds. The same dismal drama, with cats as the exterminators, took place on the Island of Herekopare. Through this and other mechanisms, associated with man and his satellite mammals, more kinds of birds have become extinct on Pacific islands than in all the rest of the world together. Sometimes it does not require active aggression. Thus the mere appearance of a man in a colony of sensitive birds, like the spoonbills, will make them desert their nests permanently. In 1967 the British proposed to convert the coral atoll Aldabra to an airbase, but fortunately Great Britain went broke before this completely virgin island, 200 miles east of Africa and 260 miles northwest of Madagascar, was opened to the rape by man and his mammals.

---

place in heaven. This comforted the children greatly since they had regarded a dogless heaven as a dismal place, as indeed it would be.

This tiny sanctuary is a sort of biological Eden, the lone untrespassed survivor of many such islands in the Indian Ocean. It houses twelve species and subspecies of birds found nowhere else and eighteen or more unique species of higher plants. It is the last home of the great land tortoise *Testudo Gigantea* and the last breeding place in the entire Indian Ocean for the frigate bird. Here is the only remaining refuge of the tiny flightless rail and the pink-footed booby. When the dog was introduced to Australia he reverted to the wild state and became the dingo. In this role he competed directly with large marsupial predators, such as the Tasmanian devil and the marsupial wolf, who were far superior to him in strength but had intrinsically inferior hunting techniques. By competition for identical prey the dingo reduced these marsupials to the extent that they exist only in Tasmania, where there are no dingoes. In this case, Man, after having unleashed the Dog, was a spectator, not a hunting companion, since the Dingo doesn't even like Man. We have played a spectator role in a similar drama in Nebraska, where competition between ring-necked pheasants, introduced from Asia, and the native greater prairie chickens has resulted in the virtual elimination of the latter. Yet, as pointed out by Virginia Kraft, even the pheasant is declining. South Dakota is an example. At one time pheasants thrived so richly in this state that in the 1940s and 1950s it was difficult to drive down a country road without running over them.

Lack of habitat has reduced the South Dakota pheasant population from about thirty million in 1963 to about three million in 1970. Most farms were once rich with shelter area but the brush stands, draws, potholes, sloughs all disappeared as modern methods and equipment allowed the farmer to use even his sorriest land. There is no place for the pheasant to hide any more.

The South Dakota landowner could, if he had sense enough, make pheasant one of his most profitable crops by retaining pheasant shelter and charging hunting fees—a system that has worked in parts of Texas. The harvesting of pheasant as well as ducks and deer by controlled hunting is by far less dangerous to all such species than the obliteration of their natural living spots. The death of the Big Thicket area in southeast Texas because of lumber companies is eliminating, among other animals, the rare redheaded woodpecker. The black rhinoceros is on its way to never-never land in Africa. Although organized poaching is flagrant, the bush country

—the rhino's natural home is fast becoming dry grassland as the result of drought, brush fires and the destruction of trees and shrubs which are food for both the rhino and the elephant. Since the elephant is by far the more adaptable and intelligent animal, it is a good bet that he will survive the rhino.

The question really is if any of the great herds of wild grazing animals will survive in Africa. Their critical ranges are being taken over by the much less efficient domestic cattle. The Serengeti Plains, thronged, as far as the eye can see, by zebra, wildebeests, Thomson's gazelle and so on, may in the next century be only an illustrated memory, filed in films. The life cycle of such animals is associated with gigantic circular migrations to take advantage of seasonal grazing and water supplies. This is like a clock—if you stop it at one point of its movement, the clock will always tell you it is midnight. Wildlife biologists are now sure that farming and ranching by the Masai tribesmen will totally disrupt the migrations. The animals will either be forced to remain in the Nyorongoro Crater, where they will overgraze the range, or they will be killed off like the American bison and antelope as they compete with domestic animals.

In many cases man resents a wild animal because he claims it reduces the profit that he can make on domesticated stock or because it devours agricultural crops. Since you will never see one, let us recall the passenger pigeon, a highly gregarious bird seventeen inches from beak to tail, colored gray with a bright iridescent vest of rusty brown. In 1871 one flock of passenger pigeons in Wisconsin was estimated at two billion. It is impossible to estimate the total number of these birds which once thrived in our country. Their community breeding grounds often covered 800 square miles, with fifty to one hundred nests in a tree. The beech was their favorite tree and their immense bird colonies started to dwindle as the great beech forests were cut down. In 1889 a large flock of young passenger pigeons flying across Crooked Lake, Michigan, became confused and went into the water. The shore line for miles was covered over a foot deep with their bodies. Farmers hated these birds and shot them at every opportunity. They were also netted and trapped, sometimes, when crops were poor, to augment the family larder. The last great commercial hunt took place in Michigan about ninety years ago. The hunters needed fifteen tons of ice to pack merely the young squabs they had killed. Evidently, like some other flocking-birds species, they needed a certain rather large minimum to survive at all, and when the constant ruthless massacre got their numbers below this threshold, they collapsed as a species. The last passenger pigeon on earth, a captive in a Cincinnati zoo named Martha, died September 1, 1914. The realization that suddenly there were no more passenger pigeons and there would never be surprised and profoundly shocked a whole generation of Americans. Although they had not been a lovable bird by rural standards, a planet forever empty of them was somehow a poorer planet. Many people today regard the starlings as the old farmers thought of the passenger pigeons, and I have a neighbor who shoots them with his air gun at every opportunity. But would anyone seriously want all the starlings on earth annihilated? It may be that the heath hen was similarly hurried into extinction when the last remnant on Martha's Vineyard fell below the numbers necessary for successful group courtship and breeding.

Sometimes the farmer's hatred of certain animals gets to the status of an ugly obsession. Ths is certainly the case with some sheep and goat ranchers and their government-aided campaign for extermination of the coyote. They want *all* the coyotes killed everywhere. So-called "wolf clubs" have been formed to encourage the financing of a federal coyote-killing program by the Federal Division of Wildlife Services and the Federal Bureau of Sport Fisheries and Wildlife. Through the virtuous combination of these government agencies, nearly a hundred thousand coyotes were destroyed in 1967. Not satisfied merely to protect the sheep herds directly in their "kill-the-coyote" campaign, the squint-eyed ranchers have put up the cash for the development of a so-called "coyote getter." This consists of hollow tubing driven into the ground, loaded with an explosive cyanide cartridge and tipped with a scented bait that is also a trigger. When a coyote (or a dog, for that matter) grabs the bait, the cyanide explodes in the animal's mouth. This ingenious device has killed a lot of coyotes, but in the long run may prove to be chiefly a "dog getter," since the wild animal is intrinsically more intelligent and learns more quickly than the dog to avoid such cute weapons. However, the obsessed ranchers would rather kill all the dogs in the state than let the chance go by of blowing poison down the throat of a "ky-yōt." In 1966 a Texas oilman was accidentally "controlled" by a homemade coyote getter and this may change the situation. As pointed out by such coyote apologists as Mary Hazell Harris of the Defenders of Wildlife organization, sheep ranchers invariably exaggerate their losses, blaming coyotes for deaths due to poor range management, starvation, exposure or disease.

The classical reply of the embattled sheepsters is that Miss Harris represents the "socialist bird watchers." The exquisite logic represented by the implied thesis—that all wildlife conservationists are communistic—finds an echoing syllogism in the belligerent question, "Who are you for, people or wild animals?"—the implication being that the Red Conspiracy is directed at the preservation of wild beasts and birds and at the destruction of humanity. Many chicken ranchers have taken up the war against coyotes and, apparently not distinguishing a coyote from a raccoon, have on occasion complained that the coyotes have learned to climb trees in finding a way into the chicken yard.

It must be noted at this point that our federal Constitution is such that technically wild animals belong to the state where they live. (Exceptions, of course, are national parks and refuges.) Thus the sovereign state of Texas could pass a law, if its electorate so pleases, making the existence of coyotes or even of cardinals (a non-migratory bird) unlawful. However, just as Texas and every other state nowadays rely heavily on federal manpower and money to prevent people from starving, so do the states lean weightly on the federal hunters and "control technologists" to solve their animal problems.

The cattlemen would like to see all the prairie dogs poisoned; they too want federal help and get it. These extraordinary town-building rodents not only eat the grass that belongs to the cattle baron but insult him by their mere presence on his ranges. Although many informed biologists have insisted that prairie dogs infest only ranges that have already been overgrazed, such statements of fact have a way of gliding off the brain of the cattle baron like water off a duck's back. He still wants the prairie dogs exterminated by poison and he is having his way. As previously noted, this has resulted in the virtual disappearance of the black-footed ferret, a compulsive predator of the prairie dog, perhaps mostly because the ferret eats the poisoned carcasses. (Indirectly, the poisoning of cattle carcasses to kill predators such as the cougar has undoubtedly been responsible in large part for the impending extinction of the California condor.)

The wolf is an endangered species for reasons perhaps still

more illogical than those used against the coyote. Recently in Minnesota a cry went up, demanding the restoration of the $35 bounty on the wolf "to save the deer," in spite of the fact that of all the large game animals in this country the deer is the safest (in fact, has enormously increased in numbers since colonial days) and that in deer-rich Minnesota the hunters enjoy the highest success rates in the world. The wolf is not only an excellent control agent to prevent the population explosion of large herding ungulates but seems to have an intrinsic biological governor to hold down its own multiplication. Wolves are monogamous for life and mating is therefore a far from capricious business. The female's preference is naturally for the pack leader, but if she cannot get him, she takes a long time in making up her mind. An indication both of the virtue of wolves as selective predators and as stable populations can be seen from the recent experience on the Isle Royale National Park in Lake Superior, which had been set aside as a moose refuge. The moose herds had built up to about 3000 animals at one time, devastated the vegetation and undergone two periods of widespread starvation. The twinning of calves, always frequent in a healthy herd, had stopped almost entirely. Then some wolves crossed the ice and invaded this questionable moose paradise. The wolves, as always, killed selectively—mostly bulls over ten years old, who were later found to be infested with tapeworm cysts in their lungs. A stable equilibrium established itself. The vegetation recovered, the moose twinning rate went up to 40 per cent, and the wolf packs stayed year after year at almost the same total number of animals.

One can compare this ideal ecological situation with the messy one in the Yellowstone National Park where the control of tremendous herds of elk is one of the Park Service's nastiest problems. Each year hundreds or even thousands of elk must be live-trapped or shot to reduce the herd. This program has aroused such public squawking that legal battles have begun over it. Although this would appear a natural place to reintroduce wolves, the cattlemen in nearby areas have raised a fuss so horrible that nobody has dared to mention the thing above a bated breath, the irrational idea being that Yellowstone would serve as a sort of wolf reservoir, which might spill over to cattle ranges hundreds of miles away.

The campaigns against coyotes, wolves and prairie dogs have some semblance of biological justification, since in simplistic terms one could say that man is trying to protect a food supply (or a wool supply) against the incursions of animals that he has not tamed. The suave aura of fake morality scarcely extends to the destruction of animals for their furs or hides or feathers. The beaver was virtually exterminated in Europe and in much of North America because in the nineteenth century men of social dignity wore beaver-skin high hats. For the most part, however, the slaughter of many animals now disappearing from the planet has been motivated by the adornment whims of the well-cared-for female human being.

The sea otter has one of the softest and loveliest coats of all animals, and when discovered in large numbers on the Pacific coast an implacable slaughter of this beautiful animal began. In the first year after the discovery of the Pribilof Islands, two Russian sailors by themselves killed 5000 sea otters at the Island of St. George. Although the Russians, always sharp fur hunters, had realized that the sea otter was not going to survive at the rate of killing then occurring and had placed restrictions on the hunters, when Alaska was bought by the United States in 1867, unlimited slaughter began again and the sea otter was pressed to the very brink of extinction. It was very easy to kill a sea otter because he was such a friendly little animal. Otters would swim up to the small boats only to be clubbed to death. Under the penalty of heavy fines, the population has slowly begun to restore itself and the restrictions have recently been relaxed, apparently at the incessant demands of fur traders, who can get as much as $20,000 for enough prime skins to make a coat. The comeback of the sea otters incidentally has made a rarity out of that tasty shellfish, the abalone. Almost alone among marine animals, the otter is able to catch the abalone in a relaxed moment and make it loose its steely grip on rocks or piers. Thus, the sea otter restoration has been the abalone's doom. (Sometimes, sighs the conservationist, you just can't win!)

The carnage in the case of fur-bearing seals was similar and contemporaneous with that of the sea otter. Uncounted millions of seals were killed on the Pribilof Islands alone. In 1867, sealing privileges in the Alaskan territory were leased by the U. S. Government, resulting in a more systematic but even higher rate of kill. The most heartbreaking and senseless assassination was the indirect one of the seal pups. The seal mother will not nurse a strange pup, hence when the mothers were killed the beaches were littered with the little bodies of pups that had starved to death. By 1911 the seals had been reduced from perhaps 270 million to 124,000.

Government restrictions on this bloody traffic saved the fur-bearing seal, but this is not to say that a lot of miscellaneous seal killing does not continue, although at a reduced rate. The seal is the salt-water fisherman's enemy and he will kill it to protect his livelihood. In 1941 the Seal Treaty was abrogated by Japan, she claiming that the seals damaged her fishing industry. The U. S. Government eventually negotiated an exclusive contract with the Fouke Fur Company of St. Louis for dressing, dyeing and selling skins at auction, although Alaska is now asking for control of the arctic fur-seal business.

A close relative of the seal, the sea elephant, barely escaped annihilation, but it was not his hide that men were after but his oil, which in the nineteenth century was found to be superior to that of even the sperm whale for lubricating machinery. A big bull might yield over two hundred gallons of blubber, which was almost pure oil. Between 1855 and 1870 these animals were killed by the tens of thousands on the southern Pacific coast and by 1892 only nine of them remained on Guadalupe Island, their favorite breeding beach. The sea elephant owes his existence to the Mexican government. In 1911 the killing of this animal was prohibited by Mexican decree. For the past thirty years a garrison of armed guards has been stationed on Guadalupe and no one is allowed even to come ashore without authorization from Mexico City. The guards are encouraged to shoot first and discuss the amenities later. As the result of such a hard-nosed policy, this unique animal has begun to increase again and in the past few years small groups of sea elephants even returned to the Channel Islands off Santa Barbara.

Among furry animals that are facing complete extinction is the lynx. This beautiful feline is somewhat on the stupid side and never learns to avoid traps. Lacking any restrictions, it has consequently almost been trapped out of existence. The booming trade in "fun furs" for teeny boppers has almost overnight resulted in near extermination of a whole feline spectrum of spotted cats, including tigers and other species, such as the jaguar, the leopard, the cheetah, even the tiny wild cats of South America. The popula-tion of very young women, whose parents can afford thus to adorn them, is a very large, solid and growing one, and if the "fun fur" craze continues at the present rate, one can confidently look forward to the complete disappearance of these species of animals. (Acts in Congress forbid the importation into the United States of all wild animals whose capture or killing is illegal in the country of export. If this legislation includes the *pelts* of such animals and, if appropriately stringent interstate restrictions are enforced, it might be possible to switch the "fun fur" trade back to the original cloth or synthetic-fiber imitations.)

Cleveland Amory, president of the *Fund for Animals,* believes we should be picketing women not the fur industry. In response to blasts from this and other organizations such as the Sierra Club, the World Wildlife Fund, the Audubon Society, the Humane Society and the new *Friends of the Earth* (FOE), feline-fur-wearing women are beginning to feel self-conscious if not guilty. The fashion press has tuned down its display of spotted furs. It takes a defiant woman these days to wear a leopardskin coat, but there are many defiant women left, including the conspicuous Gina Lollobrigida. The House of Ben Khan, where pickets have marched, protests that it is abiding by the "Red Book" and has stopped promoting the cat animals listed under threat of extinction such as the tiger, the snow leopard and the cloud leopard. George Kaplan Furs advertises it will not use leopard, tiger, cheetah, jaguar, ocelot, polar bear, red wolf, vicuña and Spanish lynx. This list contains sea otter, but these are under U. S. Government control.

Sable is not included since this animal is ranched like mink, not trapped or shot. Jean McIntyre, who heads the San Francisco branch of FOE, has attacked Mrs. Aristotle S. Onassis who was given a leopard coat several years ago. Richard Leakey, son of the famous paleontologist, is so incensed over the yearly illegal slaughter of 40,000 African leopards that he will not entertain, escort or even speak to a woman wearing a leopardskin coat.

Because the crocodilian's hide makes piquant shoe leather and handbags for ladies, the alligator in North America and the cayman in the Amazon are on their way to utter extinction. Since the killing of alligators is unlawful in the United States, the attrition is entirely due to poaching, but in states such as Florida the poacher's life is not an especially hard one. He works mostly at night when everybody else in the Everglades is asleep or drunk. Interstate restrictions are laughably inadequate. The U. S. Corps of Engineers has probably by indirection killed even more alligators than have the poachers. This animal requires a fresh-water environment, yet the ceaseless and inordinate water-carving activities of the Corps has in Florida allowed the intrusion of salt water far inland.* Another disappearing reptile is the wart snake whose hide makes an excellent leather, featured for expensive shoes.

There are many examples of birds whose lives as species have been obliterated or endangered because their feathers appealed to women as hat decoration. Many of us are old enough to remember the dire plight of the bird of paradise and of the egret. The roseate spoonbill was also nearly wiped out because its feathers appealed to feminine tastes. Now, saved temporarily, it again faces annihilation because of the destruction of its feeding grounds.

The mass killing of animals, first ostensibly for food and hides and feathers, then out of pure blood lust, is an invention of historical, not primitive, man. The majestic ostrichlike birds, the moas, survived in New Zealand until Polynesians (later to become Maoris) immigrated there and began hunting them around A.D. 1350. The world's largest bird, the elephant bird of Madagascar, lived in great colonies, with no predators except crocodiles, until the Malayans arrived in Madagascar and wiped them out completely in the ninth century. The North American bison, of course, is the classic victim of this kind of human insanity. Ernest Thompson Seton estimated a one-time buffalo population of sixty million. Not even the South African zebras, wildebeests, and other such hordes approached the multitudes of bison and antelopes of colonial America. General Phil Sheridan, shortly after the civil war, got up a hunt for the benefit of the Grand Duke Alexis of Russia, and this party of stately villains murdered some 12,000 animals in one day, not even deigning to stop and inspect the carcasses. Uncountable thousands such as these were shot for sport and never touched. Buffalo in the northern plains were killed just to destroy the food supply of the Sioux and Crow Indians. In 1889 Hornaday counted only 541 buffalo remaining alive in the United States. We now have some herds kept as zoo or refuge curiosities, but the gigantic days of the buffalo in America have vanished like an incredible bright dream and in their place we have cattle and automobiles. In order to put on a show of buffalo appearing suddenly over a hill (as was done in the first communication satellite program broadcast to Europe) an elab-

---

* In my book *Death of the Sweet Waters* I have called attention to other numerous examples of the self-perpetuating and destructive nature of this government agency.

orate and expensive roundup of scattered animals had to be carried
out—all in order to recapture one breathless moment of our fabulous
past.

Early travelers and naturalists estimated that antelope were
even more numerous than buffalo. Seton calculated a hundred
million. For centuries they furnished meat, hides and other articles
for the Plains Indians. Then came the whites and antelope steaks
were the best meat on the bill of fare on covered wagon routes.
Hunters took advantage of a fatal weakness of the antelope, his
curiosity. Disguised with buffalo or antelope skin or even with bed
sheets or waving flags, the white hunters got close enough to mow
them down. The modern antelope proved too sophisticated, after
a decade of such stalking,* to fall for such tricks, but the damage
had been done. By 1908 there were only 19,000 left north of
Mexico.

The peccary or wild pig (also called the javelina) a century
ago ranged as far north as Arkansas. Unrestricted hunting has
virtually eliminated this animal in the United States.

That noble animal, the bighorn, has been nearly extinguished
not only by shooting (since the curving horns are coveted trophies)
but by driving domestic sheep into the mountains to eat up their
forage. Legal hunting for bighorn is abolished, except in a few
restricted localities in Idaho and Wyoming, yet the poachers take
a steady toll.

As a survivor from the preglacier past, the musk ox (coeval
with the extinct mammoth and wooly rhinoceros) persists pre-
cariously in certain arctic islands and in Greenland. The high-
powered rifle, when it was made available to Eskimos and Indians,
all but eliminated the musk ox from his last stand. The natives,
who had always prized musk ox meat and fat, horn for dishes,
etc., had an orgy of killing. The ancient formation, in which the
bulls stand protectively in front of the females and the young,
was now a disadvantage to these poor creatures who were mowed
down, showing that ruthless overkilling is not a patented monopoly
of the white man. John J. Teal of the University of Alaska has
a project to beef up the economy of the North Canadian Eskimos

---

* It is remarkable that even such witless creatures as fishes can learn through
many generations to avoid the obvious lures. The groupers of the Mediterranean
can no longer be caught by the same simple expedients used on the south
coast of France a century or so ago.

by teaching them how to domesticate musk oxen. The animal sheds a cashmerelike underwool which is worth fifty dollars a pound. Thus the shy, noble old animal which the Eskimos once nearly extinguished could conceivably turn out to be their economic salvation. The Eskimos and the Indians have a bad record also with the caribou. When they acquired rifles they slaughtered the caribou, down to the last one in gigantic herds, often taking home only the tongue. (This senseless overkill reflects the savagery of certain predator animals themselves. Thus one great horned owl may decapitate fifteen or more adult common terns, although it will eat only one. And yet the tern's worst enemy is the common rat who eats the eggs and the young.)

One of the most beautiful antelopes is the Arabian Oryx, which has been nearly shot out of its native habitat by Arab princes, pursuing it in their Cadillacs. Some are preserved in zoos in this country and are included in the notable refuge for endangered foreign animals on the great King Ranch in Texas.

The living fossil, the tuatara, once lived in New Zealand but was exterminated on the main island when the white man came with his dogs and rats. All the ancient fauna of the Antipodes face extinction. Although the wallabies could graze harmlessly along with sheep on the pastures of Tasmania, since they don't eat the same kind of grass, the hatred of them by the Tasmanian sheep ranchers is as bitter as that of the coyote in Texas. The Tasmanians put down poison and endangered all the wildlife, although the poison probably does not affect the surviving thylacine wolves (marsupials). There are said to be 134 surviving Tasmanian devils (small fierce marsupials) living in an area of two square miles, kept as a reserve.

In Colombia the capybara, the world's largest rodent, who curiously enough lives on fish, is being ruthlessly slain for its meat value. They are herded by the thousands into corrals and clubbed to death. There is no sign of the slowing up of this profitable and ruthless operation.

Of all the food animals the most inevitably doomed appear to be the large turtles and tortoises. By the end of the nineteenth century about ten million of the great Galápagos tortoises had been taken by ships stopping at these islands for fresh meat. The females were easier to catch because they came down from the mountains to lay their eggs. The males are bigger and therefore more popular as zoo animals; thus there is little mating in captivity. On the islands, goats and cattle competed with these doomed creatures for food, since the tortoises are browsers and grazers. To top it all, hunters often kill them simply for their oil to which some women attribute rare cosmetic qualities.

If the great land tortoises are surely on the very edge of extinction, their kindred, the marine turtles, are swimming ponderously but inevitably toward it—a funeral cavalcade so eloquently depicted by Archie Carr of the University of Florida. Of the five genera, the leatherback may have more than a slim chance for survival, since his flesh is considered inedible, he has no carapace and no calipee (the fatty, yellow tidbit found immediately above the lower shell). Still, the eggs are considered delicacies, so he may eventually be extinguished by the same route that we have considered likely for the dinosaurs and other great reptiles of the Mesozoic.

Professor Carr used to believe that the green turtle would not be killed entirely by the fishermen who net and harpoon them for their highly salable flesh. He thought that effective protection of the nesting colony alone would save the species. But he believes it now clear that the capacity of people to consume and their ability to destroy are growing beyond the tolerance of the small populations in which sea turtles live.

The favorite, in fact the only known, Caribbean nesting beach of the green turtle is at Tortuguero in Costa Rica. With the advent of the Caribbean Conservation Corporation, protection of this nesting place has been extended to a stretch of five miles, and the "turning" of nesting turtles and the taking of eggs is legally proscribed on the whole Caribbean coast of Costa Rica. This proscription is about as effective as was Prohibition in the United States. Human poachers who "turn" the turtle do not try to carry away all three hundred pounds of this great female creature. They kill the turtle on the spot and cut out six pieces of calipee that weigh about five pounds wet. The makers of green turtle soup pay more for the calipee alone than a whole turtle brought ten years ago. Although the calipee is the primary target that is rendering these great turtles extinct, the assault on the eggs at Tortuguero is completing the destruction. The most important non-human predators are dogs and buzzards. Dogs are the worst, since they move in on a laying female and take the eggs as they are laid or prevent her from covering them. They are stronger at digging than buzzards. Other egg eaters are opossums, domestic pigs and white-lipped peccaries.

One could shoot the dogs, buzzards, opossums and peccaries, but the natives would still steal the eggs for the Mexican or Colombian trade, since these peoples put the most fervent reliance on turtle eggs as aphrodisiacs. A Mexican whorehouse without a buffet of turtle eggs to go with the frigid Margaritas (drinks, not girls) is scarcely in business.

One aim of the so-called *Operation Green Turtle* is to reestablish green turtle rookeries in places more isolated and more easily protected than Tortuguero. Batches of Tortuguero hatchlings are released at various places with the hope that they will grow to maturity imprinted by the smell, taste or feel of the place where they entered the sea and will be instinctively drawn back there at breeding time, as the salmon is drawn to its hatching brook. Yet, thinks Archie Carr, the life cycle of a sea turtle is so complicated that releasing pen-reared sea turtles may be just a laborious way to kill them.

Until recently the loggerhead turtle, which nests mainly on the Atlantic beaches and coastal islands of the United States, was believed to be secure, since it is protected by law. However, the colossal real-estate development of the beach areas has left few havens for nesting. Even where the beach itself is not built up, lights along the coastal highways confuse the turtles when they come ashore to lay, or draw the hatchlings away from the sea to be mashed by the thousands on the highways. As has been previously noted, the raccoons, who now follow man and enjoy his doings almost as much as do rats, are the worst threat on the loggerhead beaches. They can dig up turtle eggs even faster than can a dog, and (due in part to the fact that men no longer buy hounds and go on coon hunts) the raccoons along the turtle coasts are undergoing an unprecedented population explosion. Other predators of loggerhead nests are feral hogs and ghost crabs.

At one time the hawksbill turtle used to arrive on the Mexican coast in great *arribadas* of thousands of nesting female turtles. The Mexicans killed the adults, distributed the meat in the interior, dried the calipee and mined the eggs for the aphrodisiac market on a mass scale. There have been no *arribadas* for nearly ten years, and Professor Carr fears there never will be again. This turtle can't win, because it is the source of the best "tortoise shell," which has come back to displace the plastic substitutes, thus when the shell is prime and when buyers for the by-products are available, a hawksbill will bring about ten dollars.

In other kinds of marine sea food the harvesting has become so intensive, so grimly competitive that, as we have mentioned in Part I, there is no certainty that the once apparently inexhaustible oceans will not give out before the end of the century. The point of overkill has probably been reached for oysters, lobsters, sardines, tuna and whales. One must realize that the Maryland oyster lays about sixteen million eggs to the brood. If all the eggs lived and reproduced, the fifth generation of descendants from a single female would require more space than eight planets the size of the earth. Yet the oyster resources are being rapidly depleted by man and the egg or larval stage is preyed upon by almost every animal in the sea. Lobsters are getting scarce because the water in the Atlantic is getting colder every year. Off Maine the average temperature has dropped in the past twelve years from 52 degrees to 46 degrees. Because they are harder to catch, the temptation is to catch them in illegal sizes, by illegal methods and to destroy their mating rhythms. One interesting experiment by the state of Maine is to try raising the sea water temperature by distributing heated water discharged from the coolout system of a power plant near a cove on Consius Island in Casca Bay. If injected deep enough, this warm water would help the lobsters to molt more often and thus to grow faster to legal size.

Salmon long ago refused to spawn on the Atlantic coast rivers of the United States because of water pollution. Now there is danger that spawning beds on the Pacific coast may get silted up. A so-called "riffle sifter" has been developed for the U. S. Bureau of Commercial Fisheries to remove silt by a combination of high-pressure water jets and suction devices. In 1967 salmon fishing in Alaska went into a nose dive, probably because of years of overfishing in this area. The halibut has always been in danger, mainly because until a special commission made some studies, it was not known where the larval fishes were spawned or what was the nature of their migratory habits. The commission now rules on the number of pounds of mature halibut that may be taken. Iceland in 1968 was in a deep economic depression because of a sudden decline in the fish catch. The herring which traditionally clustered only a hundred miles from the coastline abruptly migrated far to the northeast and have been overfished.

It is not that men have not in recent years come ceaselessly together in bodies for purposes of talking about conservation of fishes and wildlife and have passed stern laws and signed sober treaties, it is simply that when the pressure of human voracity increases to a threshold point the laws are not obeyed and the treaties are abrogated. Thus the survival of whales is definitely threatened in spite of the existence of a voluntary International Whaling Commission. The great blue whale is practically extinct. Pelagic whaling (from ocean-going ships) is now engaged in only by Japan, Norway and Russia. Recently conservationists were unable to persuade the commission to ban the taking of fin whales from the antarctic, the commission refusing to distinguish between fin and Sei whales.

One of the most frightening and unexpected deliberate and insensate stories of animal extinction is the destruction of the Atlantic salmon by the Danes.*

That *Salmo salar* was somehow leaving the seas was first noted in Canada in 1967 and at the London Billingsgate Fish Market. In order to reconstruct this classic of marine horror we should note that the Atlantic salmon, like its Pacific cousin, swims up all northern rivers in order to spawn (that is, all rivers that are not hopelessly polluted, which confines him essentially to rivers in Canada, Norway and parts of Great Britain and Ireland, emptying into the North Atlantic). Unlike the Pacific salmon, they do not automatically die during the reproduction cycle. After being hatched in the native streams, the young salmon, as two- or three-year-old smolts, swim down to the sea. What they do, where they go in the period between smolthood and the age of sexual maturity had been a mystery. Obviously, if a large proportion of them were caught before sexual maturity the species would be extinguished.

The first clue was the discovery of a sudden increase of money

* Since the first draft of this book was written I was told in a conversation in Santa Barbara with a charming and fiery Danish lady that this whole matter was British propaganda and that she would prove it by forwarding information at her disposal. Since I have received no such information and since all the sources appeared to confirm the tragedy first prominently outlined by Clive Gammon in *Sports Illustrated*, December 15, 1969, I am forced to conclude, in spite of my personal liking for Danish people, that the facts are as stated here.

in the hands of the Eskimos of southern Greenland. These Eskimo fishermen had formerly made a meager living by catching cod, but in 1964 they were earning about $13,000 apiece in the three months between September and November. It turned out what they were doing, with the full knowledge of the Royal Greenland Trading Company (the Danish agency which virtually runs Greenland), was netting large tonnages of immature salmon which the Danes transported in refrigerated ships to the home country. Some unexplained change in feeding habits had brought adolescent salmon within the range of shore nets.

To get in on the quick buck in 1965, boats from the Faroe Islands (Danish-affiliated) turned up and, quickly thereafter, Danish fishermen themselves brought their 38-ton boats all the way from Bornbolm Island in the Baltic. The menace to immature salmon has since proceeded full steam. British and Canadian scientists confirmed by fish tagged as smolts that over 95 per cent of this catch was of less than seven-pound salmon, thus reducing a far greater potential of mature fish that would never return to the rivers to reproduce. There is no quicker way to eliminate a species than to kill off its young who have not yet experienced parenthood.

In 1967 another high-seas feeding ground for young salmon was discovered off the coast of Norway outside territorial limits. The Danes promptly moved in here. Now the great rivers of Norway —the Nansen, the Alta, the Driva—were being depleted of spawning salmon as had the Canadian rivers. The next Danish move was to intercept the sea journey of salmon off the Faroes.*

In May and June 1969 the International Commission for Northeast Atlantic Fisheries and for Northwest Atlantic Fisheries proposed a high-seas ban on salmon fishing, and in the voting only Denmark and West Germany, neither of which *produces* Atlantic salmon, voted against the ban. In fact the Danes have officially rejected the resolution. Instead they have come up with a devious explanation that "UDN," a disease that has plagued British and Irish salmon for five years, was responsble for the depopulation.

---

* As pointed out by Clive Gammon, nations have nearly gone to war over salmon. One cause of the 1904 Russo-Japanese War was the desire by the Japanese to move in on the Pacific salmon of Siberia, which they did. Although Great Britain is not about to declare war on Denmark, the question of other sanctions has been discussed. Typical stickers on cars in Scotland read *Don't Buy Danish Bacon*. They may even invoke a ban on the importation of Danish pornography.

(This obviously won't hold water, since the salmon has a five-year life cycle and the Scottish rivers did not show any infection until after 1967.) The Danes have been drift-net fishing for many years in the Baltic. From salmon smolts artificially bred by Swedes and Finns (none by Denmark) the Baltic Danes get half of the total salmon catch.

No salmon at all have been caught in British home waters outside the salmon rivers, because salmon fishing has been banned there since 1962.

But there is little time left for the Atlantic salmon as a species. Sir Hugh MacKenzie, director of the Atlantic Salmon Research Trust, Ltd., thinks we have three years at the most to end high-seas salmon fishing. Then *Salmo salar*, a beautiful and historic fish, will disappear from the universe.

Many biologists believe that the polar bear is on its way to annihilation, while others feel that it may actually be "under-exploited." The fact is that nobody knows how many polar bears there are or how they migrate. They have no home territory. They are inclined to be solitary animals, perhaps because when food pressures bring them together, they are likely to cannibalize each other, but an attempt is being made to attach radio transmitters to certain animals and thus spot their movements from the Nimbus satellite. Due to new hunting techniques, we do know that many more polar bears are now being killed than in the days when only the Eskimos hunted them seriously. For example, white hunters now use small, ski-equipped airplanes that fly over the ice in pairs to chase the bear down. In Norway hunters can charter yachts and travel along the edge of the ice pack near the Svalbard Islands, shooting bears from the deck of the ship. The International Union for Conservation of Nature and Natural Resources has put polar bears on the list of animals in danger of extinction.

There is another diabolic reason for the near-extinction of certain animals and the alarming lowering of the rate of reproduction of countless others. This is the enormous use of DDT and other chlorinated-hydrocarbon insecticides that Rachel Carson so eloquently bewailed in her book *Silent Spring*. Actually the situation is worse than the late Miss Carson imagined and we shall discuss the more recent ramifications of this self-perpetuating poison chain in Part 3.

Here we shall merely mention certain species that are definitely being destroyed by DDT and will inevitably become extinct in a matter of a few years.

The golden and the bald eagle are two of the most spectacular victims. Let us look at the way this comes about. The authorities decide to add one part per million (ppm) of DDT to a California lake to control midges. About a year later residues in the plankton or microscopic flora and fauna is at 10 ppm. Plankton-eating fish have 903 ppm and carnivorous fish as much as 2690 ppm. (This baneful multiplication is common in food chains, since the DDT is seldom destroyed but rather concentrated in fatty tissues.) The bald eagle lives primarily on carnivorous fish and therefore builds up incredible loads of DDT. The golden eagle gets a similar loading but through a food chain that starts with grain-eating or grass-eating rodents, or rabbits, where the vegetation has been treated with a DDT or other chlorinated-hydrocarbon insecticide.

Birds carrying an incubus of this sort are really in trouble, if their nesting habits are frugal and they lay only one or two eggs. The poison makes them highly nervous; there are more chipped eggshells, increased egg breaking and egg eating, suggesting a disturbance of the glands. In fact DDT owes part of its efficacy for killing insects to interfering with the normal calcium balance of the insect's nervous system. What nervous instability can be caused by the ingesting of small, sublethal doses of DDT has been shown by experiments with cowbirds in a cage. If you rattle the cage, a bird or two will flutter to the bottom, twitch and die, literally of nervous breakdown.

A widespread decrease in the calcium content of eggshells was noted after the massive introduction of DDT is the early 1950s, especially in the case of the peregrine falcon, the golden eagle and the sparrowhawk (all now endangered species). The extent to which DDT can invade the *marine* environment (due to washing down by rivers and by wind scattering) is shown by the large residue of DDT recently found in various species of shearwaters from the Pacific, eggs of numerous sea birds, coastal plankton and other marine animals from all over the world, including seals and porpoises on the coast of Scotland. A rather pathetic example is the Bermuda petrel, because once having emerged mysteriously from supposed annihilation, he is now on his way to certain extinction from DDT. Of the many oceanic birds that nested in Bermuda in 1609 when the first settlers arrived, the petrel (*Pterodroma* *cahow*) was probably the most abundant. Within twenty years man and his accompanying mammals had virtually erased this species and for nearly three hundred years it was officially written off as extinct. In 1951 a small nesting colony was discovered and in 1967 twenty-two pairs were known to be nesting on a few rocky islets off Bermuda. This total population of about one hundred made it one of the rarest of all birds. It is a wholly oceanic bird, visits land only to breed and breeds only on Bermuda. The female lays a single egg underground at the end of a long burrow. When not in the burrow she feeds far at sea, mainly on carnivorous marine creatures, such as cepholopods, and the petrel thus represents the end point of a food chain in which DDT can multiply. The extent to which even the life of the open sea ("blue water," as the Navy calls it) has been contaminated with this noxious stuff is shown by the fact that analysis of dead chicks and broken eggs of the Bermuda petrel showed high concentrations of DDT residues—so high that the species is estimated as having its second and (this time) final termination date somewhere in the 1970s.*

It is at this precarious stage in the struggle for continued existence of a species that the conservationist can often throw out a lifeline. The enlightened biologists of the Patuxent Wildlife Research Center in Maryland perform more of the species-saving services in the Bureau of Sport Fisheries and Wildlife than do their bureau mates who slavishly obey the hoarse yells of Texas stockmen. An endangered species is often safer in a cage, until more has been learned about its habits. By removing eggs regularly as laid, the female bird can usually be induced to lay two or more additional clutches for mechanical incubation. Mammal litters survive at a much higher rate in captivity. With many long-living animals, the average longevity in the wild may be below the age of most productive breeding.

* Although DDT and other chlorinated-hydrocarbon pesticides represent by far the most dangerous chemical pollutant, it should not be overlooked that lead poisoning is chronic among certain game birds. It takes the average hunter thirty-six shots to bag a wild goose. Forty-four per cent of the Canada geese examined recently in the Mississippi Valley flightway were found to be carrying shot in their tissues. Moreover, the pollution of a river with industrial waste can kill every wild inhabitant of that river. The Moshannon River in Pennsylvania into which mining acids are allowed to flow is absolutely sterile. There are no fishes, no muskrats, not even a snail. The wholesale carnage among sea birds, caused by oil leaks or dumpings, and especially by the detergents used to clean up the oil spills, is fresh in every bird lover's mind.

The federal bureau mentioned not only puts out a "Redbook" of *Rare and Endangered Fish and Wildlife of the United States* (1st edition, 1966) but the Research Center houses many forlorn creatures and sends its professionals all over the United States (including Hawaii and Alaska) to observe the habits of the harassed. Its help for the whooping crane has been much publicized because of the touch-and-go nature of this struggle in which, since the low point of fifteen in 1941, the number has increased at the agonizingly slow average rate of one bird per year to forty-seven at the Arkansas Refuge in Texas in 1968. Every bird lover knows of "Crip," "Josephine" (deceased) and "Rosie" and has fumed in wrath at the report of three drunken hunters near the refuge who shot off the leg of a whooping crane, mistaking it for a Canada goose, and every one of these bird lovers has wished that the hunters had got even drunker and shot each other instead. The Patuxent professionals view with concern the fate of honey creepers in the Hawaiian forests, the Hawaiian black-necked stilt, the Hawaiian coot, gallinule ducks or koloa and the Ne-Ne goose. In Arizona and New Mexico they try to encourage the masked bobwhite to come out of Mexico, where it took refuge when its American habitat was overgrazed. In the southeast they worry over the Florida everglade kite, the ivory-billed woodpecker, the dusky seaside sparrow, the Cape Sable sparrows and the southern bald eagle. In the west they watch carefully for the disappearing American peregrine falcon and the western burrowing owl, while in the east the peregrine falcon and the brown pelican fade away before their eyes, undoubtedly because of DDT and other chemical pollutants. Among thirteen species and subspecies now receiving direct attention by the Section of Propagation at Patuxent are three varieties of sandhill crane, the Aleutian goose, the tule and Pacific white-fronted geese, the Ne-Ne, the South American snail kite, the Puerto Rican parrot, the turkey vulture and the Andean condor.

Where a species in the wild is down to a little mite of a colony, simply an act of nature can wipe it out—the whooping crane in Texas, for example, could be erased by a late hurricane or an oil spill on their wintering grounds or even by a bad hailstorm. An anthrax epizootic could annihilate the small herds of rare tule elk, Colombian white-tailed deer or Key deer.

The Atwater prairie chicken, a near relation of the extinct heath hen, is down to less than 2000 birds from flocks of millions who not long ago flourished in the tall grass of the coastal plains of Texas and Louisiana. They filled the air with their resonant booming, but now, like the prairie chickens all over the country, they seem to be declining off to nothing. The Atwater chicken was by no means helped by Hurricane Beulah in 1967 and the accompanying floods.

The hawks have narrowly missed extinction, because any hawk was and still is often regarded as an enemy of man's chickens and of small perching birds. The truth is that the hawks most people see—that soar proudly—feed mainly on rats and mice and are the farmer's friend. Mouse hawks (called Buteos by bird watchers) include the red-tailed, red-shouldered, broad-winged and rough-legged varieties. All of them have short tails and broad wings. The troublemakers (chick-killers) are the Accipiters or blue darters including the goshawk, the sharp-shinned and Cooper's hawks. Unlike Buteos, they have long narrow tails and short rounded wings. They are elusive, stay close to cover and are not often seen. The goshawk is the largest and attacks large birds, rabbits and squirrels. There are also the harmless insect-eating, misnamed sparrow hawk, and the large marsh hawk. Most enlightened states, such as Maryland, now offer all the hawks complete protection, but it is hard to go after a farmer's boy who shoots a hawk with his .22 rifle under the impression that he is not only destroying a fierce hostile bird but a dangerous pest.

Often birds literally collide with objects that represent Western man's advanced technology. Aside from the swallowing of birds by the compressor inlets of jet airplanes, airport ceilometers under special atmospheric conditions can be the death of small nocturnal flying birds. About 50,000 birds of fifty-three different species were killed by crashing into the ground around a Georgia Air Force Base ceilometer the night of October 8, 1954. In Denmark in the years 1952–54 it was found that 35 per cent of all the white storks that had been banded for scientific purposes died in contact with high-voltage transmission lines. The automobile kills many roadside-nesting birds—especially woodpeckers.

Some birds flourish while others mysteriously decline. The bobolink has long ago disappeared from much of the eastern part of the United States and the redheaded woodpecker is now common only in certain areas in Iowa. On the other hand, birds that are nearly in the class of satellites of man, such as the house sparrow, the barn sparrow and the robin increase in number each year. Far from dying out, as predicted by the melancholy Miss Carson, the American robin is probably the number-one bird in North America, certainly exceeding the starling who in turn exceeds the house sparrow in population. It lives coast to coast, in both cities and forest, and is one of the most abundant birds in the vast 3000-mile belt of conifers stretching across Canada to Alaska. The mockingbird, fifty years ago an exclusively southern species, has found a way to make itself at home as far north as Michigan and Massachusetts. Certain wild mammals are thriving and it is possible that in sheer bulk of numbers the United States now has more wild animals than it had in colonial times. Significantly these abundant species are temperamentally similar to man; they are hardy, adaptable, have high reproductive capacity and a certain pushiness and manlike tenacity. One thinks of mice, rats, shrews, raccoons, opossums, skunks and deer. As the wolf dies out, the coyote in the face of Texas hatred has pushed eastward and northward to take the wolf's place. The deer has become a problem comparable to that of the population explosion in ghettos, and the problem has been made most serious by man's unthinking destruction of the deer's natural predators, such as the wolf and the cougar. Such predators often act as sanitary police in removing the aged, the diseased, the abnormal or the crippled. The Kaibab deer of Arizona, when the cougars and wolves were removed, rose in population from 4000 to 100,000 with starvation then ensuing. For several decades the famous "buck law" permitted the killing of male deer only, but the legislators were obviously not zoologists and knew nothing of the extremely polygamous habits of this animal. The surviving bucks never had it so good, and as many fawns were produced as before. Fortunately some of the states have seen the light, and in them the cougar is no longer regarded as vermin (or as a bounty animal) but as a trophy, coming under the game laws. Oregon in 1967 passed legislation which classifies both cougars and wolverines (another endangered species) as game animals, bringing them under the protection of the state game commission.

Although we are properly horrified at the number of elephants' feet that come into this country disguised as wastebaskets, it appears that in Kenya at least the problem is one of elephant overpopulation. At the Tsavo National Park they are considering birth control by sterilization.

It is interesting to speculate on how the animal kingdom as a whole would have fared if man had never evolved. Now that there are about three and a half billion human creatures on the planet, the rest of the animals decline or prosper to a great extent according to the way they react to this new force, an animal itself but in possession of such shattering power that it might be regarded in the context of the world of other animals as a natural disaster—like a nearby exploding supernova. Happily this animal (man) is capable of social evolution. For every knot-headed Texan or careless hunter or rapacious poacher there is at least one animal conservationist. Man has come a long way from the taming of the dog, the sheep, the horse, the water buffalo, the cow, the goat, the reindeer, the cat, to a stage at which man's ability and acumen can devote their lives to finding out how to save such a forlorn little animal as Kirtland's warbler.* Although he has wiped many animals entirely off the globe for all eternity, it is possible that in the future he will save animals that otherwise would have perished without his presence and it is even conceivable that he will learn some time to make animals that are superior in all ways to himself.

* This bird nests *only* under jack pines. These trees do not open to drop their seeds, except when exposed to a temperature of 300 degrees Fahrenheit. Hence forests are exposed to controlled burning to assure that Kirtland's warbler will have a place it deems suitable to lay its modest clutch of eggs.

PART III

Life Poisons Life

1

OFFENSIVE AND DEFENSIVE MOLECULES

The use of peculiar chemicals for inflicting harm or creating dismay among animals of a different species is of course basically as old as the existence of more than one species on the planet. A single-celled creature uses chemicals to kill its prey in the act of digesting it. Digestion is thus the primeval form of chemical warfare. Indeed, it is very probable that all the sometimes enormously complex enzyme-type protein venoms of poisonous snakes and the strange potions of stinging animals were regarded by evolution as natural elaborations of the process of eating. A non-venomous snake, such as a python, has an often difficult time in subduing a live animal so that he can swallow it, without its scrambling out of his mouth before the powerful stomach juices have had a chance to decompose it. He has to strangle it to death, whereas the viper need only inject it with a paralyzing drug and gulp it down at leisure.

Yet evolution plays the desperate game of offense and counter-offense. An incalculable number of animals and especially plants, with no quick moves or terrifying postures, can defend themselves only by chemicals that stupefy or kill, or at least prevent themselves from being eaten. As we shall see, the older plants whose chemical experience has been accumulated over hundreds of millions of years (the gingko ferns and the evergreen trees), have invented chemical weapons of the utmost subtlety to defend their all-too-vulnerable leaf tissues against the insects—that most numerous and aggressive of all animal classes. Defense and offense are in unstable balance in this interkingdom war, since the newer plants lack a hundred million years or so of pharmacological know-how and, besides, unlike the ancient ferns and balsams, often depend on insects for reproduction. Special alliances and non-proliferation treaties must be made with certain right-thinking orders of insects (such as honeybees and wasps), whereas the ferns and balsams despise them all. They were here before the insects appeared on earth and they needed only the wind to scatter their seed.

In a somewhat apocalyptic sense one can regard pathogenic bacteria and even pathogenic viruses as practicing chemical warfare and the toxin-anti-toxin Armageddon as the most fundamental of molecular confrontations, but for our present purpose this is too complicated a theater, and we shall cover here only the macroscopic chemical manipulations and tactics of animals with visible nozzles, fangs and stingers.

If we start with one of evolution's oldest many-celled phyla, we are struck immediately with the dangerous chemical guile of some coelenterates. Man is, of course, especially interested in animals that can hurt and kill him, and lately he has become conscious of the fact that in swimming in certain parts of the world he will likely be hauled out of the water covered with red welts and will die within three minutes. He has been poisoned by a species of jellyfish or medusa, *Chironex fleckeri*. If he swims at Miami Beach during early spring he may feel the ugly kiss of a Portuguese man-of-war (a semicolonial coelenterate) which puts its victim in a hospital bed with a feeling like the day after being hit by a bolt of lightning, a dryness in the throat, a bad stomach ache and trouble in breathing. The poison that he has absorbed is as lethal as that from a cobra's fangs, but the little nematocysts (the gun turrets of the man-of-war) have not been able to concentrate enough fire power on the man's large body. If the man had been a small fish, he would be long gone and digested in the rubbery shapeless interior of this ancient, omnivorous beast. The coastal men-of-war reach maturity during March and April, being blown coastward on southeast winds. In 1958, for instance, over two hundred swimmers near Miami were hospitalized in one April weekend.

The coelenterate's purposes are ambiguous (offense or defense?) but most likely he regards you in his dim decentralized way as a prey, because actually there is no personal decision, there is no "he" who as an individual decides whether you are fearful or edible. The nematocysts make up their chemical minds without central control, like sentries who have been told to shoot first and question later, or like hunters who have been instructed (throughout a billion years or so) to shoot the poison arrows at any living, moving thing. It is not unexpected that toxic weapons, invented primarily for getting something to eat, should also be used against large aliens, such as men, whose presence in the water or in an ant hill or a snake den is as unjustified in the script that evolution wrote as the appearance on earth of beings from outer space. Even the most humble coelenterate, such as the hydra, is well equipped with nematocysts. In the development of such an organ, an interstitial cell produces in its cytoplasm a minute structure like a vacuole. The vacuole is later seen to be a capsule containing a fluid and a thread. Clearly the nematocyst is not even a cell; it is more analogous to such artifacts as a calcareous coating on a single-celled alga. The discharge of the mature nematocyst involves some trigger stimulus, possibly chemical, analogous to smell, which results automatically in the sudden thrusting out of the thread, like the turning right side out of an inturned glove finger. Poison is ejected either from the free end of the hollow thread or a smear on the outside of the thread. The exact nature of the poison ("hypnotoxic") is not known.* Various kinds of coelenterates undoubtedly secrete different venoms. Nothing is so easy for evolution to arrange as a new kind of poison and, as we shall see later, the biggest problem is to assure the chemical warrior that he is safe from his own weapon. Unfortunately for the coelenterates, some fishes have found a way also to immunize themselves against coelenterate venoms. Butterfly fishes prefer a prey, such as a piece of fish, stuck in the tentacles of a stinging sea anemone, to the same prey swimming free in the water. Other cousins of this fish have developed a stronger immunity to stings and they devour the prey together with the coral animal that has caught it. Still other species disregard the stinging capsules altogether and eat coral animals, hydroid polyps and even big aggressive sea anemones, as calmly as a cow eats grass. As well as immunity to poison, parrot fish have evolved chisel-like teeth and they eat whole branches of coral. Divers can hear a crunching like a gravel mill,

---

* In spite of the embarrassment and horror of being killed by a jellyfish, the number of fatalities does not compare with deaths caused by eating poisonous mushrooms. The white or green *amanita* is responsible for 95 per cent of mushroom poisonings, since it is easily confused with the delicious meadow mushroom or champignon. Such plant poisons are especially insidious because vomiting and diarrhea do not occur until several hours after the low-molecular-weight dipeptides have irreversibly ruined the cells of the liver, after which a messy death, such as that from cholera, quickly ensues.

and know it is the parrot fish lunching off a coral reef. When this fish defecates it rains a little shower of white sand and, indeed, most of the snow-clean coral sand covering the glades of the coral forest has passed through the gut of the parrot fish.

But the hydras are common in fresh water where they do not have to fear such unauthorized specialists as the parrot fish. The hydras in a summer pond will eat anything they can get close to and sting. During one hot afternoon the insatiable coelenterate will eat thirty to forty creatures amounting to several times its own bulk.

In rather frantic attempts at developing an antidote for the fatal sting of the Australian *Chironex flecheri*, Australian biologists have found themselves in a labyrinth of big complex molecules. (J. H. Barnes of Queensland exhibits the pitiful photographs of a twelve-year-old boy, stung in shallow water, who died in hardly more than a minute.) There seems little doubt that, drop for drop, the venom of this particular jellyfish is the most vicious man-killing concoction on earth, with the possible exception of the toxin of the botulism microorganism. In the living medusa, the nematocyst discharge is set off by contact, by chemical recognition, by reflexes, by tentacle contraction and (unexpectedly) by the "mood" of the animal or the mood of its nematocysts. A small *Chironex* can easily be captured by hand (says the redoubtable Dr. Barnes, a brave man), using a firm grip over the apex of the creature's umbrella, but you have to take it easy when you draw it out of the water since, if its tentacles are stretched, the deadly little guns will fire. It is "inadvisable" (says Dr. Barnes with admirable restraint) to handle a large specimen this way since the heavy hanging tentacles feel a moral obligation to discharge, and this can add up to a rather sticky wicket. Dr. Barnes and others, concerned at the growing number of persons killed every year by *Chironex*, are experimenting with electrical stimulation of the tentacles, which appears to be a good way to recover a lot of venom without running up the funeral expenses. In order to reduce the embarrassment to Florida coast swimmers, David G. Cargo of the Smithsonian Institution is rearing a special breed of sea slug (a snail without a shell which enjoys eating the larvae of jellyfish. At this stage in its life cycle the coelenterate is a tiny cyst or polyp form clinging to a beer can or a rock and the slug can eat them by the dozen. If Dr. Cargo is successful, we may trade stingless swimming for all the East coast oysters, since the jellyfish is the only important predator of the ctenophore or sea walnut, which obtains almost its entire diet from the larvae of oysters. It is feckless to fool around with animal balances which have established themselves over the eons. Leonard Schultz of the Smithsonian has incidentally found that the best balm for stings by Atlantic jellyfish or "sea nettles" is the ordinary commercial meat tenderizer, well known to housewives. As we shall see, the horrible complexity of the Australian jellyfish poison and our present inability to identify its chemical composition, is not unusual and emphasizes one of evolution's habits: the more primitive the animal, the more complicated its venom is likely to be. (This axiom is true not only between phyla but even between species belonging to the same family or between families belonging to the same order. Progress in the world seems to consist of simplification of chemicals along with elaboration of behavior. LSD (a synthetic human product) is boyishly simple in structure—unfortunately—compared with the hallucinogenic venoms which can be extracted from the skin of certain ancient venomous toads.)

The great phylum of mollusks is not noted for poisons, except that under certain conditions bivalves, which pump in anything that will pump and filter, manage to accumulate bad food which in turn makes them dangerous to eat at certain times of the year. So-called "paralytic" shellfish poisoning from eating oysters, mussels or clams, for example, comes from digesting some water-soluble nitrogen bases that the bivalves have been wise enough not to try to digest but have put in storage in their systems and which have come from some one-celled microscopic diflagellates which the shellfish inhale at certain unlucky seasons and places. Such poisons are chemically bound in the dark glands or liver pancreas (a sort of jail for undesirable molecules) of mussels and probably somewhere in the siphon of butter clams, without change of structure. The bivalve will not have anything to do with such poisons, but leaves to such impetuous stomachs as those of men the unrewarding job of trying to break down and digest bad molecules. Some snails are poisonous to human beings, by paralyzing the skeletal muscles. The natives of New Guinea dread the bite of the *Conus* more than the sting of a ray. It is, however, only the fish-eating conid snails whose teeth carry poison glands. Those that live on other mollusks or worms, you can allow to nibble at you without trepidation. The Cephalopods have a mild poison (octopuses as a matter

of routine inject a crab or other prey with venom from their
beaks, although this is more in the nature of a condiment—
like catsup or Worcestershire Sauce—that of a lethal agent). For
most cephalopods the big thing in chemical warfare is, of course,
a cloud of ink to disappear into. A gland opening into the anus
injects "India ink" which contains pigments based on both iron
and copper, extracted from the animal's own blood. That this is a
superb product is shown by the fact that octopus ink, accidentally
preserved in fossils for thousands of years, is still usable and has been
used by an archeologist in writing a foolish letter to his wife.
Ink squirting is not unusual in the mollusk phylum, since some
small gastropods of the Aplysidae family, including the "sea hares,"
can inject enough purple liquid to discolor a bathtubful of water.
Here we see chemical warfare purely in the defensive mode—a much
more civilized and gentler type of obfuscation than the various
stinks, eye-blinding acids and pain-causing chemical insults invented
by animals outside the altogether admirable mollusk phylum.

2

THE BETTER TO STING YOU WITH

Poisonous apparatus designed for the carnivorous hunt, as in the nematocysts of jellyfish, are probably more ancient than the defensive prickles, stingers and the poisonous skin of some fishes. The tail weapon of the sting ray looks as if it were precisely designed to react to a man's foot stepping on this fish's back, but of course when it engineered this weapon, evolution had not even begun to think of man, let alone the foolish possibility that he would spend any time wading in tidal waters. The wicked spear was more likely thought of as a defense against the sting ray's primeval competitors, the sharks. The dorsal fin, over a period of millions of years, probably in Silurian time, was changed to a sharp knife, made jagged to aggravate the wounds it deals and was equipped with a glandular source of extremely stupefying venom. This is a very good dagger. Primitive men used to cut out the stinger and use it as an arrow tip. According to Greek legend (*Telegonia*) when Telegonus killed his father Ulysses without knowing who he was (one of those typical Hollywood scenarios that the Greeks kept coming up with) the patricide was committed with just such a weapon. There are freshwater as well as marine sting rays and they are found in Equatorial Africa as well as in South America and in the Mekong River of Laos. Everywhere the sting ray is regarded with great respect by natives, who follow the only prudent course in walking through ray-infested waters: they do not raise their feet but scuffle along so that the contact, if it is made, is a horizontal rather than a vertical one. Once you have been stung, you will not forget it, since it is an emotional nervous shock like being run over by a truck. The freshwater ray's sting is more localized but both are very tough on the nervous system. Man seems to be peculiarly susceptible as does the horse. Smaller mammals (say, an otter) are not very sensitive. Very little is known about the chemical make-up of the toxin but one exceedingly practical fact, at least about the poison that you absorb from being stung by a marine ray, is that it is quickly decomposed by heat. The application of steaming hot packs to the wound has helped the suffering of thousands of victims stabbed in the ankle along the Southern California beaches, where the animal is known as a "stingaree." Usually a chronic flesh ulcer forms and the only useful medication is cortisone or other corticoid drugs, since along with a host of others, mostly unknown ingredients, the venom is rich in histamine.

The bite of the moray eel is venomous but not deadly and it is better than being knifed by a sting ray or fanned by the tendrils of a stupid jellyfish. Recent research actually has found no poison glands in the moray. However, the danger of infection remains, since this fish does not brush its teeth, and they are formidable daggers full of decomposing food. The toxin, as in all congers and eels, comes from the fact that the blood itself is toxic and manages to be injected into the body of the moray's prey when the moray bites. One cubic centimeter of any eel blood when injected will immediately kill a rabbit. The moray raises hell with small octopuses and other fishes, but has never been known to go out of its way, like a shark, to attack a man.

The weever fish is every bit as dangerous as the sting ray. The dorsal fins are tipped with long, venomous spines which project from the bottom and in which the weever is hidden. Victims suffer terrible pain which lasts from twenty-four to forty-eight hours and those unlucky beachcombers who have been stung by both the weever and the sting ray claim that the weever's toxin provides a worse trip. The venom of the Mediterranean weever and that of the South American toadfish is chemically somewhat similar to the venom of cobras and rattlesnakes, which we shall examine later. The slightest pressure on the base of one of the spines protruding from the dorsal fins near the head of the toadfish causes a jet of poison to spurt a foot or more from the end of the spine. The weever incidentally is much more dangerous because of its capricious temperament. It shares with the copperhead snake a certain What-the-hellishness, in that even when a clear avenue of escape is open it may decide to go back and punish the hunter just for kicks. (Since this kind of behavior is usually associated with the use of venom for offensive purposes, it may be that, as is so often the case with armed animals and men, the very possession of a formidable, defensive weapon ultimately encourages its use for aggressive tactics. The snake's fangs are part of its hunting-feeding pattern, but the weever's poisonous spines, analogous to an electrically charged wire fence, may possibly be used in killing prey and in fact may have been designed for that purpose in the beginning.) The number of fish species that resort to chemical warfare is relatively small, but the ocean is large and there are many fishes in it. The "mad toms" are a small group of stinging catfish, where this time the pectoral rather than the dorsal fins have been sculptured by evolution into poisoned spears. They have a good many sulky relatives all over the world, both in salt and fresh water, the stinging spines being located sometimes on the dorsal, sometimes on the pectoral fins. *Siganus*, an otherwise meek fish that looks like a perch, has two stinging spines, one on each pelvic fin. The stonefish of the tropical western Pacific and Indian oceans, if you manage to see it, camouflaged as it is to look like part of a coral reef, turns out to be a hideous little creature with a head like a bulldog covered with spines based in poison glands. Divers who absent-mindedly pat a piece of coral may find that they have put their hand on a small fierce dragon, full of spit and venom. The scorpion fish (*Scorpena*) has stings all over its body like a hedgehog.

Most of man's troubles with fishes, however, have come from the fact that he likes to eat them and, in some parts of the world and at certain seasons of the year, this can be a hazardous adventure unless one sticks to a quite conventional seafood menu. That impulsive and all-too-dramatic people, the Trobriand Islanders, have as a means of suicide an alternative and less messy technique than jumping off the top of a coconut palm. They eat the raw gall bladder of the *Sopa* fish (a species of globefish) which acts with lightning dispatch. The story of the complex drug tetrodotoxin starts out in 1774 with Captain Cook's physical embarrassment one night after having eaten one of the forty species of puffer fishes near the Sandwich Islands and winds up with the isolation of tetrodotoxin as a promising experimental drug in the same class with curare. In the coral islands of the Pacific the red snapper and certain jacks (usually wholesome fish all) are reported to be poisonous to eat at certain times of the year and in certain areas.

This is undoubtedly because these fishes are at the time enjoying a diet which includes seasonal marine flora or fauna which are poisonous (a kind of *Amanita* mushroom of the sea), but the puffer fish are always poisonous, although some Japanese stubbornly claim that it is all in the way they are cooked. Many valiant modern Samurai have been laid exceedingly low from banqueting on hot *sake* and *fugu* (puffer fish) testicles, a mixture prized for imparting virility, but this method of attaining manliness is like winning in a game of Russian roulette. The annual death toll in Japan from eating puffer fish is about one hundred. In the puffer fish the tetrodotoxin is concentrated in reproductive organs and in the liver. One of the most astonishing chemical coincidences in medical history is that the same poison (originally called tarichatoxin) occurring in the ovaries and eggs of the California newt turned out to be identical to the tetrodotoxin of the puffer fish—animals separated by hundreds of millions of years of evolution. The mutual chemical is a nitrogen base of the kind called an aminoperhydroquinazoline. It acts on the nerves and is 100,000 times more powerful as a nerve block than conventional local anesthetics, such as procaine or cocaine. The first symptom is a tremendous blah feeling of complete muscular weakness. One finds it hard to raise a finger and finally one can't raise a finger or move any muscle because all the nerves actuating all the skeletal muscles have been blocked. In the hands of specialists, small doses of tetrodotoxin have proved useful as a muscle relaxant, with no after effects. Warnings against the poisonous puffer fishes occur even as early as the ancient Chinese *Herbal* (200 B.C.), yet people in land areas surrounding the South China Sea continue to catch it and eat it and die from it. (Why should this particular, rather complicated non-protein molecule be found only in one suborder of fishes and one entirely unrelated family of amphibians? And what good is it to these animals? One can guess that it is one of evolution's occasional trial runs to bet on the double-zero and see what happens. Having livers and genitals or eggs that are laced with nerve poison will not help the particular individual that is being eaten by a piscivore, such as a man or a shark. But the distressing results of such a repast presumably might teach a shark, even if it is hopeless to teach an Asiatic, that one should not eat a puffer fish or a California newt or their eggs.) Tetrodotoxin, having been identified and made available to biological scientists, has proved to be a promising paralytic agent even for insects. The insect heart continues to beat but the body tissues remain flaccid. The effect is temporary and reversible in cockroaches but in the wildworm pupas, the paralysis produced by a single injection persists for weeks without killing the animal. A strange, unexpected thing is that the pupa can undergo metamorphosis and become a complete normal moth, but it still remains helplessly paralyzed and cannot fly.

If one wants to be strict, tetrodotoxin cannot be regarded as a bona fide weapon of chemical warfare, since the damaging effects occur only when the fish is *hors de combat* and being eaten, but in the case of trunkfish, either aggression or extremely insidious defense tactics can be directly observed. If you place a boxfish, a member of the trunkfish family, in a tank, it promptly secretes a material that kills off all other fishes in the vicinity. David Boylan and Paul Scheuer of the University of Hawaii have isolated this poison, synthesized it and called it *pahutoxin*. The boxfish, called *pahu* in ancient Hawaii, was used as food without any dire aftereffects. It was taboo to Hawaiian women, a rather common kind of sexual restriction which applied also to bananas, and resulted from the custom of males and females eating apart. (The banana taboo has obvious origins in the phallic appearance of this fruit, but why the boxfish was forbidden to the ladies is obscure, unless it tasted so good that it was forbidden under the general assumption of many primitive peoples that women should have no fun.) Most trunkfishes are today considered a delicacy in some parts of the South Pacific and, like chestnuts, they are roasted in their harsh skins. The fact that such fishes are wholesome food shows that cooking destroys the rather delicate toxic molecule, which resembles somewhat a fatty chemical previously isolated from the Japanese oyster.

The trunkfish seems to be the only marine animal that can spread a poison in water. The fact that pahutoxin loses toxicity rapidly when standing in solution may be evolution's answer to the problem that the poison-spreading defender or aggressor (as the case may be) has of protecting itself from its own toxin.

3

THE SKIN YOU HATE TO TOUCH

As the vertebrates crawled out of the ocean they had a problem of skin sensitivity. A frog or a salamander's skin is more sensitive than that of a fair baby girl, and he has no attentive mother to wrap him in swaddling clothes and sprinkle him with talcum powder and gentle oil. One protection is to get back in the water again—to take a hundred baths a day, but this is no way to get ahead in the world of land, hence wandering frogs and toads conceived the idea (at evolution's prodding) of making their skin not only unpleasant to touch but definitely poisonous to insects, birds and other nuisances and predators. The same is true of the frog's amphibian relatives, the newts and unks. In addition to repelling predators, the skin secretions keep the skin moist and contain antibiotics that prevent the growth of molds and other microorganisms. Toad venoms have through the centuries become part of the human pharmacopeia, being at one time or another recommended for every ailment from canker sores to difficulty in breathing. The venom produces an action on the heart similar to that of digitalis and one of the "bufagins" it contains has frequently been tested clinically.* The toad venoms are made in small parotid glands near the eyes, so that the skin becomes poisonous, so to speak, when the toad cries. Another component

* One of the wonders of parallel chemical evolution, as we shall see in greater detail, is that certain insects, notably the monarch butterfly, protect themselves against being eaten by feeding on plants which produce digitalislike drugs. The difference is that the amphibian is his own apothecary, while the insect borrows the chemical skill of the plant.

of toad venom is cinobufagin which acts as a local anesthetic on the tongue and the eye, probably by affecting the nerve endings. Roman women used to try to poison unfaithful husbands with toad venom but had little luck, since the Roman men were very hard to kill. The venom from certain South American toads has been used, however, with good success as an arrow poison.

One of the most instructive of all animals, from the viewpoint of instant, contemporary evolution, is the Panamanian poison frog, studied in admirable detail by John W. Daly of Bethesda Naval Hospital and Charles W. Myers of the University of Kansas. One species *Dendrobata pumilio* outside of Panama shows a commendable steadiness, with little tendency to variation. In Panama, however, this species is enjoying a veritable riot of genetic explosions in every direction: type of skin toxin, color and behavior (such as extent of tree climbing). Sixteen populations show every intention of developing sixteen different ways of life. Strangely there is little connection between color (which may be flamboyant or cryptic) and degree of toxicity. There is thus even a difference in defense philosophy between these crazy mutating frogs. Since most birds have color vision and some gladly include small frogs on their menu, it would seem in the interest of safety for the frogs to have dull or protective coloration. The screaming yellow and blue and red colors of many of the populations of *D. pumilio* are self-advertising and they have apparently gone over to another basic strategem ("If you eat me, you'll be sorry, and you'll never eat a red frog again.").

The variety of poisons exuded by these and other frogs and toads and salamanders is baffling. Some individually have more killing power gram per gram than curare or strychnine or sodium cyanide. Batrachotoxin, a nitrogen base, is an exceedingly potent heart block and neurotoxin, lethal when injected under the skin of a mouse at two millionths of a gram per 1000 grams of mouse. Samanderine, a specialization of salamanders although contained also in the frog's secretions, is a convulsant of great power. Histamine is nearly always present, since it is as much of a universal pain inflicter among poisonous animals as aspirin is a general pain suppressant among men. Orthomethylbufotenine is a hallucinogen, like LSD, when injected in human blood, but it is uncertain whether non-human predators, such as birds, are caused in eating this stuff, to imagine that they have "found their identity," can experience colors as psychedelic sounds and can enjoy the mystic wisdom of the East.*

* I have often wondered whether the famous "longing for identity" is not perhaps a nostalgia for identification in ancient animalhood, for identity with the shark, the cockroach and the worm. Our sad young people assume that the identity they are looking for is a kind of forfeited manhood or womanhood, but it may be a much more basic and primitive *Drang*—the psychic cry of an animal in search of his lost instincts.

4

THE LOGIC OF THE FANG

As we have noted, the venomous fang of the poisonous snake is functionally a technique for feeding and only incidentally is a defense maneuver. Some carnivorous spiders and insects predigest their prey outside before sucking the chemically decomposed flesh into their stomachs, and the venomous snake's lethal or paralyzing bite is primarily a means of ingesting some food that doesn't wriggle. Having no paws or claws to hold the victim, the snake's problem is a rather serious mechanical one and, lacking his quietizing hypodermic needles, his only alternative is to coil and to squeeze the prey into insensibility. Often the python or boa can achieve this not by actually throttling an animal so that it no longer breathes but by simply scaring it to death. Men who are caught in the toils of such snakes are advised by Desmond Morris to allow the snake to bite them on the wrist and, then thus diverting the boa's one-track mind, to slip nimbly out of the stranglehold. It is noteworthy that man is an animal not only very hard to scare to death but comparatively difficult to drive into madness (unlike other mammals), and it is perhaps this indomitable mental toughness that has brought him through some precarious phylogenic escapades.

The notorious snake family Elopidae contains some justifiably fearsome fangsters. All the American coral snakes, who belong to this family, are shy, secretive, non-striking and dangerous only when stepped upon. (No animal on earth, including man, can tolerate the supreme insult of being stepped upon, thus stepping animals—especially big clodhoppers with shoes—are the object of instinctive resentment by a horde of ground-living animal classes whose peace or sleep they clumsily disturb.) The venom of the coral snake is extremely potent, belonging chiefly to the neurotoxic or nerve-destroying type. When a large coral snake succeeds in biting a fairly large exposed skin area with its short teeth and fangs, the chance of survival is exceedingly small. One may as well call for the morgue wagon as for the ambulance. Death occurs within twenty-four hours. When you are in coral-snake country, see whether the stranger has bands of red, yellow and black encircling the body. Don't shoot yet. Now come closer softly and see whether the head as far back as the eyes is jet black. If so, you are indeed confronting a coral snake and my best advice is simply to go in the opposite direction, retracing your footsteps, since the animal will not follow you, except with his flickering tongue, which is a sensory organ trying to find out what you are. If it finds you are a human being, it philosophically retires in dumb despair at what the world is coming to.

By far the most malign and perilous members of the Elapidae family have turned up in Australia and New Guinea. In Australia, sixty species of this celebrated family reign supreme among reptiles. Thus, quite unlike the situation in North America, the vast majority of Australian snakes are not only venomous but horribly so. Foremost and almost incredibly villainous is the taipan (*Oxyuranus scutellatur*) of eastern Australia. Ten to twelve feet in length, it carries at least twice as much venom as any other Australian serpent. None of the persons who are known to have been bitten by this terrible animal survived. A horse, bitten twice, died in five minutes. It will attack on sight and will chase a man toward his tent. Keeping one or two coils well above the rest, it waves its tail to and fro, flattens its body and suddenly delivers several bites in succession. Fortunately for the hardy race of Aussies, this creature of nightmare is quite rare. Next to the water shrew (the only poisonous mammal) it is probably the most ferocious animal on earth. (Its rarity is possibly explained by its excess of malignancy. When an animal becomes such a holy terror, other animals, its prospective prey, develop special sensitivities and tactics of evasion and in the course of time it finds it increasingly hard to obtain food. Although we commonly imagine that animals become extinct because of the pressure of their predators, which may be pathogenic bacteria, the fact is that in the majority of cases it is because their special food sources for one reason or another disappear, and they are not sufficiently versatile to find other ways of making a living.)

Of more serious danger in Australia, because it is not rare, is the tiger snake (*Notelkir rentatus*). It flattens its head and neck, raises the front part of the body, which it moves rhythmically back and forth until it strikes. No other land snake has such potent venom. Death in a bitten man results from the paralysis of the breathing apparatus. Luckily the snake is not very large and its venom glands are of modest capacity. If it possessed glands as large as those of a diamondback rattler, it would carry with it on its sinuous journey enough poison to kill over four hundred men.

The Egyptian cobra, sometimes known incorrectly as the asp, is probably the snake with which Cleopatra committed suicide. There are, however, certain true vipers which are also called "asps." (The vipers, family Viperidae, are distinguished by having extremely long and efficient fangs. When not in use, they must be folded backward and upward to rest against the roof of the mouth. The viper family in turn is divided into two subfamilies, the pit vipers, which have a facial slot and are well represented by various rattle-snakes, and the true vipers.)

The venom of poisonous snakes is commonly divided into two rough categories: hemotoxic or hemorrhagic (affecting the blood) and neurotoxic (affecting the nerves). Unfortunately this is an extremely oversimplified classification, since all snake venoms contain so many and such complex chemicals that complete analysis has been impossible. The venom of cobras, for example, is highly heterogeneous, containing a smear of toxins that affect the nerves, the heart, the blood and which release great quantities of histamine. Getting bitten by a cobra would theoretically be like simultaneously having a heart attack, gangrene, acute anemia and a virulent break out of hives, except that before all these symptoms have had a chance to develop, you are dead from the chemicals that specifically cause nerve blocks to the muscles and consequent paralysis of the breathing system. The cobra has a little for everybody. If you are an animal whose breathing mechanism is not easily knocked cold (and there are several), the heart poison will get you, and so on. The neurotoxin is *generally* the most effective, so the witch's brew is classified as neurotoxic rather than hemolytic. One purified ingredient, which however is not pure enough to be chemically identified, specifically acts on the motor nerve end plates, while the venom as a whole may inhibit acetylcholine output from the motor nerve endings or cause muscle contracture. Cobra venom also causes a sharp decrease in cortical (brain) activity. One is in a trance, but the respiratory failure is the official act of death and, in addition to the breathing muscles, may involve the cutting off of blood oxygen to the medulla oblongata. All snake venoms produce a tailspin in arterial blood pressure immediately after the bite, because of pooling of blood in the intestines and liver.

Mammals respond differently. It is perhaps unfortunate that most laboratory experiments with purified venom fractions are made with mice, since the mouse is about five times as hard to kill with snake poison as a more normal mammal, such as a dog. Nevertheless, the relative potencies of various venoms are found to be the same in the two animals and in man. The classical battle of the cobra and the mongoose is truly a life or death struggle, because the mongoose is peculiarly susceptible to cobra venom (much more so than a rat, for example) and cannot allow itself to be bitten. The battle usually ends when the head or neck of the cobra is crushed by the mongoose. Cobras are slow and are easily eluded by most animals with fast reflexes, including the young of the felines. The reason why more dogs are not killed by poisonous snakes is not any inherent resistance but the fact that the dog is an alert, quick animal with nose to the ground and knows where he is putting his feet.

There are three kinds of cobras that spit venom. It is ejected in two fine streams that mingle to form a spray that travels for several feet and high enough to reach a man's eye. The spray is harmless to the skin but if it enters the eyes, it may cause blindness. In the two inveterate spitters, the ringhals and the black-necked cobras, the fangs are modified into partial nozzles.

The mambas of Africa have a fearful reputation but this is based upon their habits rather than the potency of their venom. Actually little is known of the venom, apparently because nobody is anxious to collect the snake. It is very agile, is fond of climbing trees, and, like the cobra, has the habit of raising its forepart high off the ground when attacking. Its venom is peculiar in containing a large amount of acetylcholine which, although not lethal, causes dreadful pain. (An animal in the throes of intolerable pain may be as helpless as an animal whose nerves have been paralyzed. Thus pain may be regarded in this sense as a weapon.)

Among the pit vipers, the prairie rattlesnake is the only venomous reptile found in the northwest part of the United States. Snakes do not like to winter in country where the ground becomes frozen deep. The tropical rattlesnake is the most dangerous, chiefly because of its evil disposition, which is much like that of a mad dog. Its venom has a high percentage of neurotoxic ingredients, some of which especially affect the muscles of the neck. The victim cannot hold his head up. The sidewinder or horned rattlesnake thrives on extreme desert conditions. Its "horn" just above the eyes is a modified, overgrown scale and probably affords some protection against the desert's glare and blowing sand. There are pit vipers without rattles, including the water moccasin or cottonmouth, which live only in the Southeast and the Mississippi lowlands of the United States. The bite is occasionally but by no means invariably fatal to man. The copperhead is definitely a sneaky and disreputable character among American venomous snakes, since it snoops around and bites people when they least expect it, having a bad habit of lurking around human habitations. Fortunately its venom is not normally fatal to an adult human, although it is not a pet to encourage your children to play with.

The venom of poisonous snakes is what is known as an exocrine secretion; that is to say, just as in the skin toxins of toads, the poison was assumed not to get into the snake's own blood. However, there is now believed to be some degree of endocrine action of the venom, because of the fact that the blood of most snakes is toxic and for the same reason that the venom is toxic. The concentration is mild. Otherwise no poison snakes could ever be eaten, and many animals, including hawks and eagles, regard them as a tasty dish, even for their nestlings. The venom glands of vipers are located in the forehead and are composed of several parts. The mucous glands tie in with the venom glands in various labyrinthine connections, making plain the fact that poison secretion is an elaborate modification of the eating process. In the case, at least, of rattlesnakes, copperheads and cobras, it is a curious fact that the venom from a juvenile snake is more toxic than that of its mother or father. If you get bitten by a baby snake, the small *quantity* of venom and the shortness and delicacy of the fangs may save your life, but the power of the toxin is nevertheless going to make you very sick. This is evidently evolution's way of assuring that a very young snake, who is essentially an orphan, since its mother will never acknowledge any kinship or parental duties, has a better than even chance of survival. The change of diet may be important, since the baby snake is limited to preying on very small animals, who in general are more resistant to the lethal hypodermic than the larger ones. The toxicity reaches a peak at about six to nine months after hatching and in the case of the rattlesnake the venom is about twenty-six times as toxic as its mother's. Along with killing power, the juvenile venom differs from the adult's in chemical composition and color. When one milks enough adult snakes to obtain a glassful of venom, it looks like cloudy orange juice, while the poison extracted from the fangs of the young is colorless or the palest yellow, looking like a urine sample from a man who has been drinking beer all day.

It is not unexpected that one of the most exhaustive studies of different snake venoms has been made by Dr. J. A. Vick and his collaborators of Edgewood Arsenal, a seat of chemical warfare investigation research. On the other hand, a good deal of research proceeds on the theory that we want to protect man from the results of snakebite rather than to learn from the venom of snakes how to kill humans in a more thorough and conclusive manner. Professor C. Moroz et al. of the University of Tel Aviv from immunologic analysis of different snake venoms find that, in general, that that of serum designed against hemorrhagic cobra venom. than for a hemorrhagic or blood-destroying one. Thus serum prepared for use against the neurotoxic venom of the Russell viper (a cousin to the rattlesnake) have much more neutralizing capacity than that of serum designed against hemorrhagic cobra venom. This seems to be related in a general way to the fact that the neurotoxins are of relatively small molecular weight, while the blood destroyers imitate the toxins of bacteria in consisting mainly of higher molecular weight proteins. By using various venoms and the inert carrier carboxymethyl cellulose, the Tel Aviv investigators have been able to prepare very potent serums containing both anti-hemorrhagic and anti-neurotoxic antibodies for protection against the most venomous Middle East snakes. Some venoms, such as that of the Malayan pit viper, have the exasperating habit of preventing the blood from clotting, so that the victim is likely, if unattended, to bleed to death. The effect lasts as long as three weeks. Although there is local swelling and some pain, the anti-clotting behavior has the most curious side effect of euphoria and a sense of well-being. The victim, if he dies, dies happy. It should be emphasized that evolution, in giving poison-making facilities to animals, plays a good many subtle and sometimes cryptic chemical games. Venoms will vary in the same family, genus and even population of the same species, as we saw in the case of the Panamanian poison frogs. The chemical composition of the venoms of the jumping viper from the Atlantic coast in Costa Rica differs from that of the same snake on the Pacific coast side. The same is true of the fer-de-lance in the Atlantic and Pacific regions of South America. The chemistry is evidently far from an established feature of the animal and probably modifies itself, according to diet. In the end, the chemistry will be the kind that gives the snake the best percentage of kills in the animals that surround it.

Sea snakes (of the family Hydrophidae) are at the same time the most venomous of snakes, since their toxin is much more poisonous than that of the cobra, and fundamentally the most harmless, since they never attack a man in the water. The toxin contains at least sixty-one aminoacids and the special ingredient "erabutoxin." This blocks neuromuscular transmission by acting evidently on the postsynaptic membrane in a manner similar to that of curare. The extreme complexity and the variability of snake poisons make it tough to promise an all-purpose chemical means of curing a snakebite. Most serums are obtained from mammals, such as horses who have been bitten or injected and have survived, having built up anti-venom in the blood that may in a given case do the job of protecting a human being whose blood has never been subjected to such invading molecules. Some people, like the noted snake-venom collector Bill Haast, have been bitten by so many poisonous snakes that they act virtually as traveling anti-venom test tubes. Haast also works in milking various varieties for the Walter Reed Research Center. (The venoms are proving useful in certain medical emergencies. The pain of terminal cancers of the type that does not respond to morphine can be eased by diluted cobra venom. Venom from Russell's viper acts precisely the opposite to the above-mentioned effect of the Malayan pit viper and serves as a blood coagulant, useful in dental extractions. A fraction of the venom of the Egyptian cobra may become a key medicine in organ transplants, since it inhibits the body's tendency to reject foreign tissue.) Haast has the distinction of being one of the only humans who survived the bite of an Australian tiger snake. He was conscious at once of an incredible pain in his forehead, then blanked out. On the other hand, he found that the bite of the blue krait was similar to the middle of an LSD trip. In the hospital he could distinguish whispers two rooms away and felt gay, all-knowing and full of grace. Hours later in an iron lung, however, he felt as if all his nerve ends were on fire.

A lot of popular first-aid measures for snakebite may do more harm than good. Certainly this is definitely true of whiskey. On the other hand, some romantic scoutmasters assume that prompt cutting at the site of the bite will allow the "pocket" of venom to be drained. The affinity of the flesh and its fluids for snake venom is so great that simple bleeding at the site may do little but waste valuable blood. In the case of blood-destroying venoms, such as from a rattlesnake, if crosscuts are to be made, they should be done slowly and carefully, to *avoid* bloodletting. The intention is to drain off not blood but the lymph mixed with the venom. Mild suction is useful but not by mouth because it cannot be kept up long enough to be effective and introduces gross bacterial infections into the wound. The wound should never be cauterized or have potassium permanganate rubbed into it. The tourniquet is by all odds the single most important first-aid measure.

The wound differs with the kind of snake. The tongue has absolutely nothing to do with the venom. The most poisonous of snakes with its jaws held shut is harmless, although it can still freely extend its tongue. Coral snakes and the kraits chew in biting. The viper is apt to pierce the skin with many ordinary teeth of both the upper and lower jaw. (Most snakes have four rows of teeth in the upper jaw and a pair of rows in the roof of the mouth, plus the lateral pair lying just inside the lips. The true viper and the pit vipers lack the lateral pair, this row being replaced by the fangs.) If the venom is neurotoxic, immediate serum treatment is indicated, local cutting and draining being of doubtful value. In the United States only the bite of the coral snake responds well to serum. The embarrassing thing is that there *is* no coral snake anti-venom, hence anti-elepid anti-venom produced in South America for relatives of the coral snake should be used.

There seems to be little doubt that some animals are mysteriously invulnerable to the fangs of even the most venomous snakes and, as might be expected, most of such animals are other snakes. The Australian black-headed python has been known to devour over two hundred venomous snakes, being frequently bitten in the process. This is a magnificent triumph of immunology and suggests that the python is either born with resistance or quickly requires it, as Mr. Bill Haast did, as the result of non-lethal bites, perhaps by baby snakes.

Since lizards look like four-legged snakes, there is an extraordinary world-wide superstition that the bite of a lizard is fatal or at least dangerous. This has resulted in the stomping or stoning or beating or shooting of thousands upon thousands of inoffensive reptiles, who lead a blameless insectivorous life. Even against the big, rather aggressive monitors, a pair of trousers is enough protection against being lashed by the tails of these creatures who lose their tempers when disturbed. Only the Gila monster and the Mexican beaded lizard have venom and in amounts and type hardly as dangerous as those of an Arizona scorpion. The fact is that many more people in the United States are killed every year by the bites and stings of arthropods (spiders, scorpions and insects) than by reptiles.

5

THE HORDES OF MURDERING THIEVES

There are not only more species of arthropods than of any other phylum, there are more species of insects (an arthropod class) than of all the rest of the animals *and all of the plants on earth* put together. From a numbers standpoint, one might in fact regard the continued hot war on earth as a life-and-death struggle between bacteria and viruses, between insects and plants. Man has come late upon the scene of this planetary convulsion and is now also a source of titanic damage to all life, including his own. For one thing, he is fighting on the side of the plants, but only quite late in his sojourn on earth, has he learned that in the eon-old conflict between plants and insects, it is the plants that know more about insects than he does. If he is to keep the insects at bay, without ruining himself and killing off his friends and food animals, he must go to school (it turns out) to the most ancient of trees. The gist of what the plants can tell him we shall examine later, but, in the meantime, let us look into some of the habits of chemical warfare that spiders and insects practice in making a living and in defending themselves against attack.

In spiders, venom is definitely a means of immobilizing the prey for eating purposes, since spiders can only suck the prey dry— they cannot swallow it. Next to the venom of the Australian jellyfish (*Chironex*) and possibly that of the Australian taipan, the chemically rather similar poison of the *Latrodectus* genus of spiders is probably the most insidious brew on earth. This is a widely scattered group, the name meaning in Latin "robber bite," and the virulence of the species varies as greatly as the geographical distribution. In Southern Europe and Africa, *Latrodectus tredecimguttatus*, the *malurignette* of Italy and Corsica, gaily splashed with red as if splattered with a paint drop, has an evil reputation which probably is not earned. Farther east, the same species is mostly black and becomes the "karakurt" or "black wolf" of Russia. In India and Malaya, the *Latrodectus hasselti* is known by various folk names and is seldom liked, becoming the "katipo" or night-stinger of the Maoris. In the Americas the main species in *Latrodectus mactans*, the most dangerously toxic member of the genus, known incorrectly as the black widow in the United States (since it is not all black), in the West Indies as the *cul rouge* (red tail) or *veinte cuatro horos* (twenty-four-hour spider), in Peru as the *lucacha*, in Chile as the *guina* or *pallu*, in Bolivia as the *mico*, in the Argentine as the *araña del lino*, in Mexico (imitating the *Yanquis*) as the *viuda negra*, replacing the more interesting *araña capulina* ("cherry spider") and *chintalahua* of the Aztecs. A third species of the genus is now regarded as possibly even more dangerous, *Latrodectus geometricus*, grayish or light brown, known usually as the brown spider which is especially treacherous in that it looks and acts much like the common, harmless house spider which is distributed around the world. It has undergone a population explosion in the Middle West and Southwest of the United States but, unlike its cousin the black widow, does not seem to have invaded California.

The bite of the black widow is neurotoxic in effect, causing partial paralysis of the respiratory nerve center. There were 1300 reported cases of black widow bite reported from 1726 to 1943, nearly half of the total being in California. In spite of the chemical insidiousness of the venom, the milder venom of the rattlesnake has killed many more people because of the much greater amount injected per bite. Each year there are about 1500 snake bites of all kinds in the United States, about 5 per cent being fatal. Thus in a single year snake bites kill more people than are credited to the black widow in over two hundred years. Nevertheless, until the triumph of internal plumbing over outhouses, black widow bites were frequently a cause of intense embarrassment as well as pain. In an outhouse, which is a veritable city for flies, black widows like to spin their thin messy webs from under the seats of the privies. The ends or tie lines of these webs are sometimes touched by parts of the body (especially quite vulnerable parts of the male human). This gentle brushing of the web initiates the normal spider response. The black widow rushes to the site and bites the disturbing animal tissue, which is more than likely to be the testicles or the penis. During World War II so many soldiers were bitten by *Latrodectus* that the use of calcium gluconate became standard practice. Alcohol as an internal remedy is harmful and can contribute to total collapse.

The brown spider, in spite of its genetic relationship to the black widow, shows differences in both behavior and in venom. The females do not eat their husbands and they prefer a peculiar blood vessel-destroying toxin which acts like a case of localized gangrene, the blood vessels in the area of the wound being so thoroughly dissolved that a hollow scar results which may last for life. The web is commonly built inside of people's houses or garages —a tiny mess that would profoundly shock a true orb spinner. Since this spider is generally hanging around people's beds, shoes and clothing, the painful encounter is quite likely to be in the bedroom.

Recent laborious attempts to analyze the venom of the *Latrodectus* spider—especially that of the black widow—have foundered on the rocks of unexampled complexity. Various components seem to be segregated within the gland cells and may be incompletely mixed, even at the time of biting.

There is a good deal of confusion about the toxicity of the tarantula's bite, perhaps primarily because the European (true) tarantula is an entirely different animal from the American tarantula known in the southwestern part of the United States. The name "tarantula" is derived from the city of Taranto in southern Italy and the European spider has an evil reputation, being supposed to cause the bitten to dance and carry on until they drop dead, although none of these folk tales has been verified. There is no doubt that the true tarantula has a businesslike approach to poisoning, since she is in the habit of grabbing insects, such as the carpenter bee, and stinging them with her fangs in the nape of the neck, piercing the cervical ganglia and producing instant death. The American tarantula has extremely fine abdominal hairs. When they make contact with the mucous membranes of another animal (for instance, with the inside of the nose of a human) a terrible itching and persistent urtication result. Even the alcohol in which tarantulas have been preserved produces on contact with the human skin a characteristic itching and stinging. Unfortunately for the spider, these allergic responses do not occur in the case of the tarantula wasp—a mortal enemy.

Many of the pioneers and a few of the Indians of Central Arizona have always feared the *aphonopelma* species of large tarantula, but biologists, in trying to check out the stories, have always encountered an *aphonopelma* that either refused to bite human flesh or, when it did bite, caused no harm. Recent experiments, however, with the venom of this spider show that, if ten milligrams is injected into the groin of an adult rat, the rat within twenty minutes will have convulsions and will die within an hour. Postmortem examination shows distension of the stomach, damage to the liver and kidneys and peculiar spots on the lungs. These lesions are very similar to those caused by the scorpion *Centuroides sculpturatus* and the protein fraction of the two venoms are, in fact, identical. (These findings illustrate an exasperating dualism between popular experience and the calm skepticism of the biologist. Too often the biologist's instant tendency is to debunk all the folk tales and then to find himself in the wrong after all. Even the myths of natives should be accepted as evidence, especially when the natives have lived for many generations with the creatures they mythologize.)

The widely distributed country or hunting spider, *Lycosa*, has poisoned fangs which she protects by folding them within the case made by two powerful chitin columns. This surgical equipment, which is designed for stabbing the jugular artery of her prey, has become a multipurpose tool, since she can use it as a pickax to dig burrows. The legs take no part in carting away the dirt. The mouth acts as a barrow. A tiny ball of dirt is held between the fangs, supported by the palpi (or feelers) which are little arms in service of the mouth parts. Some spiders are specialists in prey. *Thomiseus*, a pretty spider, lurks behind blossoms and jumps out to cut the throats of honeybees. The *Epeira*, the spider so closely watched by Fabre, is the opposite and, instead of being a surgeon, she drugs or kills any small living thing she attacks at any point on its body by virtue of possessing a kind of all-purpose venom. *Epeira* does not immediately kill her prey with her delicate, remorseless bite. She poisons it so as to produce a gradual weakening and torpor, so that she can suck the victim dry before *rigor mortis* stops the flow.

Lycosa raptoria of Brazil bites with the same effect, only to an intensified degree, like the brown spider, causing gangrene. A mysterious, little-studied spider "*Araña homicida*" of the Argentine is charged with most of the human deaths from spider bite in that country. In some types, the production of venom is confused with the making of sticky stuff to ensnare the prey. Thus the spitting spider *Scytodes thoracia* spits a viscous gum from its jaws, usually at a distance of half an inch. The viscous liquid is produced in greatly enlarged venom glands, which still produce some venom *also*. One can see that this animal is not quite sure whether she wants her food paralyzed or wrapped in plastic.

The Arizona scorpion is definitely a dangerous animal, especially to children who pick it up and, after the sting, instinctively close their little fists around it. At Arizona State University there is maintained a "milking herd" of about two hundred scorpions in order to produce anti-venom. The scorpions fluoresce at night under ultraviolet light and can thus be easily collected. The two species of *Centuroides* that alarm Arizonians produce *neurotoxic* reactions in all mammals and, because of the larger amount of venom delivered by the tail stinger, are more to be feared than the black widow or the *aphanopelma* tarantula. In analyzing the venom, it is found to contain a wide variety of neurotoxic peptides and proteins, some of them resembling the incredibly potent toxin from the microorganism *Clostridium botulinum*. The species *Centuroides sculpturatus* is particularly vicious, especially in the case of children, producing paralysis of the breathing muscles. A noteworthy fact is that the venom of scorpions and of some spiders is very active when the victim is a crustacean. Since there are relatively few crabs and the like in Arizona, one must assume that the venom has changed little from the time hundreds of millions of years ago when the scorpion itself was a marine animal and used its venom to subdue prey in the shallow seas. Blocks in the nerve-muscle transmission, thus in electrical activity of the neuromuscular junctures, are obtained equally with the venom of the scorpion *Centuroides sculpturatus* and with that of the spitting cobra *Naja nigricollis*.

When we examine the chemical warfare techniques of insects, it is obvious that in large part we are dealing primarily with defensive rather than aggressive maneuvers. While a spider needs a paralyzing weapon in order to eat, a honeybee worker uses her stinger only to avoid being eaten, (or in a larger sense, to protect the hive from being destroyed). In a good many insects the weapon is not lethal, since the object is merely to tell the enemy—the aggressive species—to go away. The chemical weapon is made and housed in organs of the integument or skin, consisting of infoldings of the body wall. These glands are so variable in number, distribution and detail of form that there is no doubt they have arisen many times independently in evolution. They may be located singly, in pairs or in multiple pairs, or the head, thorax or abdomen. The weapon is usually a noxious gas that says "go away," but it may be evoked in several ways. Perhaps the most primitive fashion, one common in millipedes, is to let the secretion simply ooze from the glands onto the animal's own surface. (We saw this successfully adopted in the case of frogs.) In some caterpillars and beetles the secretion is evaporated by sticking the gland as a whole out of the body (as if one moistens a finger and holds it up to the wind). Spraying, with various nozzle devices, is a more sophisticated technique and among the arthropods who spray defensive molecules are cockroaches, earwigs, stick insects, "stink bugs" (Hemiptera), notodontid caterpillars, grasshoppers, carabid and tenebrionid beetles, whip scorpions and some millipedes. Insects that spray can usually aim the jet and economize on chemical stores. They can especially aim it toward parts of their own bodies that may be under attack or insult. The caterpillar *Schizura concinna*, whose single gland opens on the back of its head, directs the spray by pointing its head and may undergo strange contortions. In the whip scorpion the two glands open at the tip of a short revolving knob that acts like a tiny gun turret. Many of the millipedes have their defense glands arranged segmentally, one pair per body segment. A sharply localized stimulus may cause only the nearest glands to take the trouble to respond. A walking-stick insect may throw his spray accurately toward a bird in its vicinity even before the bird has made any overt move of aggression. Sometimes these sprays are accomplished by muscular compression of a reservoir, as a man squeezes a rubber ball. When muscles are missing, the reservoirs may be squeezed by blood pressure. Some glands are connected to the respiratory tracheae (external lung) and rely on air pressure to carry the chemical—a sort of arthropod aerosol dispenser. In the bombardier beetle, an explosion is involved, which we shall describe a little later.

What are these defensive chemicals? Unlike the venoms which

we have up to now been concerned with, they are simple compounds or mixtures, characterized by odor rather than toxicity, belonging to a number of common chemical classes, including acids, aldehyde, ketones, esters, hydrocarbons, lactones, phenols and quinones. They are almost always in very high concentration (for example, acetic acid is generally squirted out in 80 per cent strength). Some secretions may be complicated mixtures. The stinking discharge of the pentatomid bug *Nezara viridula* contains eighteen different aliphatic compounds, including hydrocarbons, aldehydes, ketones and esters. However, these mixtures are quite easy to resolve in the laboratory compared to the hellishly obscure, high-molecular weight blends in snake and spider venoms. Many cockroaches depend on one pure compound, trans-2-hexenal, which is also used but in mixtures by Hemiptera and one species of ant. Formic acid is secreted by ants, carabid beetles and notodontid caterpillars. Particularly popular compounds are the parabenzoquinones, which have been found to be preferred by some beetles, earwigs, millipedes, cockroaches and phalangids. The glands of arthropods producing the same or similar secretions may be very different structurally and obviously derive in different ways from the embryo. Evolution evidently resorts rather casually to a variety of retorts for coming up with the same product. More amazing, however, is the versatility of the same kind of gland. Evolution can thus also apply the same retort for cooking many brews. Thus in beetles of the Carabidae family, the same pygidial glands in various species produce compounds as different as formic acid, metacresol, parabenzoquinones, salicylaldehyde and tiglic and metacrylic acids.

The grasshopper *Poekilocerus bufonius* sprays a digitalislike compound, which, being a heart poison, is getting close to the venoms. And still closer is the salivary secretion of the reduviid bug ordinarily used as a lethal toxin for injecting into prey but also for spraying against predators. This contains at least six proteins and resembles snake venom both in complexity and in enzyme activity. Among the reduviid bug's predators who are repelled by this vicious spray are ants, praying mantises, caratid beetles, solpugids, spiders, toads, lizards, blue jays, armadillos and mice.

Ordinarily the defensive secretions act simply as skin or sensory irritants. Instead of springing upon the defending animal, the predators are forced to retreat and usually to clean themselves up. Among vertebrates, the mouth, nose and especially the eyes are the most vulnerable. Mice respond to a chemical spray from an arthropod by wiping their eyes and snout with the front feet, or by staggering away plowing their muzzles in the earth. Birds ruffle their plumage and rub their heads in their body feathers. The birds' eyes are cleaned by the nictitating membrane, acting like a windshield wiper. Frogs and toads, who are sensitive over the whole body, scratch themselves frantically with their feet. Carabid beetles and other predaceous insects brush their antennae with their feet or flee, dragging their mouthparts to let them drain. Small attackers, such as ants, whose whole bodies may become contaminated, try to bathe in the soil, rubbing their bodies in it while flailing their outstretched legs.

The success of the chemical defense may depend on many things—the mood of the predator and the time of the day. A rhythmic fluctuation or circadian rhythm of susceptibility of animals to certain drugs is well known to entomologists as well as doctors.

Some defensive maneuvers take the form of making the predator stick in his tracks. The gummy secretion discharged by Onychophora and some millipedes is a trap for ants which may struggle for minutes or even hours, and some soldier termites use the same tactic. Sometimes the chemical spray is effective for only the time necessary for the sprayer to make his getaway. Thus the beetle *Chlaenius* is safe from ants for eight to thirteen minutes after he has shot his wad. In this time he can cover about a hundred meters and get into some other kind of trouble. The glands do not automatically and instantly fill up after depletion, so the prudent animal will discharge only in a grave emergency and will shoot no more than the minimum amount required to do the job. On the other hand, some more sensitive and intellectual animals will remember the spray for a long time. After being sprayed by the walking stick, blue jays stayed away from them even when the insects were presented as food to the birds about eight weeks later.

Some insects get by with a strange con game. One of the tenebrionid beetles, which when disturbed stands on its head and sprays a potent quinoid secretion from the tip of its abdomen, is mimicked by another sprayless tenebrionid beetle. The imitator also lifts his rear end but lacks any defensive glands. Since the two both live in the Arizona desert, however, the sprayless one lives on the reputation of his cousin. This does not work in the case of some chronically hungry and insistent predators, such as grasshopper mice. In fact these mice will relentlessly pursue a real sprayer, such as the whip scorpion and, although given pause at each discharge, will eventually run the arthropod down. Grasshopper mice have developed a special technique for feeding on certain beetles by holding them upright in their front paws, while jamming them butt end down into the earth. The chemical secretion evolves harmlessly into the soil.

Some encounters are split-second decisions. The bombardier beetle, producing quinones, avoids capture by a toad by discharging a fraction of a second before he is struck by the toad's tongue. The toad instantly withdraws his insulted tongue. Chemically there is a good deal of sense to most of the secretions. In defending against large aggressive insects, the little whip scorpion uses a spray consisting of 84 per cent acetic acid, 5 per cent caprylic acid and the rest water. The acetic acid is a strong irritant but the tissue of most insects is protected by a waterproof cuticle of high wax content through which acetic acid itself could not penetrate. Caprylic acid is a wax solvent and also serves as a wetting agent that promotes the spreading of the irritating acetic acid under the cuticle. The hydrocarbons in the secretion of some Hemiptera promote not only spreading but the seepage of the active defense chemical, such as quinones, into the respiratory tracheae of insect enemies.

One of the puzzles of making and storing active chemicals is essentially the same one as to why our own internal chemicals, such as hydrochloric acid and pepsin, do not digest our stomachs. How do living cells make poisons without poisoning themselves? One of the answers may be that the gland cells responsible for the production of poisons may themselves never actually be exposed to them. Thus the millipede *Apheloria*, which produces the deadly hydrocyanic gas, has a gland consisting of two compartmented organs. In the larger compartment there is stored a compound called mandelonitrile, in itself not toxic. A smaller compartment contains an enzyme which can catalyze the decomposition of mandelonitrile to yield hydrocyanic acid. A valve shuts off the tubular connection between the two compartments, but at the moment when the millipede decides to defend itself with poison gas, the valve is opened by a special muscle, the mandelonitrile mixes with the enzyme and the mixed contents, about to evolve hydrocyanic acid, are ejected through a single outer orifice of the gland. Thus the final step, producing noxious gas, occurs not inside single gland cells but outside them. A somewhat similar and even more spectacular chain of chemical events occurs in the exocrine glandular apparatus of the bombardier beetle. In this case the final products are quinones. They are discharged with a clearly audible detonation and the spray is not only nasty but hot to the touch. Again there are two chambers to each gland, a large inner one containing the phenolic precursors of quinones, and hydrogen peroxide. Neither will react, however, without the enzyme catalyst in the second chamber. When the contents of the two chambers are mixed, the enzyme promotes the liberation of free oxygen from the peroxide and the phenols are oxidized to quinones in a highly exothermic (heat evolving) reaction. Under oxygen pressure, the hot mixture suddenly pops out of the gland. The reaction is explosive. The toxic end products (quinones) are synthesized again outside rather than inside the living cells.

It has recently been postulated by Professors Thomas Eisner and Jerrold Meinwald of Cornell University that the same principle applies to all glandular manufacture of active chemicals; that in those species where the glands appear to be only singly compartmented, the reactions which produce the final irritating or toxic compound take place actually in the cuticular ducts between tiny cells.

Aside from the protection of the chemical source cells, the defending animal must be able to protect itself against the molecules that it has put in the air. It must, so to speak, have a gas mask. Apparently this involves rather obscure specialties, such as impervious integument or detoxification mechanisms (which are not well understood.) The millipede which secretes hydrocyanic acid outlives other arthropods confined with it in a cyanide killing jar. The whip scorpion is apparently unaffected by dousing with the acid spray it receives when it is discharged. The assassin bug has a paralyzing narcotic; the giant water bug has a venom that can subdue small snakes, fishes and even birds. The ant lion as a larva has an ant-killing venom. There is a pretty copper-colored fly, *Lucillia silvarum*, which preys upon the nostrils of toads and frogs. The latter feel no pain, for they have been stung with a tranquilizer. But when the fly's larvae hatch, the hosts go blind and are eaten alive.

Soldiers of the nasute termites have pointed head nozzles from which they eject a defensive spray and in such cases the invader gets the full brunt of the gas before it spreads back to the defender. The odor also acts as an alarm, alerting more soldiers to the emergency, which is usually an invasion by ants.

Some secretions have antimicrobial activity and can protect against predators and microorganisms. The quinones of the flour beetle are multipurpose in this sense. A mutant flour beetle with less quinone is unable to prevent the nutrient medium from becoming moldy. This connection between microorganisms and insects is a shadow of the great ancient relationship (either symbiotic or deeply antagonistic) between insects and plants. Plants were on the land before the insects arrived and the two kingdoms grew to know each other very well indeed. The relationship shows up in some striking chemical parallelisms. The active components in the defensive secretions of arthropods also occur as secondary substances in plants. Two of numerous examples are 2-hexenal (mentioned above) and alphapinene (of some termites), both extraordinarily widespread in the plant kingdom. Sometimes the parallel even extends to the method of dispersion of noxious chemicals. In plants which release hydrocyanic acid, it is generated by the catalytic hydrolysis of cyanohydrin glycosides, whereas, as we have seen, the catalytic decomposition of mandelonitrile (the cyanhydrin of benzaldehyde) is used by the millipede *Apheloria*. Some of the oldest of insect repellents are derived from plants. One of the most familiar, citronellal, is also produced in the ant glands.

All of the arthropod chemical defenses we have discussed up to now have been made by so-called *exocrine* glands (i.e., glands that discharge externally rather than into the blood stream). Arthropods have also gone in for repellent substances in the blood on the philosophy which occurred to evolution eons ago, that "you'll be sorry if you eat me." Revolting or nauseating chemicals, such as cartharadin and pederin, are present in the body fluid of many beetles. There is also frequently involved here a dependence on the incalculably subtle chemistry of plants. When an insect feeds on a cyanogenic (cyanide-evolving) plant, the act of chewing is likely to trigger cyanide emission at the sites of leaf injury. If the insect has developed a biological gas mask, as many have, it derives some protection from the toxic vapors. Predators, lacking gas masks, will not attack. The digestive tract of herbivorous insects often bulges with plant matter, only partly digested. It is surely possible

that intact secondary plant substances in the gut act to repel sensitive predators. Many insects respond to aggression by regurgitating
some of the fluid contents of the gut. This may be taking advantage
of the fact that, while the defender has learned to tolerate, even
to prefer, plant tissues containing strange chemicals, they are still
repellent to most of his predators.

One of the strangest and most intimate of insect-plant chemical relationships is between the monarch butterfly and asclepiad
plants, such as the milkweed. Few herbivorous mammals will feed
on this vegetation since it is bitter with heart poisons of the digitalis
type. By using these plants as food, the caterpillars of the monarch
butterfly obtain essential advantages which have made the species
Danaus chrysippus a powerful and numerous one of sufficient appeal to men to have a statue in a California town (Pacific Grove)
dedicated to it. First of all, the monarch has a food source which
is dependable, since it is free from the munchings of most wild
mammals. This is a great luxury, since most of the animal world's
populations are restricted by the competition for reliable food
sources. It is probably the steadiness of this diet that makes for
the distinctive coloration of the butterfly. Secondly the monarch,
by absorbing into its tissues and body fluids the unconverted heart
poisons (mainly calactin and calotropin), makes itself nasty to eat
for birds, in effect borrowing inedibility from the plant. Not in-
significantly the latex of the plant has bactericidal properties, so
the monarch is feeding on very sterile food and is therefore, from
a bacterial standpoint, an unusually clean animal. There is, unfortunately, always a serpent in the Garden of Eden, and in the
case of the monarch it is not a reptile but a mouse. Mice pay no
attention to the heart poisons. Laboratory white mice, house mice
and field mice periodically wipe out hibernating hordes of *Danaus*
and even devour the monarch's food plant, apparently without
indigestion or heart palpitations. (It is a well-known medical fact
that mice do not react properly to the cardiac glycosides and are
therefore not good experimental animals for heart research.) The
monarch must wonder why in an otherwise safe and serene world
evolution allowed the appearance of such great lawless and insensitive beasts of terror. Certain other hungry animals will conquer
any revulsion they have and sometimes eat *Danaus*, including an
occasional gecko lizard and a certain large red dragon fly. In Africa,
where almost anything may happen, there are wasps who attack

the caterpillar, and the butterfly is sometimes found in the webs of certain spiders. African mantids are predators, although in captivity they refuse to eat a monarch caterpillar. Extracts of the butterfly's body mixed with cream are acceptable to certain perverted ants. Most birds reject *Danaus* on the strength of taste alone. However, blue jays and British jays have to learn the hard way and avoid *Danaus* and other insects containing calactin, only after having endured an attack of acute indigestion. Here again, the color-vision factor comes in and the "you'll be sorry" warning is reinforced for the benefit of the species. ("Never again eat a caterpillar or a butterfly with this color.")

This reinforcer is quite general and it is not an accident that all stinging insects have bright colors so that, alive or martyred for their descendants, they will be remembered. (The principle even extends to the plant kingdom, where the seeds of most poisonous plants are gaily colored.) Although stingless, the red ladybird is a very bad-tasting insect, reeking of histamine. Whether by taste or odor, the defensive insect responds to the song "Something to Remember You By." There are the blister beetles, the oil beetles, the "tobacco-spitting" grasshoppers and the "stinking grasshoppers" of Africa, the spittle bugs, the spicebush swallowtail butterflies whose larvae smell like decayed fish, the "lac" insect in which shellac serves as an indigestible and protective coating. There are also at least fifty species of poisonous stinging caterpillars which can leave welts on a baby's body.

When we review the stings of insects, we must remember that we are again chemically in the world of venoms, of protein complexity and of frequent confusion between defense and offense. Among the Hymenoptera (wasps, hornets, bees and ants) it is only the females that sting, since the stingers are actually ovipositors or egg-laying tubes modified into hypodermic needles. In the honeybee the poor worker (a chemically repressed female) can use her ovipositor only for stinging (invariably a defense maneuver), since the laws of the hive community allow her to realize her potential sexual functions only under conditions of extraordinary emergency, such as the death of queens. Associated with the stinging equipment are three sets of glands. One set secretes lubricant to oil the dagger, another the horribly complicated poison and a third an alkaline substance whose function is not clear. Lacking any further information than we have, the best slapdash treatment for the stings of bees and wasps is the injection of Benadryl and calcium lactate. Chemical analysis of bee venom discloses histamine, small peptides, mellitin, apamin, phospholipase, proteins, free amino acids, a histopeptide, some simple sugars and at least six phospholipids. Five of the eight proteins are antigenic (poisonous) to human beings. The venom of the European hornet represents a masterpiece of chemical ingenuity from the standpoint of causing human beings to moan and yowl. Biochemists, if asked to mix up a brew that would cause the most reliable pain, would include histamine, serotonin and a kinin or polypeptide such as occur in wasp venom. The added rapier thrust contributed by acetylcholine in the hornet venom is sheer evil genius. It is one of those hairy facts which run through life chemistry that acetylcholine is a necessary component of the nervous-muscular system for the transmissions of impulses, but if too much of it exists in the mammalian body, it results in terrible pain (and is therefore quite popular among venomous snakes), while if the normal acetylcholine produced in nerve conduction is not destroyed by an ever-present enzyme (acetylcholinesterase) the system goes into deadly convulsions. (The role of modern military nerve gases is essentially the destruction of acetylcholinesterase.) One of the wild stories of the Vietnam war concerned a Viet Cong guerilla who claimed to have tamed a swarm of Mekong Delta hornets and trained them to attack on order the enemies of the National Liberation Front. (If this is true, the facts have been either suppressed by one side or the hornets defected.) There is no denying that even honeybees can mount a concerted counteroffensive. From Africa it is recently reported that a colony of kamikaze bees, angered to the point of mass suicide, attacked and stung to death two dogs, their white human owner and his wife.

African bees are much more belligerent than those of the New World, as has been shown by an unfortunate experiment conceived by Professor Warwick Kerr of the Ribeirão Prêto School of Medicine in São Paulo State. Hoping to get more productivity by crossbreeding African bees (which yield more honey) with the gentle native species, he imported 170 African queens from Tanganyika. Five years ago the offspring escaped from the apiary, attacking in swarms and invading domestic hives. A six-year-old boy was killed immediately. These ferocious bees have now started to take over all of South America and it is to be hoped that they will not decide to emigrate northward. At the time of Kerr's fateful experiment, Brazil was becoming the third largest honey producer after Russia and the United States. However, the ferocious descendants of the African immigrants have driven so many honey producers out of business that by 1967 Brazil had become a honey importer.

Ants have the advantage of a non-self-destructive armory of hunting and defensive chemical stores. Just as in the case of snakes, a sting-bearing ant will normally use its venom to kill the prey it tracks down for food but if the nest is attacked the poison is systematically applied against the invader. In the various subfamilies of ants, the most primitive have specific stingers with complicated venom. As ant life becomes more sophisticated, as among the advanced Formicinae, such armament gets to be obsolete, perhaps because the life habits are diversified. Foraging may be either solitary or along odor trails and the ants may live in underground galleries, in mound nests or even in trees. Although they no longer rely on a stinger, they are still protected by a secretion produced by the old sting gland. This is usually formic acid, an exceedingly simple chemical, which used to be recovered in the seventeenth century simply by dry-roasting the ants of this family. Already the retreat from complex venom had been started by the intermediate families, such as the Myrmicinae, who no longer relied on killing other little animals for food but tended to feed on plants at sites marked by odor trails, secreted by the Dufour glands of the abdomen. In the Dolichoderivae, the development of venom glands (originally outgrowths of the salivary gland system and in larvae functioning as silkmakers) and of Dufour glands in the belly was neglected in favor of a revolutionary growth of glands in the anus, which no longer have the remotest body connection with the old venom system of the archaic ants. As might be appreciated, when one shifts chemical warfare equipment from the head to the hind end, the function shifts in a parallel way from aggressive hunting to alarm and defense. When the Formicinae adopted formic acid as their weapon, they not only lost the ancient stinger design but resorted to spraying. It is significant that in the phylogenetically older species of ants the venom is roughly like that of wasps and bees, showing that the formicine ant, as a relative newcomer on earth, descending from a wasplike ancestor, has probably evolved faster than any other insect, both in social habits and chemical simplification. Both formic and acetic acids are used, however, as defensive gases (as we have seen) in a wide range of arthropods. Not unexpectedly, some of the chemical weapons of ants are insect repellents and even insecticides worthy of man's evaluation. Iridomyrmecin, isolated from the anal glands of the Argentine ant, has definite "knock-down" power for many beetles and flies. The popular aldehyde, 2-hexenal, favored by most cockroaches and by many other stinking bugs, has been identified in at least one ant species. The occurrence of dolichodial, a complex compound, in some ants and also in plasmids (a nematode creation) shows once again that even phyla separated by hundreds of millions of years of evolutionary time may resort to the same synthetic chemistry in exocrine glands.

6

THE WISDOM OF TREES

It can now safely be assumed that practically all of the complicated compounds that plants synthesize and which seem to have no useful part in their life cycles (alkaloids, terpenes, etc.) are chemical-warfare agents to protect plants against insects. Some of these compounds, especially those made by plants relatively young in evolution, have not been especially successful since they have relied on smells, indigestion, heart palpitations, etc. and various insects have been able to develop mutant strains with iron stomachs, tolerant noses and cold invulnerable hearts. The plants that really hit the jackpot were those that invented such a smooth, insidious and indefensible chemical tactic that the insects could avoid it only by ceasing entirely to become insects. It is only in recent years that such genial biologists as Carroll Williams at Harvard have begun to put together the whole of this incredible 250-million-year-old plot of tree against insect. The discovery involves a detective story chapter called "The Strange Case of the Paper Factor."

Appropriate first is a preliminary review of the hormone chemistry of the larval insect. In order to get through the usual stages of larvahood, the insect must be infused from its own endocrine system by Juvenile Hormone (JH), which prevents premature metamorphosis into the adult. JH, however, must be absent from the insect eggs and its flow must stop and other hormones take over when the larva is to become an adult. (As an adult, incidentally, the insect again needs some JH.) If the JH is still there at the time of metamorphosis, the larva cannot shed its last skin and dies before reaching maturity. In effect, Juvenile Hormone present at the wrong time causes the insects to kill themselves. Note the matchless cunning of thus introducing JH at a correct moment of time: the insects cannot develop resistance (as mosquitoes, for example, have developed resistance to DDT) since a resistance to this hormone would also be an automatic way for the insect to commit suicide. It is the final trap—the introduction of external JH to the insect *at the wrong time*. Ancient trees learned to do this so long ago that man or monkey was then not even a twinkle in evolution's eye. For obscure and complex reasons, an actual Juvenile Hormone in any reasonable purity can only be extracted at the present time from one live insect, the caterpillar of the male *Cecropia* (silkworm) and its relative, *Cynthia*. Herbert Röller identified the active chemical as the methyl ester of the epoxide of a previously unknown fatty acid derivative. One gram would be enough to kill about one billion meal worms in infancy. However, synthesis from any known plentiful raw material is not at present feasible. The most potent substitute is obtained by the rough method of crude oil expressed from the Cecropia caterpillars. This proves to be effective in killing all kinds of insects, but this is not what we want, since only about 0.1 per cent of all the billion-times-a-billion insects alive on earth at any one time are doing man and his crops any harm. Complete or massive random insect extinction would be planetary disaster.

That *specific* Juvenile Hormones, lethal to only selected insects, exist in nature was discovered in some attempts by Carroll Williams and his associates to rear the European bug *Pyrrhocoris opterus*, which Karel Sláma in Czechoslovakia had made a popular experimental insect, and which belongs to a family which includes some of the most destructive pests of the cotton plant. Exasperatingly all the larvae of this bug died in the Harvard laboratory before reaching maturity. Their manner of death was exactly what would be expected of insects experiencing excessive exposure to Juvenile Hormone. Where in the world was this substance coming from? After checking all their procedures, Williams and his associates concluded that it could only be the paper toweling used in the rearing jars. Almost any paper of American origin was found to have the same effect, while paper of European or Japanese manufacture did not embarrass the developing bugs in the least. Paper of this sort in Canada and the northern United States is made by pulping the balsam fir and it appears that the Juvenile Hormone, which was killing Williams' young bugs, is produced by this tree and survives the papermaking process sufficiently intact to execute the original function that the tree had in mind. It now seems likely that the "paper factor" is thus a memento of the Juvenile Hormone of a former natural enemy of the balsam fir tree—a pyrrhocorid predator that is either extinct or has learned to avoid balsam firs. Evergreen trees, such as the balsam, are very ancient and in fact were here before the insects arrived. They are pollinated by the wind and thus had no reason to sign treaties with the insects, whom they detested on all counts. Consider the stroke of wisdom, the incredible chemical skill and also the conservative politics of a tree that imitates an animal hormone and continues to imitate it perhaps a hundred million years after the tree has conquered the insect.

Williams' "paper factor" is only one of thousands of terpenoid chemicals that trees synthesize for no obvious reason, and it now seems likely that they will all turn out to be related to the Juvenile Hormones of specific insect pests, many of them extinct but many still existing as descendants, now busy attacking younger, less sagacious vegetation, such as cotton, corn, beans, fruit orchards, vegetable-truck crops and even the less ancient timber trees, such as pine and Douglas fir. Carroll Williams aptly has called Juvenile Hormones the Third Generation of Pesticides. (We shall see later how desperately we need a new generation.) Not long after his discovery of the "paper factor," he found in Brazil a whole river of insecticides that as an agricultural source may, in a better century than ours, rival ammonia, petroleum and coal. This is the Amazon tributary, the Rio Negro, which runs black and aromatic because, although draining an area almost as big as Texas, it does not originate in the mountains but flows across flatland, jungle and swamps, dissolving unimaginable quantities of plant juices and tree saps. Insects avoid this river. An on-the-spot experiment, in which an extract of this dark water was injected into immature cockroaches, killed all of them before they reached sexual maturity. Apparently the only reason that all insects are not wiped out in the Rio Negro area is that not all of them touch the river's dusky broth.

Some younger and comparatively defenseless plants show signs of developing chemical weapons and, if left to their own devices before the insects could destroy them, might in a few dozens of millions of years be self-reliant. The trouble is that trees take so much time to get things done and in the meantime generation after generation of tree-destructive insects can swarm to the attack. The plants of the citrus and parsley family, although unrelated, have in common certain essential oils that are destructive or at least repellent to many insects. The female "majagua" tree has something, probably a Juvenile Hormone, that prevents the maturation of the boll weevil. The ginkgo or maidenhair is probably the most ancient of living trees and evolved from the seed ferns during Permian times. It is now found only in East Asia and is used for making fancy chessmen and lacquer ware. These trees do not reproduce until they are twenty years old but they continue fruitful until they are over a thousand years of age. They are resistant to insects, but it is not known whether this is because they have developed the ancient balsam's Juvenile Hormone or have possibly gone beyond that gambit. Japanese beetles at any rate will die of starvation rather than eat the ginkgo's leaves. The bracken fern produces insect hormones, but they are of the molt-promoting type (ecdysones) rather than Juvenile Hormone. The bracken is the first plant found to contain both of the major ecdysones and the first-known plant to be a source of alpha-ecdysone. This is an unexpected switch. Although conceivably these compounds take part in the actual growth processes of the fern itself, it is significant that the bracken is relatively immune to insect attack. It may be that causing an insect to molt, when the insect's hormonal clock has not struck the hour, may result in monsters or in death. ecdysonelike compounds has been found actually to inhibit growth system of an insect involves the Brain Hormone (not isolated), the Juvenile Hormone from the corpora allata and the ecdysone molting hormones from the prothoracic gland, which are steroids and have been identified and sythesized. The ingestion of certain ecdysonelike compounds has been found actually to inhibit growth and development in several species of insects. In following up on the bracken fern lead, the Anti-Locust Research Center in London finds that when desert locusts are fed on bracken as a sole diet, molting, growth and development are not affected. The animal has found a way to neutralize the active ecdysone and to pass it through the gut, undigested. The locust will only respond when the extract of the fern is injected into the blood.

Some promising work has been reported by William S. Bowers of the U. S. Department of Agriculture in simulating the effect of untimely Juvenile Hormones by certain "synergists" that are used to increase the toxicity of insecticides such as pyrethrum and the carbamates. Thus sesoxane, piperonyl butoxide and farnesyl ether, which are not even terpene compounds, act like Juvenile Hormones when applied to the meal worm and the milkweed bug. This somewhat opens up the field, since such chemicals are at least commercially available. Furthermore, Sláma has shown that synthetic hormones of a different sort will go a lot farther than one bug. Working with linden bugs, in which the male mates twice a day, he found that if the male is injected with this specific hormone it will not only make this male's mate sterile, but when she passes it along in mating with another untreated male, he in turn will render another female sterile, and so on, until finally the hormone becomes too dilute. The hormone thus gets around like the gonococcus of a venereal disease and the sexual promiscuity of the linden bugs becomes their doom.

7

MAN AS A POISONOUS SKUNK

Most mammals are very chemically conscious, but few of them engage in outright chemical warfare. The short-tailed shrew poisons its prey with a special secretion from the salivary glands flowing into the wounds made by the lower incisors. This slows the heart-beat and the breathing of the victim, making it possible for this very small vicious animal to kill and eat prey many times its size. The toxin is not unlike cobra venom. Perhaps the only other definitely venomous mammal known is the monotreme which has a poisonous spur on its leg.

Defensive warfare is, of course, brilliantly executed by the skunk who uses in his musk very simple sulfur compounds, mercaptans, which one can detect near any petroleum refinery which operates on crude oil of high sulfur content. With one gland on each side of the anus, the skunk seldom misses its target. Looking straight at the enemy, it can bring its rear end back around and fire directly at him; the vents of the glands protrude and usually both barrels are discharged at the same time. (A rather eerie property of the fluid is that it is phosphorescent at night, like a tracer bullet.) This caper is purely defensive and the liquid spray will cause no blindness or other permanent harm. Moreover, the skunk always gives warning. He stamps, pats the ground with stiffened front legs, may click his teeth, growl or hiss. If the enemy continues to threaten, up goes the bushy tail. Like a flash the skunk whips into a U-shape, with head and rear to the enemy. Firing begins. Swiftly he shoots to right, to left, in front or above. The two fine streams of oily, yellowish musk oil unite a foot away into one spray. The marksmanship is astonishingly accurate up to twelve feet. (If you are caught in this barrage, the best way to wash is with lead-free naphtha. Wash the clothes with ammonia, calcium chloride or dilute bleaching powder—sodium hypochlorite. Finish off with oil of citronella or oil of bergamot.)

Alas, for the chemicals with which man inundates the planet, there are no such simple ways of cleaning up! In two other books* I have considered at length the difficult poisons, respectively, of man-created air and water pollution. Still more dangerous (as the late, great Rachel Carson realized) are the stable venoms that man has invented for killing insects and, to no one's astonishment, the rhetorical defense postures of the manufacturers of established pesticides, such as DDT and other chlorinated hydrocarbons, are precisely similar to those who pollute the air and the water: anybody who objects to DDT is on the side of the insects or for the fish or for the ducks instead of for hungry human beings (as anybody who is against smog is against honest fuel-oil manufacturers or against the beautiful automobile industry which has made us the superior beings that we are). Even when we are confronted by a catastrophe of pollution, such as the beaching of the oil tanker, the *Torrey Canyon*, or the Santa Barbara gusher, we manage immediately to do all the wrong things. In the splash zone of the Cornwall beaches the use of detergents in a witless attempt to emulsify the oil killed off all the limpets, which normally graze the rocks clean, with the result that the shoreline became 100 per cent covered with seaweed. Because of loss of a food *that had been established for a million years or so*, thousands of puffins, cormorants, razorbills, guillemots and other Cornish birds disappeared—some of them possibly forever.

Dichlorodiphenyltrichloroethane (DDT) is a definite nerve poison for most insects. It blocks the specific enzyme which normally controls the excitation of electric current along nerve pathways. The insect is thrown into violent and continuous muscular spasms which end with death. The discovery of this fact some twenty-five years ago created an enormous industry which is not about to give up its equity as the result of later mournful revelations that (1) many insects, such as mosquitoes, develop complete immunity to the poisons in a few generations just as many bacteria developed resistance to sulfanilamide; and (2) the side effects

* *The Breath of Life*, New York, W. W. Norton, 1965; *Death of the Sweet Waters*, New York, W. W. Norton, 1966.

of DDT in destroying beneficial insects, fish and other marine food animals, birds and in endangering the health of mankind have made use of DDT and other chlorinated hydrocarbon insecticides (Dieldrin, Aldrin, Heptochlor, Endrin, Lindane, Chlordane, etc.) a plain case of planetary murder and self-delusion. Rather than continuing the present course it would actually be much better to go back to the old "first-generation" pest killers, such as kerosene for mosquito ponds, lead arsenate for insects that chew and nicotine and rotenone for those that suck. *Much* better would be the aggressive follow-up of various new approaches, one of which (Juvenile Hormones) we have already described and others that we shall discuss later.

The ravages of DDT are world wide in every sense, affecting not only bald eagles in Montana but penguins and crab-eater seals in the waters of Antarctica. Part of this infernal ubiquity is due to the very long life of the molecule, which loses only half its potency over a period of atmospheric or marine exposure of fifteen years. It is carried by rivers to the sea but, even without rivers, its evil breath would be carried by the world's winds, and in fact the amounts of pesticide moved by the northeast tradewinds alone is known to be comparable to all pesticides carried to the oceans by major river systems. DDT is even found in rain. Most alarmingly it attacks perhaps the most primeval breadbasket of the planet—the marine phytoplankton—without which life on this planet would have been impossible. The recent studies of Charles F. Wurster, Jr. of the State University of New York have shown that in concentrations in sea water as low as a few parts per billion, DDT reduces the rate of photosynthesis of four species of coastal and oceanic photoplankton representing four major classes of algae. Some of the unbalances DDT causes in algae populations may add up to greater planetary harm than the direct kills of higher animals. Thus the presence of DDT can favor the population explosion of a few lucky races of algae, at the expense of the normal balance, and these races may prove to be inedible or poisonous to animals further up the food chain. There is a more serious problem, however. The *over-all* destruction of marine plankton, which produce about 70 per cent of the oxygen in the earth's atmosphere would rather rapidly suffocate all higher forms of animal life on the planet. As Professor Lamont Cole has pointed out, this is by no means a Sunday-supplement fright story.

Because of the chemical obstinacy of DDT and similar compounds, there is an enormous multiplication of concentration when it progresses up the food ladder and this is the heart of the danger. For example, at Clear Lake, California, an attempt was made to rid the lake of midges by dumping in enough DDT to give a lakewater concentration of only 0.02 parts per million. A year later, the plankton was found to contain 10 parts per million, the fatty tissues of plankton-eating fish contained 903 parts per million, while the fat of the carnivorous fish (who eat the vegetarian fish) contained 2690 parts per million and the fat of fish-eating birds (most of whom died) contained even more. DDT residues have killed enormous numbers of salmon in the rivers and streams of New Brunswick. As many as 100 million fry of the coho salmon, now being tenderly reared in hopes of their eating up the obnoxious alewives in the Great Lakes system, have already been killed off by pesticide pollution, and it is now believed by realistic biologists that, as long as the pesticide peril remains, it will never be possible to bring the coho or any other salmon or trout to full growth in the Great Lakes. In fact, one of the hottest projects of the Fish Genetics Laboratories of the U. S. Government is to grow fishes that will be born with resistance to DDT. The trouble caused by DDT is mainly in the so-called "button-up" stage of growth when the final egg-sac remnants are being absorbed by the little fish. First the pesticide is transferred to the ovary of the mother where it concentrates in the oil droplets of the egg yolk. When the baby fish hatches, it draws on the yolk for its first food. The last part of the yolk eaten is that containing the DDT-infected oil. When the little fish eats this it goes into spinning convulsions, sinks to the bottom of the tank in a horrible flexed position as if frozen and dies. Chinook salmon are four times as susceptible as the coho to DDT and definitely would never be able to reproduce in water as polluted as Lake Michigan. Professor Wayne Tody of Michigan State University doubts very much if any of the lake trout now in Lake Michigan are capable of reproducing, since they must reach the age of six or seven before spawning and during this time can accumulate contragenitive amounts of DDT through the food chain. Steelhead and rainbows are also showing signs of DDT deterioration. (The complete detoxification of Lake Michigan would take about one hundred years, since—unlike Lake Erie—its geographical position does not allow flushing out any sooner.)

All fish-eating birds are, of course, inevitably caught up in this deadly cycle. The ospreys or fish hawks have disappeared from the eastern end of Long Island. The peregrine falcon has vanished from the North American continent, a victim of DDT. The damage done to birds is mainly indirect, through upsetting the metabolism of calcium, which in many cases causes the eggshells to be so fragile that the hatchlings die stillborn. In Michigan the robin kill has been so high on this account for eight successive years that, even though this bird is the state symbol, the news is now relegated to the back pages where it would scarcely be noticed even by another Rachel Carson. The nesting success of bald eagles has in some regions of the country decreased from 97 per cent in 1936 to 9 per cent in recent years. The case of the Bermuda petrel is a typical, almost classical example. This pathetic species spends all of its working days over the water, visiting land only to breed and breeds only on the island of Bermuda, arriving and departing solely at night. It lays a single egg underground at the end of a long burrow. When it is not in this burrow, the petrel feeds far at sea, mainly on cephalopods (small octopuses and squid). Since the world-wide spread of DDT, which includes all the oceans, the Bermuda petrel has been acting nervously, chipping its eggshells, sometimes eating the eggs—a symptom of hormone disturbance or calcium deficiency or both. The resultant decrease in successful hatchings has now inevitably doomed this bird. (It is significant that calcium decrease in the eggshells of the peregrine falcon, the golden eagle and the sparrow hawk occurred at the same time as the mass distribution of DDT in the late 1940s and early 1950s.)

It is ironical that at the same time that various species of birds are fighting for their existence in the midst of a growing saturation of bird food with DDT, some sea gulls never had it so good. This is because of the enormous increase in garbage that has been dumped in estuaries. This accessibility of a new "ecological niche" (another way of making a living) has more than offset the effects of pesticides. A population explosion among garbage-eating gulls, accompanied by a decline in predatory birds, is an excellent example of what biologists now call "ecosystem degradation," whereby a diverse lot of birds is being replaced by a large number of fewer species. It is quite analogous to what is thought to be happening among the marine algae, previously mentioned —and it is an unnatural and cockeyed state of affairs.

It may be that sooner or later the joke will be turned on the garbage eaters, since human garbage along with human bodies are becoming saturated with fat-stored DDT and other chlorinated hydrocarbons. A liver ailment known as "hepatic enzyme induction" has recently been observed in rats fed as little as one part per million of DDT in the diet. Since the body of the average American now contains twelve parts per million of DDT in the fatty tissues, the present generous tolerances allowed in foods may be obsolete. Both DDT and Dieldrin pass from mother to an unborn child through the placenta in mice, dogs, rabbits and man. DDT and Dieldrin are observed to perturb the synthesis of DNA and RNA in human cells. Badly fed humans are in particular danger, since the poison stored in fat is released when the fat is used up in staying alive. Such possibilities are regarded by the pesticide manufacturers as flagrant scare stories, and indeed the attitude of these people is extraordinarily similar to that of the automobile and petroleum interests who pooh-pooh the possibility of chronic carbon-monoxide poisoning in the city streets and who pretend that lead scattered everywhere from the combustion of tetraethyl lead in high-octane gasoline somehow conveniently disappears under a cosmic rug.*

There are about one billion pounds of DDT circulating through the world's air and water, ready to be ingested. At the present ungoverned rate of production and distribution, there will be about six times this amount by 1984—a year at which by some Orwellian magic all fearful extrapolations seem to converge.

What about the new, non-chlorinated type of pesticides, the

---

* In connection with lead, it should be noted that over one and a half million wild ducks are poisoned and die in Canada each year from eating lead shot. They mistake the pellets, which become dislodged from their plumage, for gravel which is necessary in their digestive process. Professor James L. Sandmeier of UCLA is of the opinion that the fall of Rome may have been chiefly caused by the fact that the aristocrats used lead oxide to prevent their wine from souring and thus came to live short, hectic lives. Because of the lead oxide from auto exhausts, he estimates that the concentration of lead in the blood stream of the average American is now about one-third the amount found in patients suffering from acute lead poisoning.

organic phosphorous-containing compounds? Aside from the facts that their chemical structure is so close to that of the secret nerve gases, (which all major countries try to keep in reserve for World War III) and that they could be used almost interchangeably to kill human beings as well as insects, they are especially hard on some insects that work for man, such as the honeybee. Their greatest virtue is that they decompose rather rapidly and without repeated applications cannot therefore continue to build up indefinitely in concentration as do DDT and its relatives. There are less than five million colonies of honeybees in the United States now, whereas about twenty times as many colonies could be profitably used in the pollination of alfalfa, almonds and other insect-dependent crops. The bees in Arizona have been knocked out by phosphorous pesticides used to harass the pink bollworms in cotton fields. Even when not killed outright, alfalfa growers complain that the colonies they rent are weak and shiftless. The beekeeper says he cannot build strong colonies because of pesticide damage and lack of safe locations to hive. Furthermore, these pesticides as well as those of the DDT type are very tough on the ladybirds, another human assistant. (During the Middle Ages, the insects were reputedly dedicated to the Virgin Mary, and were known as "beetles of Our Lady.") These bugs and their larval children hold down the populations of several agricultural pests, especially aphides and scale insects. They also feed on mealy bugs, potato-beetle eggs, white flies and the eggs and larvae of many other mean insects. Of course, the most heroic ladybug performance was the saving of the California citrus crops between 1888 and 1890, when they were on the verge of being wiped out by the cottony cushion scale, this being the accomplishment of one type (*Vedalia*), which has since been nurtured continually in California. Generally speaking, the reddish-brown bugs feed on aphides, while the blackish ones prefer scale insects, mealy bugs and white flies. About 370 of the nearly 4000 known species are scattered throughout North America. As mentioned before, the ladybugs can protect themselves against most predators by simply tasting horrible and in some species by exuding a bitter fluid from their leg joints, but they are helpless against the assassin bug, who thrives on bad tastes and smells, and are also cut down shamefully by man's powerful, senseless and indiscriminate pesticides. One can find some encouragement in the recent preferences of some large cotton and alfalfa growers for the purchase of ladybugs rather than DDT and all the other vicious, all-destroying poisons.*

Killing pest insects with the help of natural predators is not limited to ladybugs. *Trichogramma* is a wasp so tiny that four of them can crouch on the head of a pin. They lay eggs in the eggs of pesticidal moths, preventing these from hatching. Commercially they are produced in exactly that way—by first accumulating the moth eggs on wheat kernels. The praying mantis kills a wide variety of insect pests and the going price for mantis eggs is now one dollar per thousand. There is even a "praying mantis King," Eugene Mincemoger, who turns loose his pets on a likely field, then harvests the egg cases which are each the size of a ping-pong ball.

There are still other ways to kill insect pests without building up a hopelessly toxified planet. The artificial sterilization of males by radiation and their release into breeding populations has been a classic success in the case of the screwworm, a serious livestock pest. In this insect the male has a good many affairs, but the female fly mates only once, so if even only a fraction of the matings involve a sterile male, the population goes into a nose dive. The same technique is being tried with fruit flies in New Jersey and the Canal Zone. Unfortunately this is an intrinsically expensive technique and can be afforded only by the federal government. Attempts are being made to accomplish the sterilization by selective chemicals. There is an exciting parallelism here between sterilizing insects and curing human cancer. Any reproductive system always contains components with rapidly dividing cells which are strikingly similar to those in a growing tumor. Just as radiation is used for tumor control, it also sterilizes the sexual tissues; and those classes of synthetic compounds which have shown the greatest promise for cancer control also look best for insect sterilization. There are the so-called "radiomimetic" type (i.e., imitating radiation of which the best are aziridine derivatives). The most serious prob-

* The famous ditty:

> *Ladybug, ladybug, fly away home,*
> *Your house is on fire, your children do roam*

originated in Europe where these benign beetles had for 150 years successfully controlled the hopvine aphid and where hopvines were burned after the harvest. The vines were presumably full of aphids and the ladybug "children." Of course, the pest-killing virtues are not confined to the female.

lem here is to avoid getting back into the same box that we are in with DDT and the other active pesticides. The sterilizing chemicals must be harmless to beneficial insects, wildlife, plants and man. "Apholate," a sterilant developed especially for stable flies and bollworms, has had a very hard time in getting the approval of the Food and Drug Administration, whose bilious and suspicious eye, however, has seemed to falter when it comes to gross contamination of thousands of food products, especially sea food, with DDT.

A rather genial variation of the release of sterilized males is the letting loose of males who, though sexually fertile and attractive to the pest females, are basically incompatible because of some slight mutation in the germ cells. Thus Hannes Laven of Johannes Gutenberg University in Mainz, Germany, found that mosquitoes from Paris mated with the same species from Hamburg would not produce offspring. For complicated biochemical reasons, the egg cells of the females of one strain would not accept the sperm cells from males of another strain. Laven eventually found nineteen additional strains of common mosquitoes whose cell chemistries were incompatible and carried out the well-known experiment in which male mosquitoes from Fresno, California, stole the females of a Burma strain of the same species, thus cutting down the incidence of various insect-borne diseases. This technique is helped greatly by the fact that the female draws only on the first sperm she receives to fertilize all her eggs; hence if the more aggressive males have incompatible sperm, the population drops very quickly. In this general area of research, Professor George B. Craig, Jr. of Notre Dame University has found that the fluid extracted from the accessory seminal glands of twelve species of male mosquitoes renders the females sterile for a whole mosquito season (about ten weeks). Craig and his co-workers are, however, working on the theory that the best answer is to induce chromosomal changes in the pest insect which result in genetic sterility in the following generation.

Another approach is biological warfare on insects by means of specific bacteria, viruses or fungi. Most of the ideas and experience in this area derive from Japanese specialists who have spent their lives in studying (and trying to avoid) the disease germs that afflict the silkworm. Also viruses, with double-stranded RNA, that attack this insect may be useful for some pests. A double-barreled attack might be mounted by using the "DD 136" nematode, which is associated with a pathogenic bacterium, which gladly deserts its original host for the body of the insect which the nematode has bored into. This complex team has been disseminated artificially with success into populations of codling moths, boll weevils and housefly larvae. An insect toxin has been developed commercially from the *Bacillus thuringiensis*, which is harmless to other life forms and which is being experimentally marketed as "Thuricide." One of the most promising insect viruses, *Heliothis Zea*, isolated from the cotton bollworm, is being held up by FDA's insistence on more and more toxicological data. Professor Louis Falcon and co-workers of the University of California (Berkeley) have used experimental virus which attacks the larval forms of the codling moth (apple worm) and leaves unharmed all other organisms in the orchard, such as ladybugs and mantises.

Much attention has been given to the power of chemical insect lures, especially those that are identical to or resemble the sex pheromones, the nature of which has been established in the case of the pink bollworm, the black carpet beetle, the codling moth, the fall army worm, the tobacco budworm, the corn earworm, the peach-tree borer, the boll weevil and several others. These lures can be used in various ways, but the most practical seems to be the development of sufficient attractiveness that, as in the observed case of the army worm, the males swarm to pellets impregnated with the lure and leave the virgin females to die neglected. Also, as with the cabbage looper moth, when the scene of the pheromone is scattered everywhere, the male has no way of flying a course to locate the female. Insects are also attracted to other things than their mates, and the old-fashioned flypaper is based on this kind of trap. Some insects are also attracted by foolish things, such as automobile paint. At least two modern types of acrylic paints prove irresistible, for example, to sap beetles. Some people are more attractive to mosquitoes than others, due to the chemical individuality probably of the sweat components and the skin lipids. The fact that flies surround you does not necessarily mean that your bathing is too infrequent but may suggest that you are a perambulating insect attractant, worthy of closer examination by skilled chemists.

The pests that men try to repel or get rid of are, of course, not limited to the insect subphylum. Among fish pests in recent years the lamprey in the Great Lakes has been a public enemy because of its ugly habit of fastening its boring tubular mouth on good fishes and killing them. The lamprey population has been practically wiped out by intelligent chemical control, but, as we have seen, the population of good fishes is also being wiped out by chemical pollution, so sooner or later the Great Lakes lamprey would have died out for lack of prey.

Somebody is always trying to think of a new way to wipe out rats, since the standard poison may leave a dead rat inconveniently stinking between the walls. The old reliable red squill and similar compounds owe their effectiveness and discrimination to the fact that rats cannot vomit, while pet animals can. The anticoagulants warfarin and fumarin require continued reapplication. It has recently been found that mestranal, the estrogen component of oral contraceptives for women, will sterilize for the rest of their lives fetal and infant rodents up to ten days old. The effect is on the brain, probably on the hypothalamus. Males and females are equally sterilized. The treated food is eaten by pregnant or nursing rats and passed on through the placental blood or milk. It is also planned to imitate the sterilization techniques found so successful with the screwworm and loose genetically sterile rats on a population already reduced by conventional poisoning. Rats with a dominant gene for sterility have distinct black-and-white markings.

Of all mammals subject to chemical warfare, man has been most successful in developing means of destroying his own species. The only serious poison gas that is created on earth without the intervention of man or the special evolutionary skills of animals is excessive carbon dioxide of volcanic origin. In Albert Park in Africa there is an evil place called the *masuku*, deceptively surrounded with lush grasses, sedges, trees and shrubs. From about ten spots, usually at the edge of the lava flow, gas containing over 40 per cent carbon dioxide is vented from the earth. Attracted by the vegetation, elephants, hippopotamuses, baboons, buffalo and forest pigs enter and die of anoxia. Hyenas and other scavengers, eager to devour the carrion, die in the midst of their horrid feasting. Warega tribesmen (or at least the more naïve who have never heard of this green hell) add their bodies to the charnel glade. There are not many masukus on this generally mild and inoffensive planet. Yet man is rushing on his way to make the whole world a masuku. The increase of atmospheric carbon dioxide, by reason of the hurtling acceleration in combustion (in power plants, in factories and above all in automobiles), may in a century or two yield an atmosphere so high in carbon dioxide that the world weather changes to that of a hot greenhouse; the arctic and antarctic ice melts and the coastal cities are inundated. Furthermore, the concentration of oxygen may be seriously reduced to the point at which it becomes torturous to run a mile at any elevation. (Botanists have seriously advised houseowners to raise oxygen-producing plants, such as sugar cane, rather than oxygen consumers, such as grass lawns.) By that time, predicts Professor George M. Sutton, the ornithologist, we shall have an urbanized world with no other birds than domestic pigeons, starlings and house sparrows. We shall not need to smoke marijuana for kicks, for, according to the results of Dr. E. J. Malmstrom of the UCLA Brain Research Institute, the high levels of air pollutants will impart a sickly gaity—like the euphoria of tuberculosis patients feverishly giggling before death. High levels of sulfur dioxide destroy the lungs but relieve the student's anxieties. High carbon monoxide makes the student less pugnacious at the same time as it brightens his rosy cheeks (to yield a pretty corpse for the embalmer). High ozone makes even the most morose student engagingly, even revoltingly friendly. We shall not pause here to review the biologically incredible fact that men and women, boys and girls in smoking cigarettes manage to carry around with them, in the goings and comings of a species as ceaselessly restless as an ant colony, their own private means of air pollution, whereby they manage to assimilate not only nicotine and complex carcinogenic aromatic compounds but selenium compounds from the paper* and very probably some radioactive poisons as well. Professor Garath M. Green of Harvard has found that the gases even from tobacco of low tar and nicotine content depress the lung's ability to resist bacteria. He found, in fact, that the filter cigarettes giving, as advertised, the lowest tar and nicotine had the worse effect in weakening the resistance of the lungs to infection. The "stop-smoking drugs,"

---

* Cigarette papers are made from flax straw grown mostly west of the Mississippi, where the soil is relatively rich in selenium. In animals who graze on this straw, the selenium causes blind staggers, "alkali disease" or "grazing disease." This was known as far back as the thirteenth century when some of Marco Polo's animals suffered from alkaline diseases in Western China after eating selenium-containing vegetation now known to grow there.

such as lobeline sulfate, meprobamate, D-amphetamine and the like have been thoroughly debunked by Charles R. Schuster of the University of Michigan who shows that they not only fail to stop the smoking habit but often dangerously increase the heart rate and the blood pressure. Professor J. H. Thompson of UCLA finds that the flow of serotonin in the digestive tract is increased 40 per cent by smoking. This affects the stomach and the bowels and is the reason why youngsters get sick at the stomach and have diarrhea when first they take up smoking. It is the serotonin effect which results in the loss of appetite in heavy smokers.

Probably, this kind of addiction belongs to the psychiatry of drugs in general and is perhaps in the same class of phenomena with curious animal addictions, such as the crazy attachment of certain ants for naphthalene.

8

CHEMICAL AND BIOLOGICAL WARFARE

Essentially, compared with neuroses such as cigarette smoking and the vicious, know-nothing, money-grubbing way of life that has made atmospheric and water pollution a disease of the planet's layer of living scum, such activities as research in chemical and biological warfare are almost wholesome and professional. If men must for some reason fight each other in national gangs, it is inevitable that they will use the most effective weapons they can devise. Conventional bombs and nuclear explosions are not effective, since they destroy the enemy's physical plant, which one might want to occupy. The object of war is to kill the enemy or make him surrender, not to destroy his buildings, his water reservoirs, his canals and his roads. Radioactive fallout from high-level cobalt bombs would kill without blasting, but has the undesirable side effect of leaving radioactivity lurking around for an indefinite period, making the enemy's territory unoccupiable.

Chemical warfare was started in World War I by the French, who lobbed hand grenades and fired rifle grenades loaded with tear gas into the German front-line trenches, before making the "over the top" attacks. The Germans responded with tear-gas artillery shells. Chlorine gas almost immediately replaced tear gas, adding the element of lethality to one of mere embarrassment. Phosgene succeeded chlorine and mustard gas followed phosgene. Before the war ended more subtle chemicals were being used, such as the arsenic-containing Lewisite and even an "anti-Lewisite," developed by the British, which could counteract the enzyme poison. (Poisons containing heavy metals, such as lead, mercury or arsenic act by blocking many essential enzyme systems in the body.) There were 91,000 fatalities from gas warfare in this first of the world wars, both Allied and German, most of the deaths being caused by mustard gas.

The invention of nerve gas by a German chemist during World War II might have changed the course of the conflict, but for some still-obscure reason even the frenetic Hitler did not choose to use it, instead placing his faith in buzz- and V-bombs. When Germany was overrun, supplies of the nerve gas were grabbed onto by the conquering nations. Although there are variously designated nerve gases, they are all variations on a single luscious theme— the fact that a very special kind of organic phosphorus compound, when it penetrates the skin or enters the lungs, immediately destroys the body's supply of nerve-enzyme acetylcholinesterase. With this crucial catalyst out of action, the body becomes a quivering jelly. Pupils dilate, the bladder and bowels contract, the penis erects, the tear and salivary glands secrete like mad but the heart slows down and death is usually directly caused by asphyxiation, since the nerves that control the breathing apparatus have gone haywire. It is noteworthy that, aside from one detail which is supposedly still classified as secret, the nerve gases are very similar in chemical structure to the phosphorus-containing insecticides which we noted above as creating havoc among honeybees. The only known antidote (and it must be immediate) is a whopping injection of atropine. Even slight exposure will result in dilation of the pupils, and the eyes of people who visit Edgewood Arsenal or the Dugway Proving Grounds are examined before and after their tours. The killing of six thousand sheep in Utah by nerve gas, blown by the wind in a direction embarrassing to the Army, has emphasized to the public that this stuff, colorless and virtually odorless, can hardly be regarded with the nonchalance which we concede to cholera and brucellosis.

There are, of course, other sorts of war chemicals in use or under study. "Psychochemical BZ" is not meant to kill but to make the enemy stupid. (There is considerable theoretical argument about the safety of such "incapacitating agents," when used against the central-control headquarters of an enemy who also has poised a pride of rockets carrying nuclear explosives. . . . Suppose you make him so goofy that he pushes the panic button and starts a nuclear war?) New tear gases, one with the confusing fragrance of apple blossoms, were on the arsenal shelves. "Riot-control agents," such as Mace (primarily a tear gas and stupefacient) and materials that cause instant headache and nausea represent extrapolations of "adamsite," developed during but not used in World War I.

It is, of course, only a short tripping stride from synthetic chemicals to the toxins made by venomous animals, including bacteria. Here there is a scope for research that is not generally realized by the public. So vastly has our knowledge of bacterial and viral genetics grown in the last few years that it could be easy to develop new strains of some old disease organisms such as those causing anthrax, pneumonic and bubonic plague, Q-fever, encephalomyelitis, botulism, brucellosis (undulant fever), etc., which would be sufficiently changed to resist the usual antidotes or chemical therapy.* There is a still subtler type of the B W technique over the horizon, which takes off from the finding that certain viral infections can make fruit flies lethally sensitive to everyday material, such as carbon dioxide. Bacterial or viral warfare agents have the basic logistic advantages over conventional chemical agents that life has over dead matter. It reproduces. For killing or incapacitating the population of a really large city, it is almost impossible to deliver enough of a chemical, such as nerve gas, to do the job. But if one causes a virus epidemic, it is as if each nerve-gas molecule could reproduce indefinitely by binary fission. A virus of the pandemic quality of one that caused Spanish influenza at the end of World War I, if it possessed the quality, for example, of making human beings fatally allergic to some common food component, would satisfactorily depopulate a whole enemy subcontinent and possibly the planet. This is the *ultima Thule* of the progressively thinking biological-warfare expert, since in all probability it would indeed cause the world to end not with a moan of hunger or a flash of nuclear radiation but with a silent scream.

The above imaginary apocalypse was supposedly rendered academic by President Nixon's disavowal of bacterial warfare, which included as a footnote the horrible toxins such as that produced by the *Clostridium botulinum* organism, five kilograms of which if dropped in a hypothetical reservoir from which everybody in the world drank, would immediately kill everybody in the world.

Furthermore, microbiologists of considerable repute, such as Martin Dvorkin of the University of Minnesota Medical School,

* From the standpoint of durability, it is ominous to note that anthrax spores, still alive and lethal, were detected on the abandoned Scottish coastal island of Gruinard over two decades after British B W experiments during World War II.

have maintained that we simply do not know how to start an epidemic in an enemy land. Biological warfare, in his thinking, is a sort of Dr. Strangelove's farce. Either, like anthrax, it kills sheep rather than humans, or in the form of clouds of virus it is so unstable to certain climatic conditions, to sunlight and (ironically) to air pollution it is totally unpredictable and therefore totally unreliable. He believes that the only way to be sure to kill off an enemy population biologically would be to have hundreds of thousands of mad scientists at work, like the schizophrenic bacteriologist in Worcester, Massachusetts, who went around doggedly injecting typhoid cultures into chain-store bananas. By himself he did not achieve very much, for in Worcester one would have had to have a systematic team of banana stabbers, and even then not so many people as all that even eat bananas.

There is some reason to believe Dvorkin is wrong since the whole program of virus control of insects depends on the accurate targeting by stable virus "spores" (inclusion bodies) of whole insect populations. However, again we face the fundamental fact that a man or even a baby is a large animal compared with an insect and it takes a lot more virus to kill him or even to make him sick.

What would now hopefully be in the cards is that the skilled chemists and microbiologists in the Army Chemical and Biological Warfare Service would turn their talents to something useful—such as biological control of insects and nematodes or to means of decontaminating a pesticide-saturated civilization.

What we probably hope most to learn, in a sort of sociological post-mortem of our national stance on chemical and biological warfare, is why we were the only significant power that refused to sign the Geneva Protocol of 1925 banning the "first use" of chemical and biological weapons. This is a strange political story that makes one want to vomit. It shows the malignancy that can build up in a supposedly republican nation and which we cannot guarantee against building up again.

Actually the protocol was introduced at Geneva not as a no-first-use but as a *total* ban by the head of the American delegation, Representative T. E. Burton of Ohio, with the full support of President Coolidge and Secretary of State Kellogg. The language of the protocol was patterned after a ban on chemical and biological warfare sponsored by American delegates at the Washington Conference on Arms Limitations held three years earlier. This earlier

document had been accepted by the Senate without a dissenting
vote and would have become international law had it not been
for last-minute French objections to certain restrictions on sub-
marines. When our representatives signed the protocol at Geneva,
they naturally anticipated no opposition from the Senate.

But these were evil days. (Nobody who has not lived through
the 1920s can imagine how evil.) We had a weak president and
a Senate that was feeling its oats from having kicked the League
of Nations to death. The Army Chemical Warfare Service was
able to mobilize a huge group from the American Legion and
from the chemical industry. Senator Wadsworth argued that the
treaty would be torn up in time of war and, with the support of
his Military Affairs Committee, he was able to block ratification.
The protocol never came to the floor for a vote. It languished
for sixteen years in the Senate Foreign Relations Committee; finally it was sent back to the White House by Senator Vanderberg
along with all the other unratified treaties which had been accumulating dust prior to 1941.

(The Russians, incidentally, had signed the protocol.)

It can, of course, be argued that we have been using chemical
warfare ever since. Napalm and teratogenic herbicides in Vietnam
by any reasonable criterion must be regarded as chemical-warfare
agents.

9

ANTI-CLIMAX

Most of the above paragraphs have been deliberately couched in the berry-red terms of the so-called "survivalists" and were written before the partial ban on DDT. The dangers are real but less apocalyptic, much more arguable, and there is some logic, for example, even for continuing to use DDT. Since this work is not intended as a tract, we must lower the voice and consider matters in a somewhat more leisurely and subtler style. We shall have some repetition but from a different angle. I think it is helpful not only to present the angry-young-man case in our confrontations on planetary pollution but to testify in the end that the subject involves not just black and white opinions, but a sort of miasmal gray out of which we shall have to extricate ourselves by more research and fewer lecture tours by eloquent, fiery-eyed and well-paid professors. (With all due respect, for example, I think that Professors Barry Commoner and Paul Ehrlich, both younger men than I, would do well to take vacations from the nation's podia for a while and get back respectively, to their valuable research projects on the biochemical-nitrogen cycle and on insect behavior.)

Let us return to a simplification: The poisons that man makes or that he consumes in natural form divide themselves roughly into two categories: (1) poisons that have a more or less immediate effect on him or on his fellow animals, and (2) poisons that have a delayed effect, which may include an effect seen only in his children or even on his remote descendants.

It is a troubling probability that if pesticides (such as DDT) were entirely removed from the world's arsenal of chemicals, the result would not simply be to favor the survival of fish and birds and to lessen the probability of latent human cancer, but at the same time it would increase *immediately* the number of deaths from malaria, typhus and other insect-carried diseases. This presents to the individual some steely options: do I want to die of DDT-caused cancer at the age of seventy or of St. Louis encephalitis (carried by an insect vector) at the age of thirty-five? Do I want to die at seventy-five of cancer of the bladder because I take my refreshments in the form of cyclamate-sweetened soft drinks or do I want to die at fifty of heart disease because I am fond of sweetmeats containing sucrose (sugar), a probably more insidious poison?

The latency question is almost universal. Asbestos dust, for example, is practically certain to cause death if inhaled for a period of time but death may be postponed for thirty or forty years, as is substantially the case with heavy cigarette smoking. On the other hand, if a child gets in the habit of eating lead paint from the crumbling walls of slum-dwelling rooms, he will die in a short time—he will die as a child.

Let us review at a slower pace the chemical-pesticide problem and then some of the other problems. We may regard what follows as qualifying footnotes to the section entitled "Man as a Poisonous Skunk."

10

THE DEADLY SEVEN

The chlorinated-hydrocarbon types which have now been either banned or partially banned or are regarded as banworthy are DDT, dieldrin,* aldrin, endrin, heptachor, chlordane and lindane. Unlike insecticides such as pyrethrum, which are of natural origin, all of these deadly seven are new to the planet and are exceptionally stable when let loose on the world. It has been pointed out that the "half life" of DDT is greater than the "half life" of an average governor of a state of the Union.

In 1948 Paul Hermann Mueller, a Swiss chemist, was awarded the Nobel prize in medicine and physiology for his discovery in the mid 1930s of dichlorodiphenyltrichloro ethane (DDT), a highly efficient insect killer. Largely because of DDT's immense effectiveness on body lice, World War II was the first war in history in which fewer soldiers died of typhus than of bullet wounds.

Malaria world-wide has been incredibly reduced by the use of DDT. Dr. G. Garcia-Martin, chief of malaria eradication for the Pan-American branch of the World Health Organization, has insisted that complete withdrawal of DDT at the present time would constitute a regression to 1945 with the re-establishment of endemic malaria. (In 1945 the death rate from malaria in India alone was 750,000 per year. It is now around 1500 per year.) Dr. Garcia-Martin predicted that endemics would follow a period of terrible outbreaks and epidemics with high mortality because of

* The lay reader will forgive me if I do not disclose the real Christian names of all these compounds. However, as an example, dieldrin is composed of 95 per cent "HEOD," which is (draw a deep breath!) 1,2,3,4,10,10-hexachloro-6,7-epoxy-1,4,4a,5,6,7,8,8a,-octahydro-1,4-endo, exo-5,8-dimethanonaphthalene.

the loss of immunity in those populations which had been saturated with DDT. UNICEF (United Nations Children's Emergency Fund) still sends DDT around the world to kill mosquitoes and has refused even to consider reducing its shipments.

Unfortunately, as the people of India have lost immunity to the malaria bug, the mosquitoes have developed resistance to DDT. In recent years malaria has been on the increase and in Vietnam there are strains of mosquitoes who thrive on all the Deadly Seven. It has been estimated that at least 150 other insect pests have developed resistance to DDT.

The problem of the *adaptation* of insects to the Deadly Seven and to other pesticides was the chief worry of the agricultural Research Service of the U. S. Department of Agriculture years before Rachel Carson wrote *Silent Spring*. The lice which carry typhus, however, do not seem to be as genetically nimble. That is why it has been a practice, at least until recently, to spray the cabins and passengers of airplanes arriving from typhus-ridden areas of the world. Over fifty U.S. military and civilian airports have received massive ground sprayings of dieldrin to defend the country hypothetically against exotic insects of various kinds from abroad. (This seems to be senseless, since all the passenger insects have to do is get off the plane and fly. The solution would be to treat the airplane both outside and in, not poison the environment around it.)

In the matter of resistance, a curious and depressing fact of life seems to be making itself evident: DDT has killed off most of the *predator* insects that could have helped remove the pests. The insects that are on our side of the ballgame appear to be more vulnerable than the targets.

However, the complete banning in the United States of DDT, and probably of its more dangerous relatives, depends upon a very peculiar law—one that has already been applied against cyclamates, monosodium glutamate and various other chemicals that get into food either deliberately as food additives or as accidental contaminants by spraying or by ingestion.

The Pure Food and Drug Act, passed in 1906, had little teeth to it, and throughout many decades the usual processes for trying to put teeth in it followed a pattern as predictable as the workings of a farmer's mind. The proposed law always got drowned in the unfathomable depths of the Senate Agricultural Committee, then as now dominated by immovable old men elected for as long as they lived by the rural South. In 1958, however, something new was added called the Delaney Amendment (after Representative James J. Delaney of New York City). This stipulated that no chemical that could be shown *in any amount* to cause cancer of any kind in man or animals should be permitted *in any amount* in processed food, drinks or drugs. As the highly sophisticated then Secretary of Health, Education and Welfare, Robert Finch, has pointed out, this law (passed at a time when the fear of cancer from cranberries and what not was taking the spotlight temporarily away from the Red Menace) is a thoroughly inane and unscientific piece of legislation.

There are two reasons for its inanity: (1) What is "any amount"? This is a two-way absurdity. Modern methods of analysis are able to detect parts per *trillion* in any material. By this criterion, if any kind of cancer could be proved as the result of huge and unrealistic doses of a certain compound in an experimental animal, then by application of the converse absurdity, practically any food we eat could be shown to have *some* amount, no matter how small, of a carcinogenic compound; and (2) the new law contained a grandfather clause, exempting substances already employed and "generally regarded as safe" (GRAS) for their intended use.

Fortunately the grandfather clause has by general agreement been ignored. GRAS is no longer a meaningful term, and the proof lies in the recent ban on cyclamates, which barely squeezed by as GRAS before the passage of the Delaney amendment. We shall discuss the cyclamate ban later but note that now an anti-grandfather-clause action can be invoked against DDT.

Legally it is of no importance whatsoever that whole species of animals are on their way to obliteration because of causes other than cancer, as the result of saturation of the earth with DDT. (The polar bear, for example, has no recourse nor do those birds who are not normally eaten by human beings.)

It is the recently proven *carcinogenicity* of DDT that has vaguely shifted the seat of power to Health, Education and Welfare from the Department of Agriculture and the Department of the Interior. Finch had been embarrassed by this responsibility and equally embarrassed by the report of an investigating commission appointed by him, headed by Emil M. Mrak, former chancellor of the University of California at Davis. A subcommittee of this commission cited autopsy studies showing a high incidence of cancer, liver disease and high blood pressure in persons exposed to high concentrations of the Deadly Seven. Still they admitted that "present levels of DDT, aldrin, dieldrin, etc. have not produced any observable effect, in controlled studies of volunteers." (The volunteers were Georgia prison inmates.)

However, as the result of studies of laboratory animals, Dr. W. C. Hueper, former director of the National Cancer Institute, believes there could well be an epidemiclike outbreak of DDT-related cancers within the next ten to thirty years, since the latency is similar to that of asbestos or cigarette smoke. The Institute's studies showed that DDT and related pesticides caused tumors of the liver and lungs in mice. Hungarian experiments confirmed these results by feeding material containing three parts per million of DDT to mice, and as a result DDT has been completely banned in Hungary.

One can now see the box in which Robert Finch was put by the Delaney Amendment. Having banned cyclamate, how could he allow interstate shipments of foodstuffs containing *any* DDT whatsoever? Obviously he could not stop such shipments or New York City, for example, would starve in a few days. He has for the time being enforced rather high maxima on milk, meat, fish and so on.

We now have the absurd situation that the average citizen of the United States carries more DDT in his tissues than is legally tolerated in the meat he eats. A commission of scholarly sharks would conclude that the human body is not fit to eat. (This commission might compose a footnote to the effect that the bodies of Englishmen, averaging only two to three parts per million of DDT, are still acceptable on a shark menu.) The average American mother's milk would be condemned for interstate shipment. In the case of cow's milk or milk products that have been condemned, indemnity systems have been set up in thirty-one states.

We have previously mentioned the probability that the lake trout and Chinook salmon, because of DDT contamination will not be able to reproduce successfully in the Great Lakes. The coho was expected to be more successful because of a shorter life cycle. In early 1968, however, 700,000 coho fry died in Michigan hatcheries at a time when mortality was expected to be low.

The salmon and trout that had been introduced into Lake

Michigan were the pride and joy of the governors of Minnesota, Wisconsin, Illinois, Indiana and Michigan because they promised to give birth to about $100 million worth of tourist trade. (Bad times had been suffered with the population explosion of alewives because of lack of predators who had been wiped out by lampreys, but the lampreys had been put down by the use in their spawning streams of the pesticide TFM—not related to DDT and harmless to other fish. Partly to control the alewives but mainly for sport fishermen, the coho and other big fish had been introduced en masse.) The governors were not pleased when state and federal officials seized a large batch of high-DDT coho that had been harvested under state contract. Seven months later all five governors met in a motel room near O'Hare Airport and boldly pledged their faith in the purity of Lake Michigan water by drinking a glass apiece of it, perhaps flavored by a bit of Scotch. Then they pursued Finch at the Governor's Conference in Louisville but could not reach him. They had to be satisfied with Spiro Agnew. In vain, alas! The FDS established five parts per million of DDT as a temporary "action," but this eliminated 80 per cent of the common catch in Lake Michigan as commercial food.

In an incomplete but shocking survey by the Bureau of Sports, Fisheries and Wildlife, sixty-two species of fish from forty-five American rivers and lakes were found to have high proportions of DDT or other chlorinated hydrocarbons in their bodies. The highest DDT count (45.3 parts per million or nine times the FDA tentative maximum) was found in white perch taken from the Delaware River. Among other badly contaminated rivers and lakes were—in addition to Lake Michigan—Lake Ontario, the Hudson River, the Rio Grande, the Arkansas and the Sacramento. The titanic landlocked lake called the Caspian Sea is so severely contaminated that fish are all failing to reproduce, but this may be due to petroleum oil. In December of 1969 the mackerel fleet in Los Angeles harbor suspended operations indefinitely because of the finding by the State Health Department that the catches were averaging over ten parts per million of DDT.

Suggestions as to how to cook fish that you have caught yourself have been given by various agency experts. First of all, with non-fatty fish such as perch, all the DDT is in the viscera, so you remove it automatically as you clean the fish. In salmon and trout the DDT is in the fatty tissue but some of it (about

55 per cent) can be removed by deep frying. (The cooking oil should be discarded.) Pan frying, broiling and baking do not help much. (In cooking a human being, a cannibal would be advised also to use the deep-frying technique. However, this would not work with scrawny people, since in the condition of malnutrition of most of India, for example, the DDT that would otherwise be stored in the fat reserves of the body, finds it convenient to migrate to the liver or even to the brain. Recent clinical research shows a connection between high DDT content in semistarved people and softening of the brain—encephalomalacia—analogous to "crazy chick disease"; also cerebral hemorrhage, portal cirrhosis of the liver and various carcinomas.)

How does DDT do its thing in the waters of the earth? It is soluble in water only to the extent of one part per *billion* and is therefore usually brought to water bodies absorbed on soil particles. In such a form it can mainly be filtered out and modern city water systems use this procedure. However, even the few parts per *trillion* of chlorinated pesticides presently dissolved in the oceans may be critical in cases where the pesticide is consumed by very small plant or animal plankton and endures, undestroyed, up the food chain. We need much more research on the effects of much smaller than the present arbitrary-limit concentration of five parts per million on edible fish. There are indications, for example, that a few parts per *billion* of DDT can upset the temperature-selecting and -acclimating nervous mechanisms in salmon and in some other fishes chlorinated hydrocarbons at low levels make them act in a way evolution did not intend them to act: they lose their natural stealth and become easy prey for bigger fish or for cephalopods.

Some organisms do not amplify the DDT and are not visibly affected by it. Luckily this category includes honeybees.

There is an important and obvious reason why birds are more severely stricken with DDT and all other pesticides than man. Birds require more fuel than men and on the average eat one hundred times their own weight per year, while men eat only eight times their own weight per year. Big clodhopper birds such as ostriches are less affected than men.

11

OTHER POISONS, OTHER FATES

The danger of the "Deadly Seven" lies, as we have emphasized, primarily in the high chemical stability of these poisons. They help us today; they destroy us tomorrow. In substituting other pesticides that are unstable and decompose quickly even in the mere presence of sunlight, we again face up to the choice of a quick, accidental sort of death or a slow, surer one.

Most of the modern destructible pesticides are of either the organic phosphates ("parathion" type—analogous completely to the chemical-warfare nerve gases) or of the carbamate ("carbaryl") type. Both are quick acting and, unlike DDT and its cousins, very toxic to bees and other pollinating insects. A carbamate spray drifting over an alfalfa or clover field or a fruit orchard has been proved to kill off all the bees. Many of the organophosphate insecticides are acutely toxic to humans as well as to birds. Thirteen airplane pilots were killed in 1968 alone because of poisoning during spraying operations by pesticides of this kind. Moreover, the pilot's family may be the victims. He returns home with contaminated boots, wipes them clean with Kleenex which may wind up in the mouth of the baby of the family. Although fishes, with the possible exception of the mosquito fish, do not store parathion, they can be quickly killed by it. The concentration in the fish's blood is the same as in the water in which he swims, so toxicity can be easily predicted.

However, fish may not react as men or even birds do to offbeat poisons. With their cold-bloodedness they may share some of the vulnerabilities of the invertebrates. Perhaps the most monstrous fish kill in all history occurred June 18, 1969 when the pesticide *"Endosulfan"* or "Thiodan" leaked from the Farbwercke

Hoechst plant on the northern Rhine near Frankfurt. Over forty million fish were killed in a day or so. This is an intermediate sort of oddball chemical (officially classified as a sulfurous acid diester) relatively harmless to humans and other warm-blooded animals and quite unstable. Most of it has been exported to the United States where it has been registered by the Agriculture Department for protecting cotton, tobacco and corn crops against biting and sucking insects. The poison kills fish almost instantaneously by paralyzing their gills, as if they had been struck by a fish nerve-gas poison. It was the Dutch who discovered the source of the fish kill, since the Rhine emerges in Holland. Hoechst, like most American companies, was unwilling to repent. German companies now apply the same public relations techniques of Americans. Hoechst claimed that "with the Rhine in such a contaminated state [from sewage] possibly Endosulfan dealt a lethal blow to fish already half poisoned." It is interesting to note in passing that our own National Agricultural Chemicals Association has in its propaganda against restrictions against DDT, etc. advanced the public relations art to include Freudianism. Statements have been made that people who worry about birds and fish being killed by pesticides are actually concerned about their own sexual potency.

Parathion has killed a lot of migratory workers, especially in California. Symptoms of mild poisoning are frequently misdiagnosed by physicians as "flu"; indeed, pesticide poisoning is not a recordable occupational disease in forty-nine states, California being the only exception. In 1965 25 people in San Diego were poisoned by the pesticide diazinone which got into the doughnut mix in a local bakery. In 1967 in Tijuana, Mexico, 17 persons were fatally poisoned and 300 made gravely ill when parathion was carelessly spilled on a truck which later was used to transport confectionery sugar. In the same year in Colombia 77 people were fatally poisoned, 146 hospitalized and over 600 made ill from flour contaminated by traces of parathion spilled on the floor bed of a truck.

The parathion poisoning of Mexican migratory workers in California has been made a hot issue in Cesar Chavez's activities for the United Farm Workers. In one bad case 99 peach pickers were poisoned by parathion because the workers were ordered by their foremen to start picking while the poison was still glistening on the leaves. (California law stipulates a waiting period between the application of the pesticide and the crop harvestings.) Some of the lethal pesticides are stored around the workers' camps in plastic bleach bottles and are drunk mistakenly as water or wine. Other containers are either mislabeled or misinterpreted by the non-English-reading workers. This is in spite of the fact that the California State Safety Orders specifically require farm operators to inform farmworkers, even those who don't understand English. In the summer of 1969 Chavez sent legal aides to get affidavits from grape pickers about specific instances of pesticide poisoning. His aides had been barred from the records of the Kern County Agricultural Commissioner, as if these had been military secrets. The production of table grapes is a billion-dollar business. Over 100 million pounds of pesticides (20 per cent of the nation's total) are used in California. The California agricultural industry now has by far the highest disease rate of any industry in the state. Although the budget of the Bureau of Occupational Health of the California State Health Department has been cut way back by Governor Reagan and the poisoning worries of Cesar Chavez have been ridiculed by some, it must be conceded in California's behalf that it is the only state in the country where injuries among farmworkers are counted and where farmworkers are also covered by Workmen's Compensation.

In addition to workers, thousands of home gardeners contract "flu" symptoms after spraying their flowers with a parathion-type pesticide. (It must be recalled that until the end of World War II, parathion itself was the favorite candidate for standard nerve gas in the Army Chemical Corps' arsenal.)

12

ADVENTURES WITH PESTICIDES

Perhaps the triumphs and the agonies of a twenty-year pesticide adventure can best be sensed in the careful account of the changes in ecology in the state of Louisiana documented by Leo D. Newsom of Louisiana State University for the period 1957 to 1967. All of Louisiana's bread-and-butter crops—cotton, rice, sugar cane and soybeans—increased in size and value during these two decades. (Newsom's account excludes any discussion of the pesticide defense tactics used against foreign invaders, such as the fire ant and the white-fringed beetle.)

Large amounts of pesticides were sprayed to control the cotton boll weevil which in Louisiana is a heavier and longer-lived beast than elsewhere. Since 1948 an average of eight applications per acre per year included one or more of the "Deadly Seven" and organophosphate types to all of over 500,000 acres of cotton. By 1955 the tough cotton boll weevil had developed resistance to DDT and to all of the other chlorinated hydrocarbons. A shift was then made to parathion and carbamate types. Since then the cotton pests have been becoming resistant faster than the changes of many pesticides used against them, but the chemicals have proved to be incredibly toxic to some species of Louisiana fishes, some being killed, for example, at water concentrations of endrin less than one part per *billion*. Other fish species, however, along with the boll weevil seem to have become resistant to both the "Deadly Seven" and to the organophosphates.

The ecosystem of rice in Louisiana is very sensitive to pesticides, but rice has only two major pests, the stinkbug and the water weevil. During 1950 to 1960 the stinkbug was well controlled with the chlorinated-hydrocarbon pesticides. Usually the materials applied were DDT, toxophene, dieldrin or mixtures of these three. But it became apparent toward the end of the decade that Louisiana could not continue to use such methods to control both the stink-bug and to maintain its most prized wildlife. Dying off were birds such as the purple gallinule, the common gallinule, the fulvous tree duck and the precious crayfish. A shift was made in 1960 to organic phosphates and carbamates to keep the stinkbug population down. But the results were not happy. Methyl parathion was found to be the most toxic to crayfish of any chemical tested, eight times worse than endrin. At the prescribed doses for stink-bug control, any of the pesticides killed fin fish and practically obliterated the crayfish.

Aldrin was found in 1961 to be the only effective control for the water weevil, but growers found dead ducks and gallinules around the fields during the planting season. And within five growing seasons the rice weevil became 100 per cent resistant to aldrin. There has been nothing found since then to control this pest.

Until 1959 the amount of any pesticide needed for the control of the sugar-cane borer, its only major enemy, was relatively small. Since then, however, sugar cane has been treated with both chlorin-ated hydrocarbons and organophosphates. Ten years ago endrin was found to give the best kill of the borer, but tremendous fish kills resulted in streams and bayous bordering sugar-cane acre-age. These fish massacres continued during July and August of every season until the use of endrin was discontinued in 1967. The compound azinphosmethyl was moderately effective on the borer, only one-fifth as toxic to the blue gill as endrin but ten times as toxic to two other fish species in another food chain.

Newsom's story is depressing but raises two very important scientific questions. Why is it that fish that are killed by a twenty-four-hour exposure to a pesticide like endrin at one part per *billion* may tolerate one-quarter this amount indefinitely and accumulate residues in their tissues, amounting to many parts per *million*, thus continuing not only to live but to exceed present FDA levels as food? Another serious feature of Newsom's observations is that pests that develop resistance to a pesticide can store it at much higher levels in their tissues than are tolerated by a predator. This, he believes, is the principal reason that natural predators of the boll weevil, the stinkbug, etc., are now being killed faster than the pests themselves.

(It may be that the resistance-developing species are analogous to man. If their lifetimes were long enough, they might die of cancer or some other protracted disease or they might bear deformed progeny, who would not be able to keep the species going. We do not have the patience to find out.)

A quite analogous history has been chronicled for the Canete Valley in Peru. During the pre-DDT regime, chemical control of the pests of ratoon cotton (second- and third-year growth) was mainly by arsenates and nicotine sulfate. Because of a wild outbreak of aphides in 1949 the acreage yield dropped sadly. From 1949 to 1956 the growers relied mostly on DDT and toxophene. Cotton yields nearly doubled to 470 pounds per acre but the birds and the pest predators and the pest parasites disappeared. One by one of the chemicals became ineffective as resistance developed until by 1955–56 the yield dropped to an economic limit. A so-called "integrated-control" program was set up (involving, as we shall describe later, a combination of chemical and biological control) and in 1969 yields were over 700 pounds per acre.

Because of the political clout of North American agriculturists, in the legal lexicon, pesticides, no matter how dangerous, are classified as "economic poisons" and are specifically exempted from coverage under the Federal Hazardous Materials Act. One of the peculiar difficulties that reporters or scientific investigators have in finding their way around the chemical jungle is that information on the production of synthetic organic pesticides is compiled not by the Department of Agriculture or by the FDA but by the U. S. Tariff Commission. Information on ingredients in specific formulations is not permitted to be disclosed by law, to protect "trade secrets."

There is considerable doubt of the safety of insecticide strips now hanging by the millions in homes, restaurants and grocery stores. The same material (3,2-dichlorovinlyl dimethyl phosphate or "DDVP") is used in "Vapona" sprays and on flea-killing dog collars. The pesticide strip made by Shell Chemical Company ("No Pest") does not carry the legally required warnings that it should not be used in nurseries or rooms where infants or sick or aged persons are confined. The Food and Agricultural Organization of the World Health Organization has recommended a maximum acceptable intake of DDVP which is exceeded by an adult who spends nine hours a day exposed to the vapor given off by the pest strip. Research findings by Shell itself showed that vapor from the strips deposits on food. The FDA hence told the Agricultural Department that the strips should be labeled "Do not use in kitchens, restaurants or other places where food is prepared or served." Although this sounds like action, it is a hollow sound. The clanking mechanisms of bureaucracy require the Agriculture Department to request FDA for guidelines. The guidelines (in terms of food tolerances of DDVP) may take months or years to establish rigorously and may be subject to appeal by Shell. My guess is that by 1984, we will still have these damned pesticide strips hanging in our kitchens.

The matter of enforcement, even if it is agreed upon, is often rather scarily thin and, above all, the federal departments avoid publicity. They don't want to be accused of sexual impotence. A vivid case in point is the poisoning of poultry flesh by the use of heptachlor epoxide prescribed against fire ants, fleas and chiggers. This occurred in the Arkansas Valley Industry, Inc. turkey farm in Little Rock. Warnings were put out that it could harm livestock. (One Arkie grower said, "Hell, I ain't raising livestock, I'm raising turkeys.") Heptachlor epoxide is about five times as potent as DDT. The Department of Agriculture requires the destruction of poultry and poultry products in interstate shipment containing over one-half of one part per million of it. At least 350,000 Arkansas turkeys exceeded this limit, one shipment to Kansas City measuring seventeen parts per million.

It was actually the Campbell Soup Company that alerted Agriculture's Consumer and Marketing Service to the existence of all this fouled-up poultry flesh, and it was not until Arthur E. Rowe, a consumer columnist, got a tip and asked for an explanation that CMS issued a cautious press statement. The Agriculture Department still hasn't informed the public that for a while in June, 1969, the Consumer Marketing Service suspected that about 630,000 laying hens in upper New York might contain extremely high levels of dieldrin in their fatty tissues. In May, their laying days over, they had been sent to a Delaware food-processing plant to be converted into chicken spread and broth. Luckily all shipments were traced and none of the contaminated meat reached the market. During the Thanksgiving Day and Christmas holidays, however, about 2.3 *billion* turkeys and chickens are slaughtered and it is too much to expect that all the pesticide hot spots can be located. What should be possibly the most wholesome of human foodstuffs remains under a cloud of insecticides.

It is obvious that, as a result of the pesticide scare, the U.S. government control is about to undergo some kind of sea change. Up to now the Agricultural Department has had the deciding vote over conservationists and the Department of Interior on whether or not a new pesticide could be registered for sale. In the future, HEW and Interior will have some as yet not-well defined veto powers over Agriculture, which has always played footsie with the chemical manufacturers and the farmers themselves. A troika of some sort will emerge, but it remains to be seen how this three-headed monster will function.

It is interesting to note the fact that in the five-year period from July 1, 1964 to June 30, 1969, the Pesticide Regulation Division of Agriculture rejected some 1600 objections raised by HEW to registration and reregistrations of cancer-producing pesticides. In effect, Agriculture was completely ignoring the law as stated in the Delaney Amendment. Until now it has also ignored the finding of teratogenic qualities (deformed births) in certain compounds, including both pesticides and herbicides, which were specially emphasized in the Mrak report.

The President's Environmental Quality Council endorsed the recommendations of the Mrak Commission and by a little arm twisting forced Agriculture to act with some degree of activated purity on DDT and the herbicide 2,4,5-T (which we shall shortly discuss). But what statutory base of authority does the council have? It has authority only insofar as the President himself can use his power of bluffing. Legally the decision still rests with the Secretary of Agriculture. If things are not changed by the cloudily emerging troika system, the President and his council will have to determine for the Secretary of Agriculture on a case-by-case basis whether to ban the other hazardous pesticide compounds objected to as potential cancer producers or fetal deformers. This obviously would require both council and presidential attention not only far beyond their capabilities but beyond their constitutional range of authority.

The case of the lindane vaporizer is a classic one. Commencing with an FDA study in 1953, HEW concluded that a continuous vaporizer using lindane pellets that killed insects by filling the room with the chlorinated-hydrocarbon vapors caused food contamination and was cancer-inducing, especially to the aged, infants and the sick. Even the committee on pesticides of the American Medical Association (a notably sluggish organization) reported with favor in 1953 that at least fourteen states and thirty large cities had adopted measures to control the installation, the sale or the use of lindane vaporizers. Further, the Consumer and Marketing Service (CMS) of Agriculture disapproved the use of continuously operating lindane vaporizers where meat or poultry is exposed to the vapor.

But the Pesticide Division of the Department of Agriculture chose to ignore all these objections. As a result there were about one hundred registrations of lindane pellets, of which one half were for use in continuously operating vaporizers. It is estimated that at least seven million of these vaporizers have been sold and used and are still used.

In 1967 the American Medical Association's *Archives of Environmental Health* pointed out that since 1954 lindane exposure had been implicated in numerous cases of serious bone-marrow failure and leukemia. When hearings were scheduled by the House Government Operations Committee (a body which is less favorable to pesticide manufacturers than the flaccid, know-nothing committees of the Senate), the Department of Agriculture after *eighteen years* (including more than fifteen years of steady objections) conducted its own tests and after five days announced that the conclusions reached in 1953 by the FDA were correct. As a result Agriculture decided to cancel lindane registration.

In 1965 HEW objected unsuccessfully to the reregistration of lead arsenate, first registered in 1948, because it had killed so many children under five years old. The arsenicals and thallium sulfate are commonly stored in homes and are accessible to young children, who are as curious as rats but not as prudent. It is estimated that over the past ten years at least 500,000 pesticide poisonings have occurred of which about 350,000 have been children under five years old.

Despite reports that HEW would act to effect a DDT-like ban on chlordane (one of the "Deadly Seven"), no action has been taken at the time of this writing. There are limits, evidently, to the rate of materialization of the troika from the fog. HEW during periods of mental fatigue tends to fall back on the excuse that only Agriculture can ban a pesticide. HEW through the Food and Drug Administration can only rule on permissible residues in food or water.

Up to now, attempts to give FDA and Interior more authority and to require Agriculture to accept their assessments have always failed. For example, a House bill containing such provisions passed in April 1968 but failed to surface from the dark depths of the Senate Commerce Committee. It was opposed violently by both the National Agricultural Chemicals Association and of course by the Department of Agriculture.

Help, or at least publicity, has come from an unexpected source. The General Accounting Office (GAO), a separate administration agency, which can scold anybody it takes a notion to, after auditing the pesticide regulatory activities of the Agricultural Research Service, reported spitefully that in thirteen years the Service had reported not a single violator for prosecution. This was true even of firms which had been repeatedly, almost proudly, major violators. This helped tip the scales in the lindane vaporizer squabble.

Recently a new pesticide horror, almost astrological in its peculiar behavior, has hit fish and fish eaters. Mercury as methyl mercury, a form which it appears to assume no matter in what original mercurial compound it has been introduced as a grain disinfectant, is an outright killer—one need not wait around to die in a home for the aged. It took a good deal of biochemical detective work to sew together events in Japan and Sweden, which were simultaneously hit in the late 1950s. In a Japanese coastal town 30 people died suddenly of lung paralysis and 750 were invalided, while at the same time in Sweden an extraordinary number of grain-eating birds turned up dead, and chickens which ate the same grain laid eggs with a lethally high mercury concentration. A joint Swedish-Japanese investigation traced both disasters to methyl mercury, which was promptly banned in Sweden as a grain pesticide. However, the paper mills continued to use various mercury compounds and the Swedes realized that fish in their rivers were toxic and in some areas would remain toxic for sixty years. This is a nasty kick in the stomach for a country that relies so highly on fish for protein.

As in Gresham's law of money, bad pesticides have a way of pushing out good ones, and it was not long before methyl mercury was turning up as a Canadian problem. In 1969 it was disclosed that as much as 80 per cent of Alberta grain was mercury-treated to kill insects and fungus, especially in the large storage systems that are appropriate in a country that exports a tremendous percentage of its wheat. One of the results was that partridge and pheasant began to show up with high levels of mercury in their carcasses and the hunting season for these birds had to be canceled.

13

KILLING WEEDS AND DEFORMING BABIES

The Food and Drug Administration is justly proud of the fact that it clamped down fast on thalidomide in this country as soon as indications of the horrible teratogenicity (baby-deforming properties) of this German tranquilizer were demonstrated. Teratogenic chemicals or teratogenic diseases, such as rubella, are now viewed with as much alarm as carcinogenic substances, and one could have expected therefore the analogous degree of concern about food or water contaminated with such materials. One could expect a "Delaney Amendment" on teratogenicity. This is not the case. When you are dealing with therapeutic drugs, that is one industry; when you are dealing with foods you are eyeball-to-eyeball with the farmers and the farm lobby, or even with the Department of Defense.

When Finch's Mrak Commission made its famous report, it weaseled a little bit, evidently having been slightly infested with pollution politics, since it failed to back up the recommendations of its subcommittee on teratogenicity which flatly recommended that some widely used herbicides, such as "2,4-D," "2,4,5-T" and "PCNB" be immediately banned.* The chairman of the commission suggested only "additional detailed study," which is equivalent to throwing a proposed congressional bill into the bottomless well of the Senate Agricultural Committee.

The findings of the teratogenic panel are of more immediate economic significance than the uproar over DDT. Herbicides of the general nature of those found by the Bionetics Research Labora-

---

* "2,4-D" is 2,4-dichlorophenoxy acetic acid; "2,4,5-T" is 2,4,5-trichlorophenoxy acetic acid; "PCNB" is pentachloronitrobenzene.

tories' study to cause hideous birth defects in mice and rats are used in greater tonnages than the insecticides and by 1965 were being sprayed on over 120 million acres of agricultural land in this country. In Europe herbicides are used on 80 to 85 per cent of the cropland. In Vietnam vast amounts of 2,4-D and 2,4,5-T were sprayed as defoliants in the war zones.

The herbicide industry was taken by traumatic surprise when Lee DuBridge, chairman of the President's Environmental Council suddenly announced restrictions in the use of 2,4,5-T in Vietnam and in the United States. The Department of Agriculture was directed to ban the use of 2,4,5-T on food crops until such time as FDA had reached its conclusions in regard to tolerance levels. There seems to be little doubt that DuBridge's rather mystical clout in this matter resided in the public memory of the thalidomide tragedies and in the undoubted occurrence of a greatly increased deformed-baby birth rate in Vietnam villages and countrysides. Although the Vietnam use of 2,4,5-T was rhetorically restricted to "areas remote from population," there is virtually no such thing in that country. There are people trying to scratch a living everywhere. Arthur W. Gatton of Yale estimates that human beings in Vietnam could ingest as much as 50 milligrams of 2,4,5-T per kilo of body weight simply by drinking from rain-fed cisterns and ponds exposed to aerial spraying. (In the laboratory study, the proportion of abnormal rat fetuses rose to 100 per cent if a dosage of over 45 milligrams per kilo was received by the mother between certain critical days of pregnancy.) Furthermore, Clement L. Markert, also of Yale, has provided information indicating that even if the doses of defoliant used in Vietnam did not cause overt malformation of the fetus, they could lead to hidden ones such as lower brain capacity.

The possible ban on 2,4-D is more of a kick in the teeth, since it is more widely used than 2,4,5-T, both in Vietnam as a defoliant and in the United States for killing weeds in corn and wheat fields, whereas 2,4,5-T is used as a pasture herbicide, for brush control and for clearance of rights-of-way. DuBridge was wrong, however, when he stated that no 2,4,5-T is applied by home gardeners or in the residential areas. Monsanto Chemical Company has reported that a mixture of 2,4,5-T and 2,4-D is very widely used on residential lawns in the United States. They ought to know since they manufacture it.

The poetic use of 2,4,5-T for brush control integrated with
the release of sterile males of the tsetse fly has been suggested by
Dow Chemical Company as a way to make vast, dangerous regions
of Africa into one gigantic pasteurized meadow. Selective herbicides
are regarded as indispensable in increasing the productivity of small
grains, corn, rice, sorghum and sugar cane. (All members of the
grass family).

The backlash against any prohibition of such popular herbicides
will eventually be noisy but I predict that, if the teratogenic data
continue to hang in there, the backlash will not be as effective
as some of the more justified propaganda for at least the temporary
continuance of DDT and the like. There is no prospect more
horrifying to women than that of bearing deformed children.* The
news of the killing off of all the birds or of all the fish in the
world would be received by the average woman with comparative
nonchalance if by some absurd concatenation this would guarantee
that she or her daughters would always have normal babies. Women
are very hard-nosed about this.

* The much less scientifically proven and more tenuous threat of teratogenicity
and chromosome breakage by LSD has almost overnight made this a very
sex-biased drug. Pregnant girls very seldom take trips with it any more.

14

MORE ON SYSTEMATIC BIOLOGICAL CONTROL

We have mentioned briefly the possibility of imitating the wisdom of certain plants, especially the ancient coniferous trees, in which specific poisons, chemically similar to and mimicking the effect of crucial insect hormones, are offered by the tree to prevent the grub from developing to reproductive age (a subtle form of infanticide).

With the fall from grace of the wide-spectrum insecticides, such as DDT, a good deal of work has gone into biological-control systems, especially by a large group at the University of California at Riverside and by the University of Arkansas. Biological control is not a new concept and, as we have mentioned, the use of the ladybird in the last century saved the California citrus industry. Reece Saider, chief of the Department of Agriculture's parasitic insect branch at Beltsville, Maryland, recalled somewhat bitterly that government scientists were busily at work on biological controls in 1938, but after the volcanic eruption of DDT and other chemical pesticides, this group by 1955 had been shoved down to a pathetic five or six men and women suffering from inferiority complex and nervous colitis.

Work in this field requires patience and money. The commercial insecticide people have the money but not the patience. A statement from Shell Chemical Company reads: "We looked for chemo sterilants and other hormones for several years but found this very unrewarding and very costly. No one but the federal government can afford this research." The National Agricultural Chemicals Association is quoted more bluntly as saying: "There really is not much in this area for our people. They would research themselves out of a market."

This is a very frank statement, admitting that the goal of the pesticide industry is not to control pests but to make a quick buck. "If we cannot compete with natural predators, parasites or insect disease, to hell with it!"

Let me point, however, to another area of biological chemistry where the oil companies especially have deliberately chosen to ignore an immediate application or a change of emphasis of research *for which they have already budgeted the money.*

It is still an open question as to whether DDT or petroleum is the most serious planetary marine-pollution agent. From my own observations, this honor is, if not now, shortly going to belong to petroleum. The headlineworthy oil slicks from uncontrolled wells off Santa Barbara and off Louisiana, the oil-tanker wrecks on the English, Florida, lower California, Newfoundland coasts and the three successive open-seas explosions of giant 200,000-ton tankers in December 1969 (one of them near a great fishery west of the African coast)—all these represent the visible part of the filthy iceberg of marine pollution by oil. The oil-tanker transportation system is so gigantic that it now represents over 60 per cent of the value of all products sent by water. In spite of gentlemen's agreements, shipmasters do not find it convenient to separate oil from ballast water so into the sea goes the unskimmed oil. It has been estimated by oceanographers that somewhere between one and one hundred million metric tons of petroleum or petroleum products end up every year in the ocean and, as inspectional sophistication increases, it appears that the higher figure is the more likely.

The Russians, believing that it is oil spills that have ruined the reproduction of fish in the once-opulent fisheries of the Caspian Sea, have studied the problem more vigorously than the Western countries. The Russians asked themselves, what is the natural history of a globule of petroleum in the water? They found that first it is gradually attacked by bacteria or yeasts that feed mainly on the paraffinic fractions, leaving the residue heavier than water so it sinks to the bottom. Bottom organisms attack it much more slowly, and some of it may come up along with carbon dioxide to the surface, still susceptible to bacterial attack. In the end—after a long time—the globule of petroleum has disappeared, like a boneless dead body, from the ocean. *But during this time, in its various slow phases of bacterial decomposition, it is capable of killing fish and preventing fish from reproducing.*

In some areas of the ocean, where geological oil leaks have been chronic (as in the Santa Barbara Channel, where as early as 1793 Captain George Vancouver noted iridescent wavelets and the smell of tar), there has always been a goodly population of petroleum-eating marine bacteria. The result was that a lot of fish-eating birds,* but very few fish themselves, were killed in the catastrophe of 1969. The fishery is better now than before the leak, mostly because fish-eating birds were killed and the petroleum-eating bugs were right there ready to go to work.

As pointed out in Part I of this book, most of the big oil companies have programs on Single Cell Protein, based on the nurture of edible bacteria which consume petroleum. It seemed to me a golden opportunity to turn one branch of this already funded research in the direction of producing strains of bacteria capable of quickly gobbling up oil spills in the oceans of the world. Containers of such bacteria in viable form, for example, would be carried with every tanker and let loose during ballast emptying or transfer operations or just let loose where for any reason oil has accidentally accumulated in the oceans. In time this practice might make all the oceans the equivalent of a cleaned-up Santa Barbara Channel.

As it is now, there is good reason to believe that the petroleum industries are killing off more protein potential in the form of present and future fish than they are developing in the Single Cell Protein program.

With this idea in mind I have talked to persons who are in charge of the development of Single Cell Protein and to oil-company executives. The response is predictable. They do not consider this a flashy enough approach. What one needs, they imply, is something that shows spilled oil being actually scraped under the rug of the universe, so to speak. They are impressed by a continuous paddle mixer device that coats sand or other absorbent material with the surface oil and shoves it toward the ocean's bottom. As Jacques Cousteau, the celebrated oceanographer, has remarked, this is simply a method of being sure you kill *all* the fish from the surface to the bottom, not just those at the surface alone.

* Incidentally it is hopeless to try to save birds who have been soaked with oil. Even if the oil is scrubbed off they almost invariably die of pneumonia or perhaps from some insidious component of the oil which they ingest while desperately trying to preen.

Having been in the oil business myself for thirty-five years, I was hardly bowled over by this reaction. "They" are willing to spend some money in promoting "anti-air-pollution" lubricating oils and gasolines, which I can assure you are technical fairy tales,* but they cannot justify any serious reapplication of funds to help avert a planetary disaster for which they are completely responsible.

There is reason for the boys with the noxious brews of the National Agricultural Chemicals Association to be fearful, since biological control is not a pious objective but a realistic practice with a lot of accomplishments behind it. Already about 110 pests have been brought under biological control in over forty countries. For $4.25 million spent between 1928 and 1959, five projects saved in California alone $113 million in crops plus $10 million a year since 1959.

Let us examine again one aspect, that of encouraging virus diseases of pest insects. There are about 1200 different insects which plague agriculture and there are some 400 viruses already known to be fatal to these pests. Many viruses are specific to a single insect. Others may kill five to six different related species. It is now believed that these insect viruses could be produced at a cost comparable to some of the newer pesticides on a dollar-per-acre basis.

An extraordinary and brilliant development has made the virus approach click into economic focus. This is the help of some of the great National Laboratories of the Atomic Energy Commission. This is a switch probably more important actually than if the Chemical and Biological Warfare agency of the Department of Defense were to be put to some useful purpose, such as biological warfare against agricultural pests or human disease. An example is the co-operation of the U. S. Forest Service with the gigantic Oak Ridge National Laboratory in separating and purifying insect viruses. The MAN (molecular anatomy) program at Oak Ridge grew out of the development of enormously efficient centrifuges for the separation of uranium isotopes. The K-11-C rotor systems have been used to produce superpure human vaccines by removing the extraneous cellular material which is the cause of most of the unpleasant side effects of vaccination, such as arm soreness. Zonal

---

* The so-called detergent lubricating oils or motor fuels are able to cope only with one minute part of the automobile's effluent systems—the crankcase ventilating tube and valve that have been used for years to transfer blow-by fumes back into the cylinders.

centrifugation of the type used at Oak Ridge was a great help in the purification of Hong Kong flu vaccine during the 1968 epidemic.

In 1967 Mauro Martignoni of the Pacific Forest and Range Station at Corvallis, Oregon, asked Oak Ridge to purify a virus known to be fatal to the caterpillar of the tussock moth, a very mean pest which kills Douglas fir trees.

A rather complex problem is involved. The virus needed to use against the tussock moth is concentrated in particles called "inclusion bodies" located in cells of the infected caterpillar. But since the crude cell juices of the caterpillar contain many unwanted bacteria, this presents an obvious danger if the virus is sprayed in watershed areas. Oak Ridge zonal centrifuging reduced the bacterial content from an average of one bacterium per inclusion body to one bacterium for four million inclusion bodies, safe enough for use in the watershed areas.

Protected within the inclusion-body "capsule" the viruses can be sprayed as "spores," being resistant to bacterial digestion, to weather extremes and to moderate acid conditions.* The same separation principles are now being applied to studies with inclusion bodies of the gypsy moth, the European pine sawfly and the bollworm. Caterpillars of all these insects are killed by specific viruses.

In the south of France an infestation of the so-called "processionary caterpillars" (pine-tree killers) was controlled by the use of a specific virus. Since the virus only multiplies in live caterpillars, thousands were reared on virus-infected food and made up into powder containing virus spores. These were sprayed from the air and produced a massive epidemic with 95 per cent mortality among the caterpillars.

Some productive work on polyhedroses virus (so called because of the polyhedron form of the crystalline inclusion bodies) for the bollworm, the tobacco budworm, the cabbage looper and the Arkansas sawfly has been done at the University of Arkansas. Bacterial diseases have been encouraged for the cabbage looper and the fall webworm. A special fungus has been isolated that attacks the grape-root borer.

---

* The success of this technique incidentally would seem to contradict the theory of some microbiologists that we do not know how to start a viral infection in germ warfare because the viruses are too unstable.

Most viruses infect the target insect by attacking the blood cells or tracheal (lung) cells. Within two to seven days the hemolymph (blood) of a pest worm becomes cloudy and the worm gets soft, limp and decides to die. In 1965 the University of Arkansas treated cotton, soybeans and grain-sorghum fields with viruses. The first application reduced the bollworm population in both cotton and sorghum from nineteen to zero larvae per 100-foot row.

Although most insects (perhaps all) are susceptible to virus attack, not a single viral pesticide is yet in commercial production in the United States. The FDA is blocking all registration because they require more information on possible effects on other animals, including man. Although J. MacBain Cameron of the Canada Department of Fisheries and Forestry, perhaps the foremost insect pathologist in the world, has bluntly asserted that there is no known case of serious effects to a vertebrate animal from an insect pathogen, the FDA still pussyfoots and wants to be shown. There is something about the word virus that scares them. If this psychic block were removed, attack by polyhedroses virus would first be directed on the nation's number-one pest, the cotton bollworm.

A good deal of patient spy work is a necessary part of a biological control program. Take the case of the grape leaf hopper in California. University of Riverside scientists found a parasite which controlled the pest during the summer growing season by invading its eggs. But this parasite could only survive the wet winter by living in the eggs of a harmless insect that inhabits wild blackberries. The successful answer was to plant blackberries near the vineyard. One world-wide infamous pest is the green vegetable bug which has spread from Africa to attack crops of all continents. In Australia an insect parasite, introduced from Egypt, controlled the eggs of this pest but could survive only in warmer regions. A world-wide search came up with an Italian strain which was "cold-adapted." This has now eliminated the green bug in the colder areas in Australia where the Egyptian strain is not up to the job.

The gypsy moth is a terrible pest that has run savagely through most of the trees of the Eastern seaboard and is being carried, mainly by mobile homes, all over the country. When DDT lost its effectiveness on this pest in 1958, we were in trouble. Special emphasis is now on rearing parasites. At the Hicksville, Long Island laboratory in 1969, over ten million gypsy-moth parasites were reared and released in New Jersey, New York and Pennsylvania. About fifty different parasites and predators of this moth have been imported and released throughout the Northeast. Twelve have established themselves. There is now some evidence that certain parasitic wasps with a habit of stinging many hosts without necessarily laying eggs in them may be used to vector the virus diseases of the gypsy moth.

Microbe control of pests is also in the picture. Commercial populations of *Bacillus thuringiensis* have been tried, and field trials are being made with a polyhedroses virus which has the advantage of carrying over to subsequent generations. The virus is innocuous to other insects and to higher animals. Because the female gypsy moth mates just once and does not fly, the technique of releasing sterile mates is a good one, especially in spot infestation.

As in the case of mosquito hybrids, the use of Japanese male gypsy moths of certain strains, when mated with "American-strain" females, produce offspring of which all the females are sterile and one half the male offspring carry the mark of death and never grow to maturity.

As we have mentioned before, the technique of sterilizing (by radiation) a large number of males and letting them loose among love-hungry females has worked sensationally well on the screwfly (or worm), a livestock pest causing damage of over $100 million a year. The female lays eggs in an open wound or a skin abrasion of cattle, sheep and goats, but its favorite hatchery is the unhealed navel of newborn stock. When the larvae hatch, they feed greedily and often fatally on the blood and tissue of the host before dropping to the ground and metamorphosing into adult flies.

This excellently planned campaign by the Department of Agriculture began in Florida in 1957, requiring the rearing of millions of screwworm larvae. When the larvae had metamorphosed into pupae, they were given enough radiation to sterilize but not otherwise to damage them or prevent them from mating as adults.

By 1959 the screwworm fly was extinct in southern Florida, one of the four regions in the country where these insects had lived the year round. The campaign has continued since 1962 to the present in three remaining screwworm-tormented areas: southeastern Texas, the Sonora border region of New Mexico and Arizona and the lower California border of Arizona and California. In 1966 the last of the three areas was declared free of screwworm flies.

This had cost a good deal of money ($33 million), but this amounted to only one-third of the annual animal loss before the campaign. Not only does this represent a technical triumph but the cost and the result (total extinction) show why the commercial firms (members of the National Agricultural Chemicals Association) don't want anything to do with such a deal. They prefer a pest which is always threatening—always requiring more chemicals.

Another approach that requires infinite patience and biological skill rather than the facilities simply to prepare an indefinite number of chemicals and to test them on a few bugs which are currently in the limelight is to breed insect-resistant crops. This should be possible at least in the case of animals, since the productive lifetime is generally the same as the *destructive* lifetime of the pest. (In other words, genetic changes in the insects can be matched by breeding changes in the plants.) Two great triumphs were the breeding of corn resistant to the European corn borer and the breeding of wheat resistant to the Hessian fly.

Resistance takes three forms: (1) antibiosis (something in the plant's system kills the insects), (2) tolerance (the insect does the plant no serious harm), and (3) non-preference. (The insect is not attracted to the plant nor is it repelled. The plant is a neutral object as far as the insect is concerned. It might as well be a telephone pole.)

One fantastic biological attack on the mosquito has been discovered at the University of California at Riverside. Eldon L. Reeves has found that the seeds of peppergrass and shepherd's-purse trap mosquito larvae with a natural glue which forms when the seed is wet. If during its feeding excursions the larvae come into contact with a seed of one of these plants, they are stuck fast by their mouth brushes and die. The potential for killing mosquito larvae is far greater than spraying ponds with oil, which is simply substituting one form of pollution for another. As many as twenty-seven larvae have been observed stuck to one seed. There are about two million seeds of peppergrass in one pound, roughly the equivalent to the number of mosquito larvae distributed over four acres of marshland. This may be the ultimate substitute for DDT to combat malaria.

It is, in fact, noteworthy that it is precisely where a policy of devastation or DDT saturation has been followed, as in the Canete Valley of Peru (and reportedly on all of the farmland of mainland China) where pests have become hardier and more DDT-resistant than their natural parasites and predators, that biological control is the best solution. The importation of "beneficial" insects to restore ecological balance has been the common resort of following the DDT route to the point of no return.

The concept of "integrated control" has become popular as a compromise. One reduces the swarming pest population to some extent by a pesticide, or at least delimits it to a given area, then reapplies the *coup de grace* in the form of sterile males or fresh predators or (if the FDA gets off its Casper Milquetoast pedestal) specific viruses or bacteria.

One form of predator that has not easily been knocked out by DDT and is a voracious eater of the pests of cotton, soybean and other crops—being particularly fond of the bollworm moth larvae—is the hunting spider. These do not spin webs but roam around like tiny tigers looking for live prey. W. H. Whitcomb of the University of Arkansas has observed that wolf spiders generally patrol the soil surface, while lynx spiders work up on plants, protecting them against insects. Since all spiders are strictly carnivorous, no plant has anything to fear from them.

Biological control is not confined to insects. L. D. Owens of the Agricultural Research Service has found that some of the nitrogen-fixing soil bacteria secrete materials that are natural weed killers. These substances have little or no effect on animal life and degrade without residue within seventy-two hours after reaching the soil. Known as rhizobitoxin, the stuff is made by certain strains of the bacterium *Rhizobium japonicum,* first detected in the root nodules of soybeans. Against young-plant growth and new leaves the organism is effective in applications as dilute as three ounces per acre, causing no harm to mature plants. For use against weeds, it would be sprayed on the fields after they were sown but before the crop seedlings had emerged and would later be applied directly to the ground under the foliage of the maturing crop.

Upjohn has a sterilant which with one dose leaves the male rat healthy, energetic—and permanently sterile. The drug (3-chloro-1,2-propanediol) can be administered either with water or food. It causes lesions in the male's reproductive tract which result in the blockage of sperm. Although it is non-toxic to other wildlife and domestic animals, including oddly enough, mice, it may have a temporary sterilizing effect on guinea pigs, rams and monkeys. The female rats after coitus with the sterile male go as far as to show the phenomenon known as "false pregnancy" which prevents them from mating with other non-sterile males.

This is an important development since, as we know, about 50 per cent of United States grain shipped to India is destroyed mainly by rats before it reaches the ultimate consumer. One dose is enough, a great advantage over the classical rat poisons warfarin and fumarin, which are cumulative. Rats are cunning and suspicious and often become bait-shy before they have had enough of these poisons to kill them.

Of all the "natural" ways to kill pests, however, the one that most appeals to me is a development of the Agricultural Research Service. They find that the best way to kill garden slugs is to put out shallow pans of stale beer. The slugs love beer so much (as do I) that they crawl into it and drown, but they drown happy, I must insist. For this one stroke of genius I forgive the Agricultural Department all its sins of commission and omission.

15

FOOD ADDITIVES

From both the medical and the political aspects, the banning of the artificial sweetening compounds known as the cyclamates represents a rash and ambivalent action. Is it going to do more harm than good? The decision to disallow cyclamates in "diet colas" and other soft drinks and to allow only a six-month reprieve for canned fruits containing cyclamates rather than sugar syrup was ostensibly made on the basis of experiments with twelve rats which had been given for their lifetimes fifty times the dose of cyclamates recommended for human consumption. Six of the twelve rats developed cancer of the bladder. Perhaps, in view of what we said above on herbicides, a more frightening experiment reported to the public was the fact that 15 per cent of chick embryos injected with cyclamate developed into badly deformed birds. Furthermore, chromosome breakage in rats had been detected as the result of cyclamate.*

The publicizing of the last two effects is a strange, typically late twentieth-century American bureaucratic foul-up, where we see the beginning of popular government by television. FDA's Jacqueline Verrett, who had carried out the chick-embryo experiments, despairing of their receiving any attention by her bosses, took the story to the National Broadcasting Company. FDA Commissioner Herbert L. Ley denied having heard of Dr. Verrett's results until he saw them on a Huntley-Brinkley show, although the results had verifiably been sent to his desk ten months earlier. Similarly the work done by Martin Legator of FDA on cyclamate-

* Cyclamate can be used as various salts or compounds so I have used interchangeably the singular and the plural.

induced chromosome breaks in rats was referred to the National Research Council for evaluation only after being publicized by NBC.

The national scare stories over the immense audiences covered by television perhaps resulted in one of the most imprudent actions ever taken by the federal government—or maybe not. Let us listen in on a pro and con discussion by two creditable and well-qualified teams of scientists.

Stanley L. Inhorn and Lorraine F. Meissner of the University of Wisconsin, who have no visible conflict-of-interest connections with the soft-drink or artificial-sweetener industries, point out that millions of Americans, including pregnant women, have consumed vast quantities of cyclamate without statistical epidemiologic harm —in other words there are no statistical data, as there are in cigarette smoking, to connect cancer of the bladder or teratogenicity (deformed babies) with cyclamates.

On the other hand, for over fifty years, carcinoma of the bladder has been recognized as an occupational disease in people working in the coal-tar-aniline-dye industry. Crayons and hair coloring, containing such chemicals, are readily available and more danger is probably connected with young children chewing on crayons than with guzzling artificially sweetened drinks by the gallon. Too much of even an *essential* substance, such as the amino acid tryptophan, has been shown to cause cancer of the bladder. Yet in the twenty-year period during which cyclamate has been used, there has been no statistical increase in mortality from bladder carcinoma.

Regarding teratogenicity and chromosome damage resulting from cyclamate, although Jacqueline Verrett's work showed deformities in 15 per cent of chick embryos, studies on animals closer to us in evolution, such as rats, were negative. Furthermore, a smear of foods and drugs have been found to be teratogenic in one or more species: excess vitamin D in the rabbit, excess vitamin A in the rat and *aspirin* in the rat. (If all the pregnant women who with bad colds had been told by their doctors to take two aspirins and go to bed and drink plenty of liquids—probably diet soft drinks—were added up, one might expect a world full of monsters, but then perhaps in a sense we *do* have a world full of monsters.)

Work in the laboratories of Inborn and Meissner and elsewhere has shown no mutagenic effect—chromosome damage—when very high concentrations of cyclamate were put into cultures of normal human cells.

Inborn and Meissner do not claim that the cyclamate ban is going to kill off a lot of diabetics, since the ban still allows cyclamates to be bought under prescription, but they are worried about people who are "prediabetic" (with a genetic disposition toward diabetes) who can now prevent the development of a clinical stage of the disease by a prudent diet with artificial sweeteners. The dental profession has acclaimed the role of cyclamate in the prevention of tooth decay.

How can new artificial sweeteners be developed for market during 1970, ask these professors, when it took a ten-year development period of careful testing of cyclamate before its introduction in 1950?

For the other side of the coin, we go to a specific rebuttal of Inborn and Meissner by Samuel S. Epstein of the Children's Cancer Research Foundation; Alexander Hollander of Oak Ridge National Laboratory; Joshua Lederberg of the Stanford University School of Medicine; Martin Legator and Howard Richardson of FDA, and Arthur H. Wolff of the Consumer Protection Environmental Health Service.

These gentlemen claim that, contrary to Inborn and Meissner, the widespread use of low-calorie drinks containing cyclamate is a recent fad and resulted from high-power advertising campaigns on the part of Coca-Cola, Pepsi-Cola and others. Thus from the epidemiological viewpoint cyclamate has not had the time that, for example, cigarettes have had to get out of the twenty-year latency period. Furthermore, the evidence of bladder cancer in Connecticut men at least in the last twenty years has doubled. More recent rat data than those quoted by Inborn and Meissner shown that cyclamate salts fed to rats produced bladder cancer in three out of twenty-three animals and extreme hyperplasmia and polyps in the bladders of ten out of twenty rats. Although no specific teratogenic effect has been proved on mammals, damage has been shown to rat germ cells by cyclohexylamine, a metabolic product of cyclamate in the body, so that one could assume that sooner or later congenital or genetic effects would show up in generations of rats fed on cyclamate.

Umberto Saffiotti of the National Cancer Institute says that a ratio of fifty times the normal human dose, as used in the rat experiments, actually represents a low safety factor. In testing food additives under the Delaney Amendment, a factor of one hundred is usually applied. Recent FDA work shows that a factor of eight times normal causes bladder cancer in rats. Saffiotti protests that it has evidently escaped general attention that the amounts of cyclamate and cyclamate derivatives that caused birth defects in Jacqueline Verrett's chick-embryo experiments were infinitesimal, comparing with only one bottle of a cyclamate-sweetened drink for humans.

Perhaps the most serious and least publicized black marks against cyclamates are that they appear to interfere with the action of oral antidiabetic drugs and also to interfere with the efficacy of certain important antibiotics. Furthermore they often cause diarrhea in children.

What is one to think? More to the point, what is one to do?

Since the cyclamate ban, many soft-drink manufacturers are going back to saccharin combined with small amounts of sugar. Saccharin's chief sales disadvantage is that, although it tastes sweet enough at first, with most people there is a ghostly and very disagreeable aftertaste of extreme bitterness.

Since the cyclamate ban, there has naturally been a vast rustling around to find low-calorie sweeteners that are not at least instantaneous poisons.

The firm of MacAndres and Forbes has been making ammoniated glycyrhizin for fifteen years. This comes from the root of the licorice plant in Mediterranean regions. The root is shredded and cooked and the resulting liquid is 100 times sweeter than sugar, and can be processed to a solid. If you like the taste of licorice this may be your baby, and some must like it since the sales have increased by twenty times in the last year. But this compound has not received the biological laboratory study that cyclamate has had. It may turn out to cause galloping cancer of the penis in mice, for all we know.

Foodways Incorporated's Weight Watchers Sugar Substitute is a blend of saccharin, dextrose, sodium gluconate and sodium citrate.

"Sweet 'N Low" of the Cumberland Packing Corporation contains lactose, saccharin and potassium bitartrate. (Because of the lactose content this may cause trouble with people who cannot digest milk.)

G. D. Searles and Company has come out with aspartyl

phenylalanine derived from soybeans. This is an amino acid 150 times sweeter than sugar but one must remember, as mentioned previously, that tryptophan is also an amino acid and an essential one but was found in excess amounts to cause bladder cancer.

The U. S. Department of Agriculture itself holds the patents for naringin dihydrochalcone (from grapefruit peel) and neohesperidin dihydrochalcone (from the peel of Spanish oranges). The latter is 1500 times sweeter than sugar and is being put into pilot-plant production by the Western Regional Research Laboratories in Albany, California. It takes four chemical steps to convert naringin, the extremely bitter principle of grapefruit, to the sweetener. The operation would be simpler if they started with neohesperidin itself, but this is found only in Seville oranges and is not commercially available. Neohesperidin dihydrochalcone's sweet taste differs in "character" from that of sucrose and existing sugar substitutes. The sweetness is longer lasting (it may in fact be "cloying") but is slower to develop. Meanwhile many biochemists, in particular John E. Amoore, who for many years has been trying to relate the *odor* of chemicals with their molecular structure, will seek to uncover the secret behind such sensory mysticisms as the production by minor chemical changes of extremely bitter flavors into extremely sweet flavors. Perhaps the tongue can be *trained* in infancy to accept bitter or insipid for sweet. Or possibly we can teach children by the newly established neurology of the autonomic nervous system to regard anything—except fruits—tasting like sugar as nasty.*

Needless to say, all the proposed substitutes for *cyclamate, including especially saccharin and sugar itself*, are now being given high-priority tests along the same line as those that got cyclamates banned.

It is my prediction that sucrose (sugar) itself will turn out to be in practically every clinical sense an undesirable food substance, better for making rum than candy and pie. It will be ironic indeed if we cannot only blame it for atherosclerosis (as we can) but for various cancers. The soft-drink industry is, however, betting that saccharin, a product of the coal tar-dye industry, is more likely to

* This discovery, perhaps the greatest in neurology since the establishment of the neuron theory, makes it possible by "instrumental learning" to get people to control their heartbeat, their blood pressure, even their kidney functions. Rats, for example, can be made to pump more blood into one ear than the other. This is discussed in my book *An Ark of Wiser Animals*, to be published later.

be the next to go under the ban; hence the scramble for new supersweet substances, all of which in turn will probably in the end be shot down under the Delaney Amendment. In view of the enormity of the sugar industry, any discoveries of carcinogenicity under the terms of the Delaney Amendment will simply result in the repeal of the Delaney Amendment.

(It is noteworthy that in cuisine-conscious France artificial sweeteners of any kind have been banned since 1902. The French, however, are hardly models of health and are interminably complaining about their livers.)

The furor about monosodium glutamate (MSG) or "Accent" started out from vague reports of dizziness, temporary loss of memory, and the like, after eating in Chinese restaurants. This was in fact called the "Chinese restaurant syndrome." (The Chinese restaurant owners of New York City have, however, denied that they use as much MSG as is commonly applied for flavor enhancement in French and Italian restaurants.) From this modest beginning the MSG controversy grew in absurdity to a point at which the Food and Drug Administration committed the farcical mistake of reporting the results of experiments it had never carried out.

Most of the heat was provided by some work that John W. Olney of the Washington University School of Medicine at St. Louis performed in which he injected small amounts of MSG into the veins of baby mice, then examined their brains with an electron microscope. He detected shattered and pitted cells in certain areas and found the same effect with rats, rabbits and rhesus monkeys. This kind of study is new to nutritionists and toxicologists who rarely consider such advanced techniques in screening a new additive. And FDA had never told them to consider such techniques.

The predictable backlash from the MSG people, including the Ajinomoto Company, world's largest producer of MSG, was to the effect that the average Japanese consumes two grams of MSG daily which is only 0.1 per cent of the two kilograms of glutamic acid naturally and necessarily present as a protein ingredient in the adult human body. MSG was thus held up as the most "natural" of all flavorings. Others complained that Olney's subcutaneous injections were not the same as eating the stuff. But Olney popped right back with the same result on baby mice that had been tube fed rather than injected with MSG. Moreover he made the important point that MSG was not a substantial danger to adults, only to babies. Furthermore, it is a completely silly thing to flavor baby foods with MSG since the baby's taste buds have not developed sufficiently that he knows the difference. MSG is added because it makes baby food taste better to the mother. He deplored the fact that the GRAS list which evolved from the Delaney Amendment did not provide separate adult and infant categories. When the Senate asked FDA's opinion of MSG in July 1969, it hastily put together a report showing that MSG presented no significant threat for either babies or adults—so hastily in fact that it reported as definitive the results of five experiments that had barely been set up. (In college research reports of this kind, not infrequently turned in by desperate young people for getting a Ph.D. degree, are termed "carboning.") Quite obviously FDA had made a fool of itself, but Olney's work was impressive enough to result in Gerber Baby Food removing all MSG from the contents of its cans.

John Olney had made an exceedingly important point in respect to the difference between adult and infant foods. It became evident that a review of baby-food additives was long past due.

First of all, why is so much salt put in baby foods? Here again it is added to please the mother's palate and, if not positively dangerous, it is habit forming and may lead to excessive use and perhaps disease later in life. Most medical authorities believe the nation consumes far too much salt.

The trend at present is to re-examine very critically all, or at least as many as can be handled, of the extraordinarily long and varied list of food additives that have gaily and almost automatically been accepted as GRAS before the Delaney Amendment was passed.

One is carboxy methylcellulose (CMC) that had been found in the 1950s to cause cancer in animals. It is used indiscriminately today for the thickening of ice cream, jellies, chocolate drinks, icings, some candies and even some baby foods. It has been used in cyclamate-sweetened soft drinks, thus providing a double threat.

A complicated acid known as "NGDR," used to keep fat from going rancid, was banned by the Canadian Food and Drug Directorate in 1967 for carcinogenicity. It is still being used in the United States in shortenings.

"Red No. 4," an aniline dye used to color maraschino cherries is definitely poisonous. The FDA once attempted to take it off the market but left it on after a piteous outcry from the food processors. It is still used today.

Nitrites, added to baby foods and meats to keep the product "red," can be converted in the child's body to nitrates. Sufficiently concentrated, dietary nitrates can lead to respiratory failure and even death.

The list in canned foods is almost endless. Who reads the fine print on food packages indicating the presence of propylene glycol, calcium silicate, butylated hydroxyanisole, sorbitan monostearate, methyl paraban, etc., etc.? The consequence of additive ballooning in the United States is that Americans are each ingesting about three pounds annually of exotic chemicals if they eat the average of 1400 pounds of processed food per year. Included is benzoic acid or its salts, used for nearly a century and regarded rather uncritically as being GRAS because it occurs naturally in berries and in some fruits such as plums. The food processors find every excuse in their bitter competition to add something for a specific function: *anti-caking agents* (in salt, sugar, milk products, etc.); *preservatives*; *emulsifying agents*; *sequestrants*, which keep trace materials from turning fats and oils rancid, and prevent beer and soft drinks from turning cloudy. As flavorings, FDA also has at least eighty "miscellaneous" GRAS materials from alfalfa to zedoary (an aromatic East Indian herb), from pipsissewa leaves to ilang-ilang.

16

THE PLANTS THEMSELVES MAY KILL YOU

As we have mentioned in Part I of this book, one does not have to go to the trouble to *add* poisons to many foods to kill oneself. The brave Swedes who took a balloon close to the North Pole (*The Discovery*) perished not from cold or starvation but from eating the poorly cooked flesh of a polar bear which was afflicted with trichinosis.

N. Sapeika in his searching monograph *Food Pharmacology* gives synthetic sweetening agents a light scolding while he fires all his guns at sucrose (ordinary sugar), which spreads ischemic (artery-narrowing) heart disease around the modern world.

Many plants contain allergens, but most of these can be decomposed by pressure cooking, while ordinary boiling has little effect. Plants also may contain protease inhibitors (preventing protein digestion), hemagglutinins, goitrogens, cyanogens, saponins, gossypol, lathyrogens, favism-inducers, and so on. It is not necessary to tell you precisely what all these things are: none of them does your body any good. But the trouble is the lack of a convenient animal-model test to predict the effect of these toxins. This is especially so of lathyrogens, present in the leaves of the *Lathyron* plant, a popular Asiatic food. It causes spastic paralysis of the legs.

Some of the toxic symptoms are much worse in people suffering from semistarvation. Favism, a condition in which acute deterioration of the red blood cells occurs, can result from inhalation of pollen and the eating of beans of the *Vici faba* plant, the active poison being "dopa" (3,4-dihydroxyphenylalanine).

The fact is often overlooked that *all smoked foods* contain some concentration of cancer-forming compounds. This is true of "charcoal-broiled" steaks. It seems very likely to be true of "crisp" bacon.

Philosophically the Delaney Amendment has started us in the wrong direction by using the premise that only food *additives* should be investigated, while the foods themselves, being "natural," are above suspicion.

The very dangerous substance 1,5-vinyl-2-thiooxazolidine-1 which is toxic to animals and humans is identified in various amounts in raw rutabaga, turnip, kale, cabbage, cauliflower, kohlrabi, Brussels sprouts and broccoli.

Phytic acid, present in whole wheat, oatmeal and other cereal foods, may be injurious to health because it interferes with the assimilation of iron and calcium. Raw egg white contains small amounts of a hazardous poison, avidin, which inactivates the essential vitamin biotin. Other vitamins such as A and C are destroyed by carotenase, lipoxidase, ascorbic acid oxidase and other enzymes found in "natural" foods. The only reason why we can survive is that the amounts of poisons, designed by plants for the war against insects, is too small to kill us spectacularly. It is on the whole much safer (as many primitive tribes realized) to eat the insects themselves rather than the plants, but it would be best to cook them. Eating raw fish is as safe as playing Russian roulette. The harmful enzyme thiaminase is found in raw fin fish and in raw shellfish. Oysters, uncooked on the half shell, have probably killed many people, unless they accompanied these delicacies with drinks so potent that the enzyme was destroyed by alcoholysis. Fortunately this is usually the case. We have mentioned the oxalic acid in certain leafy vegetables. On the whole, the child takes an instinctively self-protective stand in objecting to spinach.

The caffeine contained in coffee and tea and the theobromine in cocoa are, of course, dangerous drugs which cannot be purchased in pure form without a prescription, and recently caffeine has been found to be a mutagen. (We shall have more to say about this later.)

It has recently been established that certain fats in the diet may trigger the development of goiter, if the body isn't getting enough iodine. Olive oil is the worst (mainly from mayonnaise), followed by corn oil, soybean oil and chicken fat. Incredibly iodine deficiency is now becoming worse in this country after having been nearly eliminated several years ago. The reason seems to be that new developments in food processing call for salt that has not been iodized. The continuous bread-mix process, for example, avoids the use of iodized salt. All food processing is accounting for a tremendous and unhealthy salt consumption, but without a corresponding iodide use. On a low-iodine diet, butter, pork and beef fats result in a lower incidence of goiter. In this case you can't win. You choose between goiter and atherosclerosis.

In some cultures plants of known toxicity are venerated but occasionally eaten in a rather playful sense as if to be naughty and challenge the gods. What is so great about staying alive anyway? *Obrus prectorious* is such an ambivalent shrub in India. Its seeds are known as *rati* and have been used from time immemorial by goldsmiths since they are persuaded without scientific basis that the weight of all the seeds is the same. The seeds are also used as beads for necklaces. The principal poison contained is *abrin* which was once used as a remedy—although a dangerous one —for granulated eyelid. Bruised seeds were used in darts for poisoning cattle and people. A poultice is claimed to cause abortion. The broiled seeds have been used as famine foods in Egypt and India where they solved the famine by killing off everybody who ate them.

Wyeth Laboratories of Philadelphia put out a poetic booklet called *The Sinister Garden*, in which a list of plant poisons and their symptoms is neatly set forth. Potato sprouts, leaves and stems will cause mental confusion, cardiac depression and clammy skin. Rhubarb leaves may make you vomit until you throw up bloody foam. Some unexpectedly poisonous things which you are unlikely to have at your table but which you might consume if you went on a gnawing fit are the twigs, leaves and bark of the cherry tree, the shoots, leaves, bark and root of the elderberry; acorns and young shoots and leaves of oak trees, and especially the elongated pods and their seeds of wisteria.

Some plants may cause cattle and sheep to die from hydrocyanic-acid poisoning under certain conditions. Sudan grass, Sudan hybrids, sorghum and Johnson grass are especially unpredictable when plant growth is checked by drought, frost, trampling, mowing or wilting. The *second growth* from these plants should be viewed with particular suspicion. Cattle raisers have sometimes been wiped out in Oklahoma by such cyanide poisoning. This can be viewed as an ancient evolutionary defense mechanism, especially effective against insects. Grazing cattle is a relatively new thing in the world compared with the tens of millions of years that the grass plants have been fighting the insects by chemical warfare.

17

LEGACIES FOR THE FUTURE

A distinction of the most portentous kind must be made between agents that cause deformed babies (teratogenic) because at some critical period of pregnancy they affect the fetus in its development, and agents that strike a dagger at the germ cells so that a stable *mutant* is produced, perhaps a *delayed* mutant if the insulted gene is a recessive one. The distinction in a social population of animals, such as men, is sometimes hard to make because the generations succeed themselves much more slowly than the development of medical curiosity and public concern.

Thalidomide was undoubtedly a teratogen but, although we are not quite sure (since the surviving children have not yet produced their own children), it is probably not a *mutagen*. In other words, the thalidomide did not permanently affect the *germ* cells of the afflicted children. We guess at this on the basis that it does not seem to be mutagenic toward other animals with which we have tested it.

The most popular way of achieving mutations has for a long time been by means of radiation. Herman J. Müller in 1926 dramatically increased the rate of mutations among fruit flies by exposing the males to X rays. When some nineteen years later the atomic bomb was developed, it was assumed that both the first flash and the fallout of radioactive materials from its explosion would develop human mutants. A careful study of the survivors of Hiroshima and Nagasaki and of their children and of the marine life exposed to terrible radiation from experimental explosions in isles of the Pacific Ocean has rather disappointed those chroniclers who looked for a race of mutant monsters to emerge. (Literally hundreds of science-fiction novels have been based on the weird mutants remaining on an earth scarred with generations of nuclear warfare.) Of course, it is too early to determine whether recessive mutant genes have been established, but those first Hereford cattle, caught in the fallout from the Hiroshima blast, were brought to the United States and shipped to Oak Ridge. After they recovered from their lesions they produced normal, healthy calves as long as sixteen years after the explosions. In this case the radiation did not even appear to have been teratogenic.

Arguments about radiation flare up frequently because of the increasing number of nuclear power plants proposed in this country and because of the planned ABM system.

There is the great "Sternglass controversy," for example.

Professor Ernest F. Sternglass of the University of Pittsburgh attributed an increase in fetal and infant death rates to strontium-90 or other insidious fallout from the Trinity Test in Alamogordo in 1945. In the magazine *Esquire* he predicted that these and other horrors would result from a full-scale ABM system which, if successful, could cause the extinction of the human race. Indeed, he claimed that hundreds of children who died before their first birthdays in the 1960s were victims of peacetime nuclear testing. The genetic effect has become evident, according to Sternglass, from an increase in infant mortality along the path of the fallout cloud in 1945 and from detailed correlation of state-by-state infant-mortality excesses with yearly changes of strontium-90 levels in the milk.

While elsewhere, in the United States infant mortality was continuing to decrease as expected, "downwind" of Alamogordo it did not. There was no change in the infant death rate in 1946— the year after the Trinity test—but by 1950 the rate in Texas, Arkansas, Louisiana, Mississippi, Alabama, Georgia and both Carolinas had deviated upward from normal expectancy. Thus the Alamogordo blast appears to have been followed by death before reaching the age one, of at least one out of 100 children in the downwind area. In April 1957 a sizable amount of nuclear debris from a test explosion in Nevada wafted downwind some 2000 miles to the east and, thirty-six hours later, deposited by a rainstorm over the Albany-Troy region of New York. Ralph Lapp drew attention to this heavy local fallout. Subsequent examination of the childhood leukemia pattern in the area showed that leukemia doubled over a period of some eight years after the fallout, then decreased.

As shown by Representative Chet Holifield of California, who is a recognized expert on the nuclear peril, Sternglass' data on infant deaths in the states mentioned may be interesting demographic records, but they prove nothing whatsoever about the effect of fallout because *that was not the direction the Alamogordo cloud went.* The cloud went *north,* not south from the site of detonation and finally wrapped itself around Gallinas Peak, sixty-five miles to the north, there to break up and disappear for good. While the major deposition was in New Mexico itself, smaller portions of cloud did pass into Colorado, Nebraska and Kansas. The infant mortality in New Mexico continued to decline steadily until 1958—thirteen years after the Trinity shot—when the decline slowed, as it did nationwide. Holifield characterizes Sternglass as a "blowhard" who became an "instant expert" in order to sell a story to *Esquire,* which pays well.

The level of radiation to which the population of the United States was exposed to fallout has been relatively small. The best estimates are that the increased exposure due to fallout when added to background radiation (always present in the earth or from cosmic rays) has added less than 5 per cent to the total, and strontium-90 probably accounts for only a few per cent of the genetic dose.

John Storer of the Biology Division of Oak Ridge says that there is just no evidence that very small amounts of radiation have caused leukemia or bone cancer any place in the country or any place in the world. In regard to mutation, Storer points out that experiments with strontium-90 and mice, carried out by Swedish scientists, which show genetic damage, should not be extrapolated to man. The reason is that the *range* of radiation from strontium-90 is very short. A mouse is a small animal. The reproductive tissue is close to the bones. But in man the reproductive tissue is out of range of any strontium-90 that has substitued itself for calcium in the bones.

This matter of the *size* of a man compared to a fruit fly or a mouse may be extremely important. Recently, however, the arguments about radiation effects have involved much smaller and livelier materials than strontium-90. The main villain feared in the case of nuclear power plants is tritium (superheavy hydrogen) in the form of T_2O or "superheavy water." The controversy has raged especially bitter in regard to the installation of a nuclear power plant at Cliffs of Calvert, Maryland, which would get its cooling water from the Chesapeake and return it there. Richard F. Beers of Johns Hopkins University maintains that the T_2O produced in the cooling water would make the whole bay mutagenic, would case a large number of infant deaths and possibly a race of two-headed monsters.

The Atomic Energy Commission does not think so. T_2O acts chemically like other water. Even if one assumes that a person drank undiluted cooling water from the power plant and also that he got his entire food supply from plants and animals grown in the same water, the over-all result would not total over one millirem* per year for the whole body. This amount of radiation is one five-hundredths of the exposure considered acceptable for the general public and one-hundredth of what a person receives every year from natural sources. The Atomic Energy Commission has been unable to detect any biological effects due to natural background levels of radiation. The natural background in most sea-level regions averages 100 millirems a year, which is 100,000 times the exposure that would result from the Cliffs of Calvert reactor.

If a person living in Baltimore moves to Cumberland, Maryland, his average annual exposure from natural background cosmic radiation alone would increase by three millirems per year. This difference is 3000 times higher than any exposure that might be expected from eating Chesapeake Bay fish or shellfish containing tritium from the Cliffs of Calvert reactor. Extensive measurements of tritium concentration available from the Nevada Test Site and Savannah River Project, where the ambient tritium levels in certain areas are far higher than those anticipated near the Cliffs of Calvert reactor, confirm that there is no evidence for the concentration of tritium in organic molecules as tritium passes up the food chain.

Professor Beers does not believe that the AEC has gotten the idea through its thick skull. What is argued is not the effect of radiation from T_2O but tritium embedded in the DNA double helix of young children or fetuses. If the true biological effects of tritium were taken into consideration, the AEC experts would have to account for the fact that just one tritium atom can produce a mutation when it is at the right spot at the right time; it can

---

* "Rem" stands for "roentgen equivalent man" and is the dosage of any ionizing radiation that will cause the same amount of biological injury to human tissue as one roentgen of X-ray or gamma-ray dosage.

kill a bacterial cell, and in general does not display the simple dose-response curves observed with X rays and other high-energy radiations that distribute their energy along a diffuse path. As long as the tritium remains as water, the AEC conclusion is correct. But it does not all remain in the form of T_2O. It may end up as part of the DNA molecule, thus in the growing fetus or child resulting in personal deformations or, more importantly, it may incorporate itself into the germ cells of growing children, the oögonia and the spermatogonia. This does not mean that the tritium would be concentrated or enriched at levels higher than those observed in the environment or in the food chain. It simply means that the distribution in the human organism, the fetus or baby, will be unequal, depending on relative growth rates, the state of metabolism of the tissue or the form of the tritium-containing molecule. At the wrong time and place even one tritium atom is like a bomb exploded in an immense and crowded cathedral. But, unlike the bomb, its repercussions, warns Beers, may persist for centuries, even for millennia.

Aside from worries about certain color television sets and microwave ovens, mostly expressed by Ralph Nader, it is the fashion now to worry more about mutagenic chemicals than ionizing radiation.

In spite of the enormously complex and specific venoms invented by the plant and animal kingdoms over millions of years, one must realize that within the last few decades thousands of synthetic chemicals have been made by man that are not natural. They are not found in evolution. Their effect on evolution is therefore unpredictable. Some of them may, upon reaching the germ cells, cause immediate or long-delayed mutations. Take the nitrogen oxides. These are simple enough little units of misery, representing perhaps the most important part of air pollution from burning fuels at high temperature as in internal-combustion engines. (One must realize that evolution did not anticipate that animals would deliberately burn things under pressure. Nitrogen oxides are rare from forest fires when the temperature of burning is relatively low and hence the nitrogen fixation reaction of nitrogen and oxygen in the air is not favored.)

Now some of the nitrogen oxides react with water to form nitrous acid. This simple substance has been found definitely to be mutagenic in lower organisms. As we have mentioned previously, there is a more deliberate way nitrous acid can get into the human body: by the use of sodium nitrite as a preservative and color enhancer in frankfurters, sausage meats, smoked salmon and other foods. In the acid environment of the stomach, the salt evolves the free nitrous acid. The question is, can a chemical which causes mutations in a very small animal such as a fruit fly or even the *Escherichia coli* microorganism, be regarded as mutagenic for a human being? In order to be mutagenic for a large multicellular animal such as man, the chemical must reach the nucleus of the germ cells (in the ovary or in the testicle). In the single-celled creature the one nucleus *is* the germ cell.

If we could be certain that any chemical under suspicion had some infallible way of reaching the germ cells of man, we would be really scared since there is an extraordinary biochemical unity in all living cells. The DNA molecules of a microbe are made of the same constituents as the DNA molecules of a man, only they are much smaller molecules. If a chemical is mutagenic in *Escherichia coli* because it reacts with a specific DNA nucleotide base (e.g., adenosine) it should also react chemically with adenosine in human DNA. It is a question of accessibility of the germ cells in large creatures like babies or even mice. Ozone, another component of air pollution, is mutagenic in *E. coli* but not in mice. It probably does not reach the mouse's germ cells.

Some geneticists, such as Ernst Freese of the National Institute of Health, believe we should play it safe and ban any compound shown to be mutagenic in lower organisms. He makes an exception of isoniazid which is an extremely valuable therapeutic drug for tuberculosis, although it is definitely mutagenic to lower organisms.

Some of the common chemicals, either natural or synthetic, that are under grave suspicion as mutagens are: caffeine, cyclamate, urethane, various alkylating agents, hydrazine and its derivatives, epoxides, hydroxylamine, benzopyrene, various anti-cancer agents, various anti-depressant drugs, some antibiotics, anti-nausea drugs and oral contraceptives. Even more definitely suspected are the fungicide captan, the plant-growth inhibitor maleic hydrazide and the sterilants triethylenephosphoramide and triethylenemelamine.

Bruce N. Ames of the University of California (Berkeley) emphasizes the delayed-fuse effect of only a slight amount of genetic damage. Cumulative effects a century hence may be catastrophic. He believes caffeine may be partly responsible for the relatively high level of spontaneous abortion, miscarriages, Mongolism and deformities that we see today.* We are beginning, he thinks, to feel the effect of three or four centuries of coffee and tea drinking. This has not made Professor Ames very popular, and there are battalions of people who have sprung to the defense of coffee, tea, cola soft drinks and the use of caffeine as an adjuvant drug in a large number of patent medicines such as Anacin, Excedrin, Bromo Seltzer, No-Doz, etc.

In fact we must admit meekly at the present time that no one has yet shown *conclusively* that any chemical induces mutations in the germinal cells of man. How can we prove such a thing? Obviously we cannot, under our present ethical system, use human beings as experimental animals, and besides the so-called "generation time"—the average length of time between the birth of parents and their offspring—is much too long for research purposes. In the bacteria it is thirty minutes, in the fruit fly two weeks, in mice fourteen weeks and in rats seventeen weeks. Certain statistical methods have been considered but are regarded as embarrassingly difficult and costly to apply.

For example, in respect to caffeine, Sydney Mittler of Northern Illinois University suggests, on the basis of laboratory experiments with animals, that caffeine may increase the incidence of Mongolism. Why not statistically examine the relative occurrence of Mongolism in those people in this country whose religions bar the use of caffeine-containing drinks, such as the Mormons and the Seventh-Day Adventists, with the Mongolism incidence in all others? This is easy to suggest but very hard to carry out. Another statistical survey of value would be to examine the occurrence of defective births in the children and the grandchildren of the seven to eight million men who were injected during World War II in the South Pacific with quinacrine ("Atabrine") as an anti-malarial drug. This has since that time been found definitely mutagenic to *E. coli* and to fruit flies.

A great deal of publicity has gushed forth on the supposed effect of the hallucinogenic drug LSD on the breakage of chromosomes. This whole matter is in a rather awkward scientific posture,

* Actually such statements are not very reliable, since unlike the Scandinavian countries only a few of our hospitals have systematic and comprehensive registries of birth defects.

since chromosome breakage* in the first place may not constitute an act of mutation (the *point* distortion of chromosomes, without breakage, is apparently more likely to be assuredly mutagenic), and moreover the bulk of recent evidence from carefully controlled experiments shows that LSD does not even cause a statistical increase in chromosome breakage. It appears that some of the LSD work may have been biased by moral attitudes. This appears likely in the reports of Cecil B. Jacobson at George Washington University School of Medicine, which ostensibly showed that in a study of seventy-five female users of LSD four out of fourteen therapeutically aborted fetuses from these women showed serious brain or skull deficiency. The white blood cells of the babies as well as of the mothers showed abnormal chromosomal breaks. This may have been teratogenic rather than mutagenic or may have been imaginary. As the result of an impressive number of rechecks of Jacobson's work, he seems to have been out of step with nearly every other researcher in the field. At the present time, in fact, the case against caffeine is actually stronger than that against LSD. On the other hand, the subject is so full of emotional and political reverberations that the eager refuters of Jacobson's data may also be suspect. Indeed, LSD as a mutagen or even as a teratogen is somewhat in the same status as alcohol seventy years ago. There were very learned professors, especially favored by the Woman's Christian Temperance Union, who succeeded in proving to the satisfaction of these fanatics that alcohol affected the germ cells and would produce a race not only of chronic drunks but of babies born from one generation to another with bloodshot eyes and hand tremors. Since alcohol has been used by man for some 7000 years, it appears the least likely of all the drugs to be mutagenic. Furthermore, it is a common natural product so that numerous other kinds of animals get seasonally drunk, including fruit-eating birds and even elephants.

The first proof of a chemically induced point mutation rather than mere chromosome breakage was accomplished by Charlotte Auerbach and John M. Robson at the University of Edinburgh. In the early 1940s they discovered that mustard gas (dichloroethyl

---

* When a chromosome break does occur in a cell and the break is not properly repaired, the cell usually dies. Thus the effect of the break is neatly canceled out.

sulfide), other sulfur mustards and nitrogen mustards cause mutation in fruit flies. (This discovery was not made public until 1946 because of the government secrecy restrictions during the war.) Unfortunately there does not seem to have been any rigorously conducted follow-up on the possible genetic damage done to mustard-gas survivors of the previous war, their offspring and grandchildren.

In regard to the all-important question of caffeine, a new theory has been advanced that caffeine itself may not be a mutagen in man or any mammal but may generally inhibit the natural repair of DNA damaged by radiation or by other chemicals.

We do know of mutations in the human race, most of them being lethal or threatening, some of them beneficial under unusual circumstances.

The sickle-cell gene is a mutant of value in countries, such as parts of Africa, where man has been threatened for millennia by extinction due to malaria. Its value is that the red blood cells in the mutated (sickle-shaped) form are unable to carry the malaria organisms. However, if both parents carry the gene, the red blood cell is so distorted that it cannot survive and the child usually dies of anemia.

Most genetic disorders are in fact caused by a defective recessive gene. The disorders will usually show up plainly only in the offspring when both parents transmit the same recessive trait.

But it is much easier to monitor mutation from a dominant gene, even if only one parent confers it. Geneticists have proposed a comprehensive "chemical dragnet" to determine the possibly increasing incidence of hereditary disorders such as achandoplasia (a form of dwarfism), retinablastoma (a hereditary disease causing cancer of the retina), neurofibromatosis (causing benign tumors in the tissues of nerve fiber) and partial albinism with deafness. All these are caused by defective dominant genes.

Other genetic disorders, at some time in the past caused by mutations, are cystic fibrosis, muscular dystrophy, complete albinism, phenylketonuria, agammaglobulinemia (lack of gamma globulin in the blood), alkaptanemia and glactasemia.

Since most mutations now can be detected by blood analysis, a "genetic-alert" program has been sponsored by the Albert Einstein College of Medicine, the National Institutes of Health and the

National Foundation for Neuromuscular Diseases, to examine some 5000 to 6000 children per year. "Cord blood" obtained at the time of cutting the umbilical cord at birth would be analyzed for such key factors as gamma globulin, ceruloplasmin, transferrins, alpha-1-trypsin inhibitor and others associated with various genetic diseases.

There is one rather self-complacent attitude that runs as a *leitmotif* through all this bustle and concern. That is the assumption that man is such a perfect creature that any mutation must be for the worse: either it is lethal or incapacitating or at least it leads away from standard *Homo sapiens*.

It seems to me that, although statistically and medically this may be a satisfactory way of viewing mutagenesis, philosophically it is an absurd point of view. Man is one of the most recent animals on earth. He has run very fast because he has learned some unusual tricks. He has learned a *tradition* of learning to learn. But this tradition is a social not a biological phenomenon. The truth is that man, far from being the crystallized wonder of creation, is as a species a singularly self-destructive, passionate and dangerous animal.

It would appear that we should be alert to *favorable* as well as debilitating mutations. I cannot help wonder whether, for example, in Wolfgang Mozart we did not have an extraordinary mutant which in a genetically alert society might have been bred to a new race of musical man. In the extraordinary Huxley family it appears reasonable to suspect a favorable mutant that perhaps was eventually allowed to dilute itself.

The National Laboratory at Oak Ridge has produced by radiation at least sixty new stable lines of mutant plants. As a result of such work, Florida has a good new oat variety, South Carolina a new lespedeza, North Carolina a new peanut. Commercial chrysanthemum growers have been successfully using radiation-induced mutations for some years.

Are we so proud of what we are that we cannot imagine the day when we can view mutagenesis as perhaps our only hope rather than merely another form of catastrophe?

18

MAN AS A CHEMICAL ADVENTURER

We have seen throughout most of this book that the chemistry of food and of poisons dominates the lives of small animals. Getting food and avoiding the experience of being devoured is a planetary theme of the utmost, even exasperating, complexity. When man ceased being simply a skilled carnivorous animal and took to food gathering and to agriculture, he found himself mixed up in the ancient warfare between plants versus small animals such as insects and nematodes. He attracted the interest of new parasites; he exposed himself to peculiar natural toxins.

In this no man's land, we had one advantage, our size, but this was offset by a disadvantage—our long generation time. Whereas a small animal that breeds a new generation every year or perhaps every week quickly adapts to poisons, we have not even had time during our industrial period to adapt either to the toxic materials that we invented a generation or so ago or to our own natural waste products that in crowded cities we dumped in rivers and lakes and oceans and found returned to us in the form of cholera or hepatitis or typhoid.

In a vast enterprise of synthetic organic chemistry, we have since the nineteenth century introduced on earth great quantities of unnatural compounds, such as those containing chlorine or heavy metals, in a single-minded fury of counterattack upon the small animals that compete with us for vegetable food or upon the still smaller animals which spoil our food. It turns out that this cataract of new chemicals—this blind but superficially cunning planetary war has had some essentially immoral effects. It has led to the destruction of friendly animals, even of helpful animals, such as bees and birds and fish. In the long run the campaign may have had the same moral effect as Hiroshima. By extinguishing whole species of lovely or remarkable animals we feel—or should feel—a dreadful pang such as that which does—or should—accompany our recollection of having radiantly roasted babies and housewives and shoemakers and 100,000 other little people going about their business of living.

Worst of all is the moral fact that many of us do not feel the pang. Franciscan love continues to be hidden behind the money chest.

I feel there is real danger—physical as well as spiritual—inherent in anti-ecology, in the coyote-haters, in the sneers about the bird watchers. With poisoned minds, we not only eventually poison our bodies but prepare ourselves for mutual destruction in a thousand Hiroshimas of the future. If we treat a sea bird as a dispensable piece of sponge for oil, sooner or later we will treat a Chinese or a Russian peasant as a cockroach and will find ourselves in return treated as malevolent insects. DDT and petroleum spills now, tomorrow the apocalypse of nuclear fire.

Again I advance the prayer: Help us, dear Francis!

TABLES

FIGURE 1

GEOLOGIC COLUMN AND SCALE OF TIME

SYSTEM AND PERIOD	SERIES AND EPOCH	DISTINCTIVE RECORDS OF LIFE	1000 YEARS*
		CENOZOIC ERA	
Quaternary	Recent	Modern man	44
	Pleistocene	Early man	1000
	Pliocene	Large carnivores	
	Miocene	Whales, apes, grazing forms	(21,000)
Tertiary	Oligocene	Large browsing mammals	(50,000)
	Eocene	Rise of flowering plants	
	Paleocene	First placental mammals	70,000
		MESOZOIC ERA	
Cretaceous		Extinction of dinosaurs, flora with modern aspects	130,000
Jurassic		Dinosaurs' zenith, primitive birds, first small mammals	160,000
Triassic		Appearance of dinosaurs	200,000

PALEOZOIC ERA

Permian	Conifers abundant, reptiles developed	(230,000) 235,000
Carboniferous Upper (Pennsylvanian)	First reptiles, great coal forests	260,000
Lower (Mississippian)	Sharks abundant	285,000
Devonian	Amphibians appeared, fishes abundant	320,000
Silurian	Earliest plants and animals	350,000 (380,000)
Ordovician	First primitive fishes	400,000
Cambrian	Large faunas of marine invertebrates	500,000

PRE-CAMBRIAN TIME

No known basis for systematic division	Plants and animals with soft tissues, few fossils	(520,000) 1,420,000 1,800,000 2,680,000 3,310,000 3,500,000 4,000,000

* (Italicized figures are from radiocarbon analyses; figures in parentheses are reliable values from radioactive minerals found in rocks that belong in time divisions indicated; plain figures give estimated dates at start of corresponding time units)

FIGURE 2

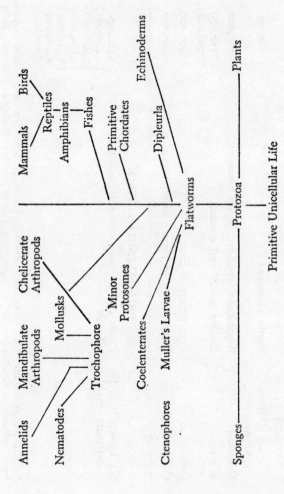

FIGURE 3

TWO EXAMPLES OF ANIMAL CLASSIFICATION

	MAN	AMOEBA
Phylum	Chordata	Protozoa
Subphylum	Vertebrata	—
Class	Mammalia	Rhizopoda
Order	Primatiformes	Amoebiformes
Family	Hominidae	Amoebidae
Genus	*Homo*	*Amoeba*
Species	*sapiens*	*proteus*

BIBLIOGRAPHY

Since this book is not intended as a scientific treatise, I have not tried to attach a learned reference to every name and statement given in the text. In the case of especially crucial references, where a periodical rather than a book is involved, I have used footnotes.

In addition to the books listed later, my reliance has been upon the following sources:

Scientific and Technical Periodicals

Advances in Marine Biology, Advances in Pediatrics, Agricultural Science Reviews, Agronomical Journal, American Journal of Botany, American Journal of Clinical Pathology, American Journal of Orthopsychiatry, American Journal of Tropical Medicine and Hygiene, American Naturalist, Annals of Applied Biology, Annual Review of Phytopathology, Archives of Biochemistry and Biophysics, Archives of Diseases of Children, Archives of Environmental Health, Archives of Internal Medicine, Audubon Magazine, Auk, Bamidgeh, British Medical Journal, Business International, California Agriculture, California Medicine, Canadian Journal of Plant Science, Ceres, Chemical and Engineering News, Chemical Engineering, Chemistry and Industry, Comparative Biochemistry and Physiology, Conservation News, Ecologic Management, Ecology, Environmental Education, Environmental Science and Technology, Evolution, Experientia, Experimental Neurology, Experimental Parasitology, Foreign Affairs, Gastroenterology, Johns Hopkins Medical Journal, Journal of the American Medical Association, Journal of Applied Ecology, Journal of Clinical Nutrition, Journal of Economic Entomology, Journal of Experimental Medicine, Journal of Fish Research Board of Canada, Journal of Genetic Psychology, Journal of Neurochemistry, Journal of Neuropathology, Journal of Nutrition, Journal of Nutrition Education, Lancet, Limnology and Oceanography, Medical Journal of

*Australia, Medical Tribune, Natural History, Nature, Nematologica,
New Scientist, Occupational Safety and Health Abstracts, Oceanology
International, Oceans Magazine, Pediatrics, Pharmacological Reviews,
Physiological Zoology, Phytopathology, Plant Disease Reports, Prairie
Farmer, Proceedings American Philosophical Society, Proceedings Royal
Society of Biology, Proceedings World Symposium on Warm Water
Pond Fish Culture, Progressive Fish Culturist, Quarterly Review of
Biology, Review of Applied Mycology, Science, Science Journal, Science
News, Scientific American, Smithsonian, Systematic Biology, Transac-
tions of American Fish Association, Transactions of American Fish
Society, World Health Organization Chronicle*

Popular Journals and News Services

Associated Press, *Business Week, Chemical Week, Congressional
Record, Fortune, Frontiers of Science, Home Garden, Look,* Los Angeles
Times News Service, *National Geographic, National Wildlife,* News-
paper Enterprise Association Service, *New Yorker,* New York Times
News Service, Science Service, *Sports Illustrated, Sunset, Time,* United
Press International, *Wall Street Journal,* Washington Post News Service.

BOOKS

AGRIOS, G. W. *Plant Pathology.* New York: Academic Press, 1969.

ANDERSON, E. *Plants, Man, and Life.* Boston: Little, Brown, 1952.

ARDREY, ROBERT. *The Territorial Imperative.* New York: Atheneum, 1966.

BENTON, H. H. and WERNER, W. E. *Field Biology and Ecology.* New York: McGraw-Hill, 1960.

BERRILL, N. J. *The Person in the Womb.* New York: Dodd, Mead, 1968.

BLAIR, W. F., Ed. *Vertebrate Speciation.* Austin, Texas: University of Texas Press, 1961.

BOUGHEY, A. S. *Ecology of Populations.* New York: Macmillan, 1966.

BRUN, F. et al. Eds. *Galathea Report.* London: Allen & Unwin, 1957.

BRYSON, V. and VOGEL, H. J. Eds. *Evolving Genes and Proteins.* New York: Academic Press, 1965.

CAHALANE, VICTOR H. *Mammals of North America.* New York: Mac-millan, 1961.

CARLANDER, K. D. *Handbook of Freshwater Fishing Biology.* Dubuque, Iowa: Brown, 1950.

CARR, DONALD E. *The Breath of Life.* New York: Norton, 1965.

———. *Death of the Sweet Waters.* New York: Norton, 1966.

————. *The Sexes.* Garden City, N.Y.: Doubleday, 1970.

CLARKE, G. L. *Elements of Ecology.* New York: Wiley, 1954.

DASMANN, RAYMOND. *A Different Kind of Country.* New York: Macmillan, 1968.

EKMAN, S. *Zoogeography of the Sea.* London: Sidgwick & Jackson, 1953.

ELTON, C. S. *The Ecology of Invasions by Animals and Plants.* London: Methuen, 1958.

FABRE, J. HENRI. *The Life of the Spider.* New York: Dodd, Mead, 1958.

FEINENDENGEN, L. E. *Tritium-Labelled Molecules in Biology and Medicine.* New York: Academic Press, 1957.

FISHER, JAMES et al. *Wildlife in Danger.* New York: Viking Press, 1969.

GAUSE, G. P. *The Struggle for Existence.* Baltimore: Williams & Wilkins, 1934.

GERKING, S. D., Ed. *The Biological Basis of Freshwater Fish Production.* New York: Wiley, 1967.

GERTSCH, WILLIS J. *American Spiders.* Princeton, N.J.: Van Nostrand, 1949.

GROSSMAN, MARY LOUISE and SHELLY and HAMLET, JOHN H. *Our Vanishing Wilderness.* New York: Grosset & Dunlap, 1969.

GROTAN, S. W. and EDWARDS, R. L. *Fish and Nutrition.* London: Fishing News, 1962.

GUTHRIE, MARY J. and ANDERSON, JOHN M. *General Zoology.* New York: Wiley, 1961.

HARDY, ALISTER G. *The Open Sea: The World of Plankton.* London: Oxford University Press, 1956.

HAY, JOHN. *In Defense of Nature.* Boston: Atlantic, Little, Brown, 1969.

HERSH, SEYMOUR. *Chemical and Biological Warfare: America's Hidden Arsenal.* Garden City, N.Y.: Doubleday, 1969.

HICKEY, JOSEPH J., Ed. *Peregrine Falcon Populations.* Madison, Wis.: University of Wisconsin Press, 1969.

HILL, M. N., Ed. *The Sea.* London: Interscience, 1963.

HOPCRAFT, ARTHUR. *Born to Hunger.* Boston: Houghton Mifflin, 1968.

HUTCHINS, ROSS E. *Insects.* Englewood Cliffs, N.J.: Prentice-Hall, 1966.

HUTCHINSON, G. E. *The Ecological Theater and the Evolutionary Play.* New Haven, Conn.: Yale University Press, 1965.

KARMONDY, F. J. *Concepts of Ecology.* Englewood Cliffs, N.J.: Prentice-Hall, 1969.

KERSHAW, K. A. *Quantitative and Dynamic Ecology.* London: Arnold, 1960.

KLAUBER, LAURENCE M. *Rattlesnakes: Their Habits, Life History and Influence on Mankind.* New York: Berkeley, 1956.

LATIL, PIERRE DE. *The Underwater Naturalist.* Boston: Houghton Mifflin, 1958.

LEVINS, R. *Evolution in Changing Environments.* Princeton, N.J.: Princeton University Press, 1968.

LIENER, IRVIN I., Ed. *Toxic Constituents of Plant Foodstuffs.* New York: Academic Press, 1969.

LIFTON, ROBERT JAY. *Death in Life: Survivors of Hiroshima.* New York: Random House, 1968.

LORENZ, KONRAD. *On Aggression.* New York: Harcourt, Brace & World, 1966.

McCARTHY, RICHARD D. *The Ultimate Folly: War by Pestilence, Asphyxiation and Defoliation.* New York: Knopf, 1969.

MAGNUSON, W. G. and CASPER, JEAN. *The Dark Side of the Marketplace.* Englewood, N.J.: Prentice-Hall, 1968.

MUNRO, H. N. and ALLISON, J. B. Eds. *Mammalian Protein Metabolism.* New York: Academic Press, 1964.

MOMENT, GARDNER. *General Zoology.* Boston: Houghton Mifflin, 1967.

NAPIER, S. R. and P. H. *A Handbook of Living Primates.* New York: Academic Press, 1967.

NELSON, RICHARD K. *Hunters of the Northern Ice.* Chicago: University of Chicago Press, 1969.

ODOM, E. P. and H. T. *Fundamentals of Ecology.* Philadelphia: Sanders, 1959.

OLDROYD, HAROLD. *The Natural History of Flies.* New York: Norton, 1965.

OLSEN, JACK. *Nights of the Grizzlies.* New York: Putnam, 1969.

OOSTING, H. J. *The Study of Plant Communities.* San Francisco: Freeman, 1958.

PADDOCK, WILLIAM and PAUL. *Famine 1975!* Boston: Little, Brown, 1968.

POPE, CLIFFORD H. *The Reptile World.* New York: Knopf, 1966.

RUDD, R. L. *Pesticides and the Living Landscape.* Madison, Wis.: University of Wisconsin Press, 1968.

RUSSELL, FINDLEY E. and SAUNDERS, PAUL R., Eds. *Animal Toxins.* London: Pergamon Press, 1967.

RUSSELL, FRANKLIN. *Watchers at the Pond.* New York: Knopf, 1961.

SAPEIKA, N. *Food Pharmacology.* Springfield, Ill.: Thomas, 1969.

SCHEFFER, VICTOR B. *The Year of the Whale*. New York: Scribner's, 1969.

SCHENKEL, RUDOLPH and LOTTE. *Ecology and Behavior of the Black Rhinoceros*. Hamburg, Germany: Heeliger and Perey, 1969.

SCHULTZ, LEONARD B. *The Ways of Fishes*. Princeton, N.J.: Van Nostrand, 1948.

SCRIMSHAW, N. S. and GORDON, J. E., Eds. *Malnutrition, Learning and Behavior*. Cambridge, Mass.: MIT Press, 1968.

SEBRELL, WILLIAM H., JR. and HAGGERTY, JAMES J. *Food and Nutrition*. Palo Alto, Calif.: Burdett, 1967.

SMITH, R. L. *Ecology and Field Biology*. New York: Harper & Row, 1966.

SNELL, E. E. et al. *Chemical and Biological Aspects of Pyridoxal Catalysis*. London: Pergamon Press, 1963.

SOLER, F. DE. *Strategy for Conquest of Hunger*. New York: Rockefeller Foundation, 1968.

STEVENS, N. F. and A. B. *Disease in Plants*. Waltham, Mass.: Chemica Botanica, 1952.

THOMAS, W. L., Ed. *Man's Role in Changing the Face of the Earth*. Chicago: University of Chicago Press, 1956.

TROWELL, H. C. et al. *Kwashiorkor*. London: Arnold, 1954.

TURNER, JAMES S. *The Chemical Feast*. Washington, D.C.: Center for Study of Responsive Law, 1970.

WALKER, J. C. *Plant Pathology*. New York: McGraw-Hill, 1950.

WATT, K. E. F. *Ecology and Resource Management*. New York: McGraw-Hill, 1968.

WEAVER, J. E. and CLEMENTS, F. E. *Plant Ecology*. New York: McGraw-Hill, 1938.

WELTY, JOEL CARL. *Life of Birds*. New York: Knopf, 1963.

WHITTEN, JAMIEL. *That We May Live*. Princeton, N.J.: Van Nostrand, 1966.

INDEX

Abalone 201

Acarology, as study of ticks and mites, 41

"Accent." *See* Monosodium glutamate

Adaptive radiation evolutionary explosions, 187

Agricultural revolution, 140, 171; effect of, on nutrition level of man, 140, 171; and application of modern technology to present-day farming, 144

Air pollution. *See* Pollution of air and water

Airport ceilometers, death of small nocturnal birds caused by, 216

Ajinomoto Company, 320

Aldabra, coral atoll of, as bird and animal sanctuary, 195–96

Aleutian goose, 215

Alewives, 70, 268, 289

Algae: role of, in coral reef-building, 21, 184; eutrophication of lakes by, 154; cultivation of marine algae, 155–56; unbalances in populations of, caused by DDT, 267, 270

Allergens in plants, 323

Alligators. *See* Crocodilians order of reptiles

Ambidextrousness of advanced apes, 133

Ambrosia beetles, 55

American continents populated by bands of Paleolithic hunting peoples from Siberia, 137

American Medical Association, 299; Archives of Environmental Health of, 299

Ames, Bruce N., 332–33

Amino acids, lack of, in diet, 142, 143, 157

Ammonites, of cephalopods, 182

Amoeba, food hunting and digestive process of, 6–7

Amoore, John E., 319

Amory, Cleveland, 203

Amphibians: evolution of, from lungfishes, 71–72, 74; frogs, salamanders, toads, 74–77; stegocephalians, 75; body plan of, designed for capturing arthropods, 75; diet of, and evolutionary principle of competitive exclusion, 76; hibernation of, 76; large urinary bladder of, 76–77; Permian decimation among, 181

Amphipods, or beach fleas, of malacostracan crustaceans, 44

Angelfishes, 69

Angler fish, 71

Animal classification, two examples of, 343 (fig. 3)

Animal kingdom, mammary glands as revolutionary in evolution of, 103

Animals, destruction of, for their furs, hides, feathers, 201–4

Annelids phylum: earthworms, 30–33; leeches, 30; segmented body of, 30; five classes of, 30

Anopheles mosquito, and malaria, 11, 39

Antelopes, of artiodactyls, 128, 206; of colonial America, 204, 205

Anthropocentricity of Christianity, and the animals, 194

Anthropoids, platyrrhines and catarrhines groups in, 132–33

Anti-Locust Research Center in London, 263

Ant lions, of Neuropteriformes, 43*n*, 54, 253

Ants, of hymenoptera, 14, 58, 62–64, 250, 256, 258–59

Aphids, 51, 271, 296